PHYSICAL TECHNIQUES IN BIOLOGICAL RESEARCH

Volume III, Part C

Cells and Tissues

Contributors to This Volume

M. S. BURSTONE

JEROME J. FREED

A. W. POLLISTER

E. RASCH

FRITIOF S. SJÖSTRAND

H. SWIFT

SEYMOUR S. WEST

PHYSICAL TECHNIQUES IN BIOLOGICAL RESEARCH

SECOND EDITION

Edited by

ARTHUR W. POLLISTER

DEPARTMENT OF ZOOLOGY
COLUMBIA UNIVERSITY
NEW YORK, NEW YORK

Volume III, Part C

Cells and Tissues

 1969

ACADEMIC PRESS   New York and London

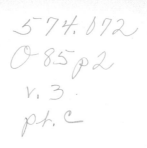

ACADEMIC PRESS, INC.
111 Fifth Avenue, New York, New York 10003

United Kingdom Edition published by
ACADEMIC PRESS, INC. (LONDON) LTD.
Berkeley Square House, London W.1

LIBRARY OF CONGRESS CATALOG CARD NUMBER: 54-11056

PRINTED IN THE UNITED STATES OF AMERICA

List of Contributors

Numbers in parentheses indicate the pages on which the author's contributions begin

M. S. BURSTONE,* Department of Zoology, Columbia University, New York, New York (1)

JEROME J. FREED, The Institute for Cancer Research, Fox Chase, Philadelphia, Pennsylvania (95)

A. W. POLLISTER, Department of Zoology, Columbia University, New York, New York (201)

E. RASCH, Department of Biology, Marquette University, Milwaukee, Wisconsin (201)

FRITIOF S. SJÖSTRAND, Department of Zoology, University of California, Los Angeles, California (169)

H. SWIFT, Whitman Laboratory, University of Chicago, Chicago, Illinois (201)

SEYMOUR S. WEST, Department of Engineering Biophysics, University of Alabama Medical Center, Birmingham, Alabama (253)

* Deceased.

Preface to First Edition of Volume III

It is the broad task of cytology, the study of cells, to determine the morphology, chemical characteristics, and functions of the cellular organelles, such as nucleus, mitochondria, etc. In these structures of the intact cell, the chemical constituents—studied as isolated and relatively pure substances by the techniques described in Volumes I and II of this series—are intermingled in complex physical states that are by no means yet precisely definable; their general nature is suggested by such terms as nucleoprotein or lipoprotein. For modern cytology, there are many new or more highly refined methods which are largely responsible for a current unprecedented growth in our knowledge of the cell. The authors of Volume III discuss such of these approaches as involve mainly physical techniques. The apparatus and principles, in most instances, are those described in earlier volumes, but with the very different requirement that the result is in each case directly referable to the relatively intact cell or part of the cell. Wide use of these methods of modern cytology is rapidly bridging the gap between the older cellular biology and the molecular biology that is the goal of physico-chemical studies of unique chemical compounds extracted from cells. Thus, the electron microscope, at its lower limit, makes visible the larger biological molecules; the absorption techniques detect specific substances in subcellular volumes of a fraction of a cubic micron; an autoradiograph can demonstrate a specific metabolic process that involves less than a hundred isotope atoms in a single nucleolus; while the techniques of differential centrifugation have achieved isolation of units for specific synthesis that probably contain no more than a score of enzyme molecules. The Editors and Authors of this volume are hopeful that its juxtaposition to the other two in the series will in some measure serve to accelerate this convergence of all applicable physical techniques on the central biological problem of the full significance of the cellular structure of living matter.

The Editors wish to express their warm appreciation to the Authors for taking time from their active research careers to make these useful contributions to the field.

New York, N.Y.   ARTHUR W. POLLISTER
May 25, 1956   GERALD OSTER

Preface to Second Edition of Volume III

During the long period since the first edition was written there have been many improvements and innovations in every physical technique used in biological research on cells and tissues. This progress has made it imperative to present a new edition. The main chapter headings of the first edition have been retained since no widely useful methods have been developed that are different in principle from those current earlier. For one reason or another there have been a number of changes in authorship. All authors have been given freedom of choice in adherence to the original organization and in retention of the material of the first edition. However, in nearly every subject the revised manuscripts were considerably longer than those of the first edition. Therefore, it has become necessary to publish Volume III in three parts: A, B, and C. Volumes IIIA and IIIC cover all subjects except autoradiographic techniques; the latter is the subject of Volume IIIB.

March, 1969   ARTHUR W. POLLISTER

Contents

Chapter 1

Cryobiology Techniques in Histochemistry, Including Freeze-Drying and Cryostat Procedures

M. S. BURSTONE

Chapter 2

Microspectrophotometry in the Ultraviolet Spectrum

JEROME J. FREED

Chapter 3

Electron Microscopy of Cells and Tissues

FRITIOF S. SJÖSTRAND

Chapter 4

Microphotometry with Visible Light

A. W. POLLISTER, H. SWIFT, and E. RASCH

Chapter 5

Fluorescence Microspectrophotometry of Supravitally Stained Cells

SEYMOUR S. WEST

PHYSICAL TECHNIQUES IN BIOLOGICAL RESEARCH

Volume III, Part C

Cells and Tissues

CHAPTER 1

Cryobiology Techniques in Histochemistry, Including Freeze-Drying and Cryostat Procedures[1]

M. S. BURSTONE

I. General Aspects of Low Temperature Techniques

Emphasis in the low temperature field during the past decade has been in cryobiology. This term was first used by Parkes (1964). The temperatures involved in cryobiology as constrasted with the highest known temperatures is shown in Fig. 1.

Cryogenics, the science of producing and using extremely low temperatures, employs the so-called cryogenic gases, whose boiling points are below $-100°C$ ($-148°F$) or $173°K$. These gases, which can be liquefied, include the atmospheric gases nitrogen ($-196°C$), oxygen ($-183°C$), and argon ($-186°C$) and also some of the rarer atmospheric gases including neon ($-246°C$), krypton ($-153°C$), and xenon ($-108°C$). Other gases of the cryogenic group include helium ($-296°C$), hydrogen ($-253°C$), methane ($-162°C$), and fluorine ($-188°C$) as well as ethylene, which boils at $-104°C$. The first four of this group are available in the greatest

---

[1] Doctor Burstone's untimely death occurred in 1966, shortly after this chapter was completed. It is published essentially as he wrote it except for the interpolation of brief discussions of several more recent references. (Editor)

1

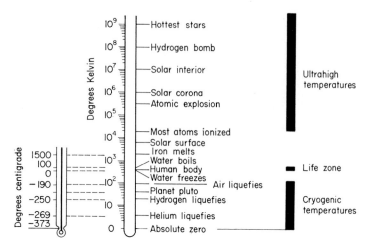

Fig. 1. Comparison between degrees centigrade and degrees Kelvin. (After Sittig and Kidd, 1963; Coriell *et al.*, 1964.)

quantities and thus are more available for general use (Sittig and Kidd, 1963; McClintock, 1964; Rose-Innes, 1964).

In addition to the familiar temperature range scale in degrees centigrade, the Kelvin range is also applied in low temperature procedures. Thus absolute zero is 0° Kelvin or −273°C. Figure 1 indicates the scale of absolute zero temperatures in degrees centigrade and degrees Kelvin. From zero degrees Kelvin there is one continuous logarithmic scale to the hottest temperatures known. However, the attainment of this full scale is not possible according to the third law of thermodynamics, which rules out the production of an absolute zero temperature. In the field of cryogenics, temperatures of −150°C, or about 123°K, are generally employed, although from the standpoint of freeze-drying this may be a relatively low temperature to use. Nevertheless, with extremely high vacuum procedures as well as good heat exchange between the tissue and the surrounding container, it may very well be possible to freeze and dry tissue at 123°K (−150°C). An interesting characteristic of liquid helium is its superfluidity, which occurs at temperatures of about 20°K (−253°C) and 2°K (−271°C) and which has been employed in the freezing of tissues for electron microscopic studies as discussed by McClintock (1964), Mendelssohn (1960, 1961), and R. B. Scott (1959). Above the lambda point the viscosity of liquid helium, although less temperature dependent than the viscosity of other liquids, behaves in no unusual way. Its value is much lower than that of other liquids (about 1/100 that of liquid nitrogen), but this low value is easily explained by the high zero point energy of the liquid which "inflates" it somewhat and gives it many gaslike qualities, among them low viscosity. Aside from the fact that the viscosity of liquid helium is more nearly the same as that of a gas than a liquid, there is no unusual behavior from the critical point, $5.20°K$ ($-267.95°C$) down to about $3.0°K$ ($-270.15°C$). At this temperature, according to the lambda transition, the viscosity begins to decrease sharply. There is a continual decrease in the viscosity through the lambda transition until about $1°K$ ($-272°C$) or until the liquid has nearly zero viscosity. For example, an ordinary fluid will flow in a downward direction, while liquid helium II will creep upward and cover a slide which has been partially immersed in the helium solution.

New cryogenic techniques are entering into many diverse fields. Researchers have developed techniques for freezing of whole human blood for an indefinite period. Other live cells as well as bacterial cultures can also be frozen and stored indefinitely. Williams (1957) has studied the appearance of influenza virus of rabbit papilloma by freeze-dry techniques and the morphology of poliomyelitis virus type II has also been studied. The conclusions from these investigations is that none of the animal viruses show any indications of polyhedral form as is found in some of the plant viruses. The small ($27 \, m\mu$) poliomyelitis appears spherical when frozen-dried, while the larger viruses appear like spheres that have shrunken during dehydration. The size and shape of the poliomyelitis virus is very uniform, and it has now been demonstrated that this type of virus can be crystallized into fairly large three-dimensional crystals similar in appearance to those formed by some of the smaller plant viruses (Williams, 1957; Bourne and Danielli, 1957).

Cowley (1964) has discussed various aspects of cryobiology from the engineering standpoint. It is pointed out that a bath of isopentane at $-120°C$ results in faster cooling of an immersed specimen than does liquid nitrogen at $-196°C$. Therefore, basic knowledge of heat transfer becomes important in order to understand the reasons behind such phenomena and to utilize them in low-temperature techniques. An understanding of heat transfer characteristics of a boiling fluid, such as liquid nitrogen, has led to techniques for varying and controlling the cooling rates of specimens immersed in it by the application of a thin layer of thermally insulating material to the sample container.

Two somewhat diverging views dealing with the handling of tissues for low temperature work have been proposed. In one view, it is recommended that tissues be frozen as rapidly as possible, even to the extent of applying cryogenic gases such as helium II. The other view recommends the application of relatively slow freezing in conjunction with cryoprotective substances (e.g., glycerol or DMSO).

In a recent book by Smith, "Biological Effects of Freezing and Super-cooling" (1961), methods for supercooling animal tissues as well as entire animals are discussed. The highest incidence of supercooling was among hamsters which had been drinking 20% propylene glycol and had received no other fluids in their diet. Smith also reported the work of Kalabukhov, who suggested that it was possible to store animals for long periods in the supercooled state at temperatures as low as $-40°C$ ($233°K$). Smith also reported the application of radiofrequency radiation in order to warm the frozen hamsters and other animals. In one case a galago (*Crassicaudatus agisymbanus*), one of the smaller primates, which was frozen for approximately 1 hour was revived by microwave diathermy and artificial respiration. It was found also that rats which had been trained prior to freezing to find food in the maze retained their ability upon survival. Postmortem examinations revealed a pulmonary edema that may have resulted from terminal cardiac failure. These results suggest that it is possible to resuscitate adult nonhibernating mammals as complex as primates after cooling of the body temperatures below zero and after partial freezing of the fluid in superficial and internal organs.

Jacob (1964) has studied the freezing of organs by perfusion of liquid helium, which enters the renal artery at $-190°C$ under 3 pounds of pressure through a metal cannula. It requires about 2.5 hours for the temperature in the center of the kidney to reach $-180°C$. The kidney can then be positioned in a Dewar flask cooled in liquid helium and the vapor pressure dropped to 80 μ of mercury, the equivalent of $-272.2°C$.

The problems of cryobiology encompass various areas including what happens to an entire animal or a single cell when it is cooled and subsequently warmed, to techniques for preserving blood cells or destroying neoplastic cells. Of particular interest is the problem of finding what occurs in the salt, protein, and water molecules in a freezing solution that may contain glycerol or other materials. Cryobiology is therefore a technical problem area, not a well-defined realm of organized science or technology. Of interest is the review by Doebbler and Cowley (1964). It is believed that the answer to the control of biological and biochemical changes lies in the low-temperature area. Temperature is an important parameter to physicists and chemists as well as biologists. As Doebbler and Cowley have pointed out, temperature is exponentially important in that life turns upon chemical reactions, and reactions slow down as temperature decreases—almost by one half for every $10°C$. Thus the refrigeration industry is based upon preservation of changeable biological products, such as foods. From the tissue research standpoint there are the more difficult problems of keeping living cells preserved for longer periods. The key to such "suspended animation" or prevention of aging lies in keeping living cells cold, since at sufficiently low temperatures it is known that chemical reactions or even physical processes such as diffusion do not occur at significant rates or at all. But the basic problem is bringing a live cell to low temperature and back to warm temperature again without harming the cell. While cold does have a preserving influence, it also kills most living cells unless it is employed under certain very limited conditions. One of the most important areas of cryobiology is the mechanism by which living cells or organisms are killed, or avoid death, by freezing or thawing. Since water constitutes the major component of most living systems and it is this substance that undergoes, physically, a qualitative change, study of the state of submicroscopic organization of water molecules with relation to the structures of living cells, including their proteins and protein complexes and lipids, are significant. In addition to the aforementioned macromolecules, specific components of the cell including the nucleus, mitochondria, ribosomes, cytoplasm, lysosomes, and cytoplasmic membranes have been studied with reference to the effects of low temperature freezing and thawing.

One of the most difficult aspects confronting the research attempts to lower the temperature of a living biological system is "phase transition." When water in such a system freezes as pure ice, a dehydration process occurs. This results in a rising concentration of solutes in the remaining unfrozen liquid, and changes in pH then follow. As can be expected, the cells deform as they are channeled between the growing matrix of ice crystals. Soon, sufficient salts have accumulated to begin interacting with the lipid components of the cell membranes so as to alter their permeability characteristics and permit the leaking away of various metabolites. The fact that salt concentrations induced by freezing play an important role in cell injury can be demonstrated by adding salt to blood in the same proportion as would be created by lethal freezing. The same pattern of dissolution of erythrocytes by liberation of their hemoglobin occurs. It is believed by some that the crushing effect of ice crystal formation is not as important as the above-mentioned salt concentration, with reference to tissue damage. This is the case if ice crystals are formed outside the cell. However, most types of cells are unable to survive formation of intracellular ice crystals. Figure 2, adapted from a paper by Doebbler and Cowley (1964) outlines a hypothesis concerning cell injury—salt concentration and intracellular ice—and the influence of these factors on viability as a function of cooling rate. The cells at the left of the diagram are distorted or crenated because they have cooled slowly enough for water to be lost by diffusion, while cells at the right retain their shape and size because they are cooled so fast that intracellular water is retained.

The quantitative relationship between viability and cooling rates may differ considerably, but the overall pattern is essentially the same.

Cooling rates may be classified as ultrarapid, 150°C/sec; rapid, 15–

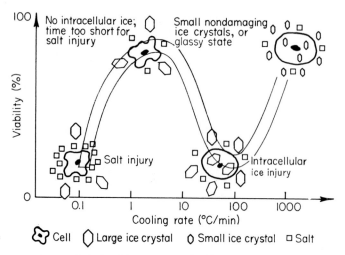

Fig. 2. Relationship between viability and cooling rate.

150°C/sec; moderate, 0.5–15°C/sec; and slow, up to 0.5°C/sec (Cowley and Rinfret, 1963).

Pryde and Jones (1952) demonstrated that water could be frozen into a vitreous state and that it crystallized at −129°C as it was rewarmed. Subsequently, Stephenson (1956) calculated that to produce vitrification in tissues it would be necessary to have a cooling below −100°C at the rate of 5000°C/sec, −100°C being the estimate of the temperature at which vitreous water in the tissue would crystallize.

Very slow cooling allows formation of large ice crystals, concentration of the liquid surrounding the cell, and withdrawal of water from inside the cells; since intracellular ice formation is unlikely, injury that does occur will be caused by some concentrated solute (salt, hydrogen ion, etc.). On the other hand, more rapid cooling diminishes the time of the exposure to concentrated constituents of the medium and thus reduces further damage by them. Since adequate cell permeability is retained, intracellular water can still be lost through the cell membrane, so that intracellular ice crystal formation is unlikely. Thus viability rises in this cooling-rate range. If the cell is cooled at an even faster rate, injury by concentrated constituents of the medium is probably avoided because of the short time of exposure. Because of permeability changes in the cell membrane, however, water may not escape from the cell rapidly enough, and intracellular ice crystals of size to cause damage may be expected. Without actually attaining "vitrification" (e.g., the absence of crystalline ice), it may be assumed that highly rapid cooling rates can be employed to reduce the size of ice crystals both inside and outside the cell. This also would result in a higher viability of the tissue. With the application of such high cooling rates, however, the question of thermal shock arises. There is probably some high velocity of cooling at which injury can occur because of differences in the coefficients of thermal expansion of different cell constituents. Which mechanism is at work at very high rate—intracellular ice damage or thermal shock—is not clear.

The general principles involved in ultrarapid cooling of biological materials is discussed by Cowley *et al.* (1961). The temperature-time relationship in a material at a given temperature which is suddenly exposed to a considerable variation in temperature change is a complex function of several variables. If a phase change occurs anywhere in the sample during the period under study, the complexity is further increased. The degree of cooling or warming which the material goes through at a given time after exposure to a given environment is a function not only of its thermal characteristics and geometry, but also the heat transfer coefficient is mainly determined by the characteristics of the environment. In this particular study, tissues including liver and kidney cooled at a much higher rate when immersed in liquid nitrogen if they had been previously coated with a thermally insulating material such as glycerol.

Hypothetical aspects of freeze preparation of tissues are shown in Figs. 3 and 4. Figure 3 has four regions: water in the specimen cools to the freezing point (*1*); then it supercools (*2*); ice crystals then form, usually abruptly, and phase transition goes to completion (*3*); and finally, further cooling occurs in a solid state (*4*). Biological changes may occur by heat removal during any or all of these phases. The curve's shape—the two slopes and the duration of phase-change plateau—sums up the transient heat transfer relationship between biological specimens and their cold environment.

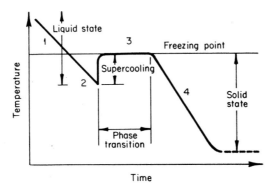

Fig. 3. Cooling diagram according to Doebbler and Cowley (1964).

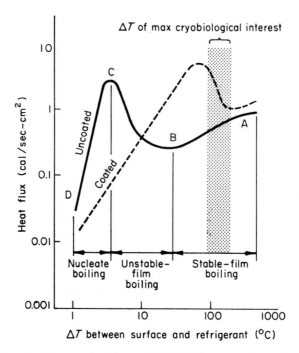

Fig. 4. T between tissue and refrigerant (°C). With some cells, such as blood cells, heat must be withdrawn rapidly. Immersion in liquefied gases, such as nitrogen, provides the initial low temperature, but cooling rate is limited by localized boiling, which occurs as heat leaving the specimen evaporates the refrigerant. This is the stable-film boiling region AB. The film continually exhibits a breakup and reformation as ΔT declines—region of unstable-film boiling BC—and heat flux all show rapid changes. Finally, as the surface of the biological substance cools to a temperature closer to that of the refrigerant, a less effective heat transfer mode, called nucleate boiling, occurs (region CD). Low heat transfer is indicated in the area of cryobiological interest, specifically that of T. However, by applying certain coating or possibly by the use of helium II, the more effective region of unstable-film boiling can be made to coincide with the region of higher ΔT's. Thus, the heat-flux curve can be shifted to the right as shown by the dashed curve. (According to Doebbler and Cowley, 1964.)

Although the present discussion primarily involves the effects of ice crystals and related changes, it should also be mentioned that it has been suggested that when liquid water freezes as ice, the dry protein macro-molecules of the cell structure may physically approach one another and undergo chemical interaction by disulfide formation. Such disulfide forma-tions are not reversible upon thawing. Therefore, protection against low temperature injury might be afforded when natural or artificial factors in the system prevent the physical association of macromolecules that allow this chemical interaction (Andrews and Levitt, 1967).

From the standpoint of solidification, it is apparent that most liquids and solutions pass from the liquid state to the crystalline solid state when cooled. Solidification without crystallization (or supercooling) is an additional possibility, as shown in Fig. 3. This phenomenon of "vitrification" has been studied by Luyet and associates and will be further described. On the basis of this work on the so-called "glassy state," it has long been thought that early experiments that appeared to "vitrify" vinegar eels probably resulted merely in the formation of extremely small crystals of ice. Thus, the old view of the solid, amorphous state has given way to a concept of "vitrification" as a semicrystalline state, as in glasses. In water, extensive and detailed light and electron microscopy and X-ray diffraction observations of solutions frozen at high velocity have indicated some evidence of ordered structure or crystallinity. In recent years, it has been observed that dissolved compounds can alter the formation and size of ice crystals and even their crystalline shape. More important, solutes retard nucleation and drastically retard the rate of growth of ice crystals. One of the significant observations is that compounds like glycerol increase the likelihood of supercooling to lower temperatures before crystallization can occur, if at all. Therefore, if the amount of ice that forms in the presence of such a solute is small, the concentration of possibly damaging electrolytes in the solution will be reduced.

Recently a conference on cryobiology, sponsored by the American Cancer Society (Stowell, 1965), was held. In this conference studies on water/solvent interaction and the determination of recrystallization temperatures were elucidated. When a solution has been frozen rapidly, so that it is not permitted to reach its phase equilibrium and still has some of its water in a nonfrozen state, a rise in temperature will complete crystallization. A range in which this happens, designated as a recrystallization temperature, depends primarily on the molecular weight of the solute and is little affected by the concentration. Thus glycerol solutions recrystallize in the neighborhood of $-60°C$, gelatin solutions at about $-10°C$, and sucrose solutions around $-31°C$. The recrystallization range is apparently related to the mode of binding of water to the solute. Apparently the conditions for the formation of a vitreous state, the ability of any substance to exist as a "glass," is determined by two parameters, the crystallization velocity and the rate of nucleation. Both these quantities have a maximum value at a specific temperature (not necessarily the same), being limited at a low temperature by lack of molecular motion, as measured, for example, by viscosity. A "glass" forms when the nucleation rate (the number of nuclei formed per cm^{-3}/sec^{-1}) does not exceed that at which significant crystallization can take place. This will depend on the length of time spent by the specimen at different temperatures, glass being more likely to form at high cooling rates. In the case of water alone, the viscosity data show that a glass is unlikely to form until well below $-100°C$.

In the same conference on cryobiology the effects of freezing on enzymes systems have also been reported (Chilson *et al.*, 1965). The denaturation of proteins during freezing and thawing appears to be primarily due to the effects of pH change. It has been suggested that actual physical contact between protein molecules may occur as water is removed by freezing and that this might cause nonspecific disulfide bridging and aggregation. Whatever the mechanism involved, the data presented by these authors suggest that the protection of sulfhydryl groups is important in reducing the extent of protein modification caused by freezing and thawing. The effects of freezing and thawing on sulfhydryl groups does not appear to be due to oxidation of these groups, since freezing in a nitrogen atmosphere does not prevent inactivation of the enzymes. Among the enzyme systems studied by these workers were triosephosphate dehydrogenase, glutamic dehydrogenase, alcohol dehydrogenases, malic dehydrogenase, α-glycerol phosphate dehydrogenase, and muscle aldolase.

The protection against freeze-thaw inactivation of enzymes shown by ethylene glycol, propylene glycol, glycerol, DMSO, and sucrose is not clear, but it may be a function of the colligative properties of the solutions. It has been suggested that glycerol prevents hemolysis of blood by reducing the concentration of salt in the eutectic mixture. Protection against inactivation or inhibition due to specific binding of the reagents to the proteins and modification of solvent structure must be also taken into account in any study of low-temperature effects on enzymes. Irrespective of the mechanisms involved, the above-mentioned compounds are very useful as additives for storage of enzymes at low temperatures. It is interesting that the agents that protect against the inactivation of enzymes during freezing and thawing also are effective in preventing damage to intact cells and organs. The usefulness of these compounds in the freeze-dry process depends upon their vapor pressure. In the case of glycerol, it is unlikely that even under high vacuums this reagent could be removed. The effect of enzyme hybridization induced after repeated freeze-thaw cycles has been observed. One cycle at very low temperatures resulted in little or no hybridization; thus, under conditions of rapid freezing and rapid thawing the rate is slow. However, after many fast freezes and fast thaws there is indication of hybrid formation. With reference to cryostat techniques, it might be feasible to control the conditions of thawing rates in order to maintain reproducible activity.

It appears that the effects of denaturing agents upon the hydrophobic bonds of proteins and nucleic acids are accompanied by changes in the structure of the solvent. Thus the influence of salts of compounds of the ureaguanidinium class on the denaturation, dissociation, and solubility of proteins does not appear to result directly from any simple effect of these compounds on the structure of water itself. The formation of "ice-like" or structured regions in the water which surrounds tissue proteins and occurs in ice itself requires further study.

The preservation of blood by freezing has been described in a recent review by Meryman (1964). This review deals also with an evaluation and review of effects of cryoprotective agents such as glycerol, DMSO, and DMSO followed by sucrose. According to Sherman (1965) the protective effect of 5% DMSO was equivalent to that of glycerol. Lovelock (1954) has proposed a number of protective agents, including their requirements, but the mode and site of action of such agents including glycerol is open to question. Nevertheless, as previously mentioned, these agents may be tried in conjunction with cryostat techniques for the preparation of frozen sections.

Doebbler and Rinfret (1965) have studied physical and chemical factors in the rapid freezing of human blood. In their paper they review previous literature which has explained freezing injury to erythrocytes as a result of exposure to concentrated electrolytes arising as water is converted into ice. Thus, glycerol and other small molecular weight solutes appear to protect by "buffering" the concentration of salts in equilibrium with ice at any subfreezing temperature above the eutectic point. Freezing injury has been interpeted as due to molecular disturbances in protoplasm caused by crystallization of ice. Thus the rate of cooling may inhibit ice crystal formation. As previously indicated, the view that glycerol and other solutes inhibit the rate of ice crystal growth, and thereby prevent seeding of cross membranes and formation of intercellular ice crystals, several difficulties in that it does not account for specificity among cryoprotective solutes, and requires at least two separate mechanisms of injury by freezing to be postulated as one goes from slow to rapid cooling conditions. Doebbler and Rinfret (1965) have studied cryoprotective agents containing one or more hydroxyl, carboxyl, amino, amide, or carbonyl functional groups. At equimolar concentrations, protection increases with the number of functional groups per molecule. With the particular water-soluble compounds studied, all groups were capable of hydrogen bonding. Some fifteen water-soluble polymers of molecular weights from 500 to 400,000 were studied. Some of these which afforded more protection were polyoxyethylenes, polyvinylpyrrolidone, and dextrans; albumin, gelatin, gum acacia, polyproline, polyoxypropylene, however, afforded little or no protection. Polyvinylpyrrolidone and polyoxyethylene were effective cryoprotectants at 7% concentration (w/v).

Doebbler and Rinfret also found that solutions of cryoprotective agents gave evidence of vitreous ice in addition to crystalline hexagonal ice while only crystalline hexagonal ice was observed in solutions of structurally similar nonprotective solutes. Of interest is the fact that concentrated sodium chloride behaved like a protective solute; also 30% aqueous concentrations of glucose, methylglucose, and polyvinylpyrrolidone gave vitreous plus hexagonal ice formation. The biochemical effects of freezing were also studied with reference to the enzyme nucleoside triphosphatase. This enzyme is localized in the erthrocyte membrane and is reportedly involved in cation transport. Since phosphatase activity is known to be changed or altered by several kinds of disruption, it may serve as an indicator system in deciding which of the possible agents of injury during freezing inflict hemolytic or other damage. Similarly, it may be of value to study the effects upon freezing of enzyme systems related to cytoplasmic, mitochondrial, and nuclear membranes.

Other compounds that reduce freezing damage have been studied by Vos and Kaalen (1965). Protective effects in freezing of human kidney tissue culture cells were found with ethylene glycol, diethylene glycol, propylene glycol, dimethyl sulfoxide, pyridine N-oxide, and hexamethylene tetramine. Less protective were acetamide, dimethylacetamide, formamide, dimethylformamide, monoacetine, d-mannose, d-ribose, glucose, d-mannitol, sorbitol, and inositol. Little protection was observed with dimethyl sulfone, polyvinylpyrrolidone, and serum. It is of interest that lower survival than in control experiments was found if methanol, ethanol, phenol, resorcinol, or sodium chloride were added to the growth medium.

Coriell et al. (1964) notes that, with reference to tissue cultures during ultrarapid freezing, ice crystal growth does not occur below $-130°C$ and is retarded by the well-known additives glycerol, alcohol, sugars, urea, sodium citrate, and polyvinylpyrrolidone (PVP).

From a histochemical standpoint, Turchini and Malet (1965) have found that various tissues kept in 50% glycerol–water at $-20°C$ for 9 months exhibited good preservation of tissue architecture as well as maintainance of a number of enzyme systems including 5'-nucleotidase, ATPase, monoamine oxidase, succinic dehydrogenase, and alkaline phosphatase.

The freeze-drying of microorganisms and the protective action of the suspending medium in the freeze-dry process have been described by Morichi (1964). About 150 different low molecular weight compounds were studied including acidic compounds related to glutamic acid, neutral compounds related to glucose, and basic compounds related to arginine. In most instances, a 0.06 M aqueous solution adjusted to pH 7.0 was used as the suspending medium. The protective effect of the suspending medium was evaluated in terms of the survival rate which was determined by the number of surviving bacteria before and after lyophilization. It is know that glucose, sucrose, and lactose have highly protective bonds. The protective effects of sugars against blood hemolysis which have been observed during the freezing and thawing of erythrocytes is believed to be related to the ability of such sugars to form hydrogen bonds.

Nei (1964) has also studied the effects of freezing and freeze-drying of microrganisms. Included in this work were electron micrographs of yeast cells showing the drying process of extra and intracellular water (ice in the frozen state). This author notes that glycerol, which is useful in freezing, cannot be used in freeze-drying because of its high vapor pressure (see above, page 10). He notes that the unfreezable water content in *Escherichia coli* cells is 18%. The percentage of cells surviving decreases as the amount of residual water in the cells decreases. Since the surviving rate in the cells immediately after freezing and thawing was 90%, and the survival rate was approximately 80% when the residual moisture content was reduced to 18%, it was concluded that there is only a slight decrease in the survival rate during the period in the drying process when only the freezable water is removed from the cells, and therefore the major alterations in survival rate occur during the period when unfreezable water is removed. This interesting point, that is, the evaporation of nonfrozen water during the drying phase, may have an important relationship to electron microscopic studies of frozen-dried tissue.

Stowell *et al.* (1965) have studied structural, chemical, physical, and functional alterations in mammalian nuclei following different conditions of freezing, storage, and thawing using light and electron microscopy. The best structural preservation of nuclei appeared to be obtained with the most rapid possible cooling 0°C (273°K) to below −100°C (173°K). As other investigators have reported, rather slow conditions of freezing which are better in general for preservation of chemical constituents and viability of cells lead to large intranuclear ice crystal formation during the frozen state with marked displacement of the nuclear structures, including chromatin and nucleoli. Under conditions of rapid thawing they report structural reconstitution of the nucleus so that in some tissues which are rapidly thawed it is difficult to recognize any changes other than slight clumping of chromatin, some shrinkage, and an increased affinity for certain basic dyes. If the nuclei are thawed slowly, on the other hand, there may be large residual areas of displaced necleoplasm. The physical and chemical changes that accompany freezing of the nucleus appear to be caused by the formation of ice crystals and the resulting concentration of the solute in the nucleoplasm. Some nuclear enzymes, for example NAD-phosphorylase, are not appreciably affected by freezing. Although the total amount of DNA is not altered by freezing, a reduced synthesis of DNA as measured by tritiated thymidine uptake does occur. In one report a reduced amino acid incorporation into protein has also been demonstrated.

Trump *et al.* (1965) also have reported on the effects of freezing and thawing on the morphology, chemical constitution, and function of cyto-plasmic structures. They discuss correlative electron microscopic and biochemical techniques and indicate morphological and biochemical alter-ations in virtually all cytoplasmic organelles and subcellular systems after freezing and thawing of individual cells. It appears that, in general, cyto-logic alterations after thawing tend to be minimized with relatively slow rates of freezing and rapid rates of thawing, particularly in the presence of protective agents such as glycerol or DMSO. Although cells and tissues frozen slowly are extensively distorted by large extracellular ice crystals, if stabilized in the frozen state, a striking structural reconstitution after thawing is reported.

The injury to cells following freezing and the various methods that may be used for prevention of this phenomenon have been discussed by Mommaerts (1965). With freeze-drying techniques to preserve sites of ice formation, convincing evidence has been presented that these cells do survive the formation and dissolution of intercellular ice as tested by transplantation, oxygen consumption, and mitotic activity. Specifically, human spermatozoa and human erythrocytes are in this category. Para-doxically, there is evidence that more rapid rates of freezing, with accom-panying smaller ice crystals result in greater functional damage to certain cells than lower rates with larger ice crystals (Sherman, 1962, 1964a).

Huggins (1965) has reported techniques for the preservation of cells and cell fragments that depend for their success upon control of three important variables: rates of freezing and thawing (with or without extracellular additives such as sugars or polyvinylpyrrolidone), storage temperature, and the presence of small molecules such as glycerol and DMSO (the latter class of compounds must penetrate the cell in order to be effective and can be called endocellular cryophylactic agents, or ECA's). Huggins indicated that the use of ECA's in maximally tolerated conditions would appear to be the only possible approach to the practical problem of preserving organized tissues, whole organs, and animals by freezing. In this method one accepts major osmotic problems associated with the addition and removal of ECA's to accomplish the safe passage of cells to cryogenic temperatures. Optimum protection of blood cells, for example, was obtained when DMSO was present in concentrations between 5.0 and 5.7 M.

At our present state of knowledge, there may be two possible methods of keeping cells dormant but potentially alive at low temperatures. One method, which was originated by Luyet, is to cool the cells very rapidly at a low temperature and subsequently to rewarm them very rapidly (Luyet and Gonzales, 1951). The Luyet technique was used to cool microscopic preparations of isolated cells including striated muscle fibers and frog spermatozoa. It was also used to cool and rewarm embryonic tissues; for example, embryonic chick hearts survived exposure to low temperatures of cooled and subsequently rewarmed at a rate of hundreds of degrees per second. Rinfret and co-workers (1962) found that survival of red blood cells as judged by the degree of hemolysis after thawing and their survival after transfusion was improved by including comparatively high concentrations of polyvinylpyrrolidone (PVP) and lactose in plasma in which the cells were suspended before freezing. Smith (1965) has posed the question: Could such extracellular protective substances be brought into contact with every cell in organs such as heart, kidneys, lungs, spleen, and liver of adult mammals? So far as is known the normal capillary endothelium is not permeable to molecules of this size, and diffusion through extracellular spaces would be slow. The next problem would be to thaw all cells within solid organs at a uniformly rapid rate. Smith (1965) adapted a magnatron microwave diathermy apparatus in order to thaw hamster heart at a uniform rate from $-75°C$. These organs weigh only about 5 g. It was difficult to supply the heat necessary for the fusion of ice inside the auricles and ventricles and the deeper layers of muscles without "cooking" the pericardium, coronary vessels, and superficial fibers of the myocardium, where a uniform rate of heating is required. For a large bulk of material, such as heart or kidney of a dog or man, immersion in a warm fluid would be inadequate and radiation methods must be used. At infrared wave lengths penetrations are small and there is a preferential heating of the peripheral surface. With radiofrequency heating, the absorption depends upon the loss factor of the material acting as a dielectric. Because organs are not homogeneous and there are preferential heating gradients, it is indicated by Smith that radiofrequency methods might be used where rapid reheating is necessary.

The other method currently used for preserving cells in a potentially living state at low temperatures involves the glycerol, DMSO, and other nonelectrolytes which enter cells and protect them during comparatively slow cooling to and rewarming from low temperatures. One advantage of this method is that rates of cooling of the individual cells are less critical so that large volumes can be cooled by a simple means. This method has extensively used during the past ten years in the banking of bull semen for subsequent artificial insemination. It has also been used for banking bacterial protozoa as well as mammalian cells of many types and tissue cultures. The main disadvantage is that the DMSO has to be removed, but this can be done by the technique described by Huggins in which ECA's are interchanged.

It is important to note that whether fast or relatively slow cooling is employed, it is imperative to avoid the concentration of solutes (electrolytes) which can occur in microregions of a specimen as a consequence of freezing.

Smith (1965) has also investigated the preservation of adult mammalian cartilage at low temperature. Living chondrocytes were isolated from fibrocartilage and from hyaline cartilage of rabbit, dog, monkey, and man and the matrix was removed by successive treatment with the proteolytic enzyme, papain collagenase. The isolated cartilage cells were suspended in media containing DMSO and cooled to −79°C. After thawing, their viability was reassessed and a high proportion of the cells was found to have survived. These frozen cells were then grafted into prepared sites of cancellous bone in adult animals.

From the histochemical and electron microscopic standpoint, vitrification is the least destructive type of freezing, but this is difficult to achieve even during ultrarapid cooling. Thus the formation of crystallized ice inside the cell most frequently occurs during relatively rapid cooling, e.g., when the temperatures decreases at a rate of 20°C per minute, and after supercooling. Intercellular freezing, as a rule, results in the death of organs and organisms; therefore most investigators believe that the organism can endure freezing even when crystallization takes place outside the cell. Lozina-Lozinsky (1965) studied the processes within cells and their nuclei during freezing and thawing by means of fluorescent microscopy. The tissues were located in a special cooling chamber on the table of a fluorescent microscope and the preparations were stained with acridine orange (AO) before freezing. The rate of cooling of these objects in the chamber was altered by: a gradual decrease in the temperature of the isopentane in which the preparation was submerged, by immersing the preparation in cooled isopentane, or by plunging the specimens directly into liquid nitrogen. The moment of crystallization and thawing was established microscopically and by measuring the temperature of the surrounding media in the chamber. The time of freezing is easily determined by observing the whitening of the tissue media; approximately 1 sec later the fluorescent structure of the cells becomes visible. Studies of salivary gland and ascites carcinoma were made by means of this fluorescent microscopy technique. Lozina-Lozinsky believes that there is every reason to assume that biological systems such as extremely cold-resistant organisms and cells of certain types can tolerate intracellular crystallization without the use of outside protective agents. The reversible character of changes in some types of proteins and nuclear proteins, and the capacity of the latter to acquire resistance to freezing during the life cycle of the animal and under the influence of environmental conditions of living systems may allow the study of the mechanisms of resistance to cold.

Fernández-Morán (1960) has utilized a cooled specimen support employing liquid nitrogen. A liquid nitrogen cold stage is also available with the Siemens Elmiskop I electron microscope for controlled cooling of the speciman holder from −10°C to −120°C. This cold stage minimizes specimen damage, especially with frozen-dried or freeze-substituted material, including specimens embedded in water soluble media.

Cooling stages and specimen chamber devices are available for both RCA and Philips EM 200 electron microscopes. In both systems, liquid nitrogen is employed as the coolant. Basic work on the design and physical aspects of cooling stages is described by Heide (1962).

II. Freezing of Tissues for Cryostat Application and Freeze-Drying

From a historical standpoint, interest in so-called suspended animation has been of paramount importance in many aspects of biological research. Liebow (1963) indicates that relative immortality for animal tissues may be obtained by cryogenic procedures. Thus preservation of cells may be considered the preservation of life. From a broader biological sense, reaction to cold has provided clues to the nature of protoplasm and to its survival in a hostile environment (e.g., outer space). With current interest in exobiology, cryogenic approaches may give an inkling of how living matter could be transferred from one planet to another. In the study of disease it has been exceedingly helpful to freeze-dry rare biological materials (e.g., specialized neoplasms) and to store these materials intact so that they may be made available more widely for special study.

Cryogenic techniques have also been employed in so-called "cryogenic surgery" for the treatment of neoplasms (Cooper, 1965). In this technique, liquid nitrogen is passed through a small cannula to a freezing tip. The cannula is supplied with thermocouples at the freezing tip so the temperature may be monitored throughout the procedure. Cooper has applied this technique in the treatment of various malignant growths and various other tissues, and has found that virtually all living tissues subjected to temperatures of −20°C or below for 1 min or longer will undergo cryogenic coagulation leading to necrosis.

When a tissue specimen is frozen, the free water is removed from the organic matrix and deposited in the form of ice crystals. The organic matrix which is compressed by the forming crystals appears as a honey-comb and in tissue sections is referred to as the ice-crystal artifact. In general, freezing should occur as rapidly as possible in order to minimize the size of ice-crystal artifacts. However, in many instances, particularly involving tissues that have high water content, rapid freezing does not appear to reduce appreciably the size of the crystals. Goodspeed and Uber (1935) called attention to the fact that various conditions, including unknown factors, might determine the rate of freezing of tissues; that slow freezing gave rise to intercellular nucleocytoplasmic surfaces; and that, on the other hand, rapid freezing increased the number of centers of crystallization and determined the degree of reticulation (ice-crystal artifact) produced.

The ideal situation would be the direct transformation of water in tissues to a vitreous or completely amorphous state with no evidence of crystalline pattern. In recent years the transfer of water out of solution into ice crystals has been studied rather intensively. Pioneering work in this area has been done by Luyet (1960), who has studied transitions from the liquid or amorphous state into a crystalline state, and also other transitions such as solidification into the amorphous state, vitrifi-cation, and transformations within the amorphous state in the form of incomplete crystallization. The possibility of obtaining complete vitrifi-cation has been considered (Luyet, 1951). With regard to obtaining an amorphous state of protoplasm after freezing, he feels that rapid cooling can hinder the crystallization process somewhat but does not prevent it entirely. Electron micrographs of frozen-dried tissues often reveal obvious ice-crystal artifacts or else areas showing no apparent crystallization. Stephenson (1956) feels that samples which show no obvious ice-crystal artifacts are vitrified. It is reasonable to assume that some areas of small tissue specimens may be frozen in the vitreous state. At approximately $-150°C$ crystal formation ceases and any remaining water remains un-crystallized. As previously mentioned, it has been estimated that to avoid crystal formation the specimen must be cooled below $-100°C$ in less than 0.02 sec (Figs. 5-7).

The earliest form of ice crystal is called a crystal nucleus. This nucleus is made up of an aggregation of molecules that may grow to form a larger crystal or series of crystals. Thus, for formation of crystals of small size, a rapid rate of nucleation and a low rate of growth are to be desired. The addition of glycerin or similar substances may reduce the amount of water available for crystallization. However, this approach has not as yet found application in the histochemical use of freeze-drying. Meryman (1964) has carefully reviewed physical principles of ice-crystal growth *in vitro* and *in vivo*. Of interest is the fact that in tissues subjected to slow

FIG. 5. Frozen saline solution; approximately 50% of the photograph is $NaCl \cdot 2H_2O$. In this area there is a 50-fold increase in concentration relative to the distribution of solute as compared with an unfrozen solution. The depletion of salt from adjacent microregions may result in damage to cells subjected to osmotic pressure extremes during a warming process. Thus part of the cell surface would be exposed to a highly hypertonic medium, and another part to a highly hypotonic medium. In addition, extreme salt concentration could be damaging to the cell membrane through interaction with its lipid-protein components. $\times$ 24,800. (Courtesy of Dr. A. P. Rinfret.)

freezing, crystal nucleation is subordinated and nuclei appear uniformly throughout the specimen. Although the crystal size which occurs during rapid freezing is generally many times smaller than that occurring with slow freezing, experience has shown that viability of tissue is enhanced by slow freezing.

Mathematical factors that influence ice-crystal formation during rapid

Fig. 6. Electron micrograph of blood plasma frozen at −20°C (253°K) showing relatively large ice crystal structure. × 12,000. (Courtesy of Dr. A. P. Rinfret.)

freezing of biological material have been considered by Stephenson (1960). He has pointed out that two closely related problems arise during the rapid freezing of tissue specimens. The first is the dependence of the cooling rate on the sample size, shape, and thermal properties, on the velocity of immersion, and on the temperature and physical properties of the coolant. The second is the relation of the size and number of ice crystals to the thermal history of the sample. Thus as soon as ice crystals begin to form throughout a specimen they may act as numerous small heat sources evolving heat as they grow in size.

Recently Fernández-Morán (1960) studied the formation of submicroscopic ice crystals by means of electron microscopy. It was possible to stabilize thin ice crystals at low temperatures and to obtain high resolution electron micrographs and electron diffraction patterns of these. By oriented deposition of ice crystals on films of mica, characteristic moiré patterns were observed. These ingenious techniques may elucidate the changes in submicroscopic structure that occur in tissues during the freezing procedure.

Danielli (1953) has determined some of the time relationships in freeze-drying, as compared with routine aqueous fixation, by plunging a specimen containing a thermocouple into a freezing mixture. It was found that the temperature in the center of a 2-mm section of tissue fell

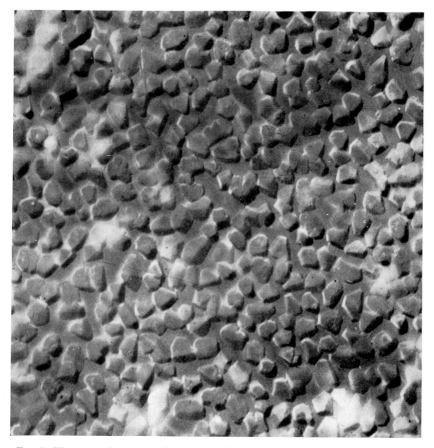

Fig. 7. Electron micrograph of specimen of human blood plasma rapidly frozen at −79°C (194°K). Note the smaller crystalline structure as compared with Fig. 6, although the magnification is greater.

to below $-50°$ in less than 10 sec and below $-170°$ in less than 30 sec. A 2-mm specimen is thoroughly frozen in 2–3 sec as compared with a minimum of over 300 sec which is required when a rapidly penetrating fixative solution is used. Thus freezing in isopentane cooled by liquid nitrogen results in a fixation time approximately 1% of that required when a chemical fixative is used. With the application of material exhibiting thermal superconductivity, such as liquid helium II, even shorter fixation times may be achieved (Fernández-Morán, 1960). Even though freeze-drying presents great advantages over chemical fixation, artifacts at the submicroscopic and microscopic levels may still arise. It has been observed, for example, that gels frozen at low temperature exhibit a laminated structure; and at times similar laminations may be seen in frozen-dried tissues at high optical magnification (Bell, 1952a). When specimens over several millimeters thick are frozen, gross cracks may be seen. These, however, do not as a rule interfere with subsequent processing or study. Small pieces of tissue are to be preferred.

Since the probability of formation of ice-crystal nuclei is low below $-33°C$ and increases considerably between $-33°C$ and $-43°C$ (Fisher et al., 1949), various rapid cooling procedures have been employed since the inception of freeze-drying. These include direct cooling in liquid oxygen, nitrogen, hydrogen, and helium or else fluids cooled by these liquefied gases (Luyet, 1951). Gersh (1932) used liquid air which, despite its low temperature, offered relatively poor surface fixation (Gersh and Stephenson, 1954). Although the temperature of liquid nitrogen was satisfactory in establishing a large temperature gradient, poor conductivity resulted because of the formation of a vaporized air film adjacent to the specimen. Various other quenching liquids and mixtures have been employed; these include: isopentane cooled by liquid nitrogen (Hoerr, 1936; Simpson, 1941; Stowell, 1951; Glick and Malmström, 1952), isopentane containing dry butane cooled by nitrogen (Emmel, 1946), propane and isopentane cooled by nitrogen (Bell, 1952a), propane cooled by nitrogen (Bell, 1952a; Moberger et al., 1954), Freon 12 cooled by nitrogen (Bell, 1952b), Dry Ice–pentane mixture (Zlotnik, 1960), and liquid helium II (Fernández-Morán, 1960).

Moline and Glenner (1964) reported the use of different powders for the coating of tissue specimens prior to immersion in liquid nitrogen and found that powder-coated tissues cooled more rapidly in liquid nitrogen than in isopentane liquid nitrogen. The powder coating procedures prior to immersion in liquid nitrogen have been reviewed by Cowley et al. (1961, 1962) and Luyet (1961). For histochemical application it is recommended that tissues be dipped into a very fine Santocel (Monsanto Chemical Company).

The temperatures of previously mentioned quenching media are given below:

Liquid nitrogen, $-195°C$ ($78°K$)
Isopentane, $-165°C$ (approx.)($108°K$)
Isopentane–butane, $-190°C$ ($83°K$)
Propane–isopentane mixture, $-190°C$ ($83°K$)
Propane, $-185°C$ ($88°K$)
Freon 12, $-158°C$ ($115°K$)
Dry isopentane, $-125°C$ ($148°K$)
Liquid helium II, $-272°C$ ($1°K$)
Ucon 12 (CCl_2F_2), $-30°C$ ($253°K$)
Freon 22, $-40°C$ ($243°K$)
Freon 502, $-45°C$ ($238°K$)
Freon 113, $-35°C$ ($248°K$)
Freon 215, $-80°C$ ($193°K$)

It may be mentioned that Freon products are organic compounds containing 1–4 atoms and fluorine.

Freezing in isopentane cooled by liquid nitrogen gas found widespread use for routine histological and histochemical studies. For more specialized cytochemical work, propane or propane-isopentane mixtures are recommended. Stephenson (1956) found that propane gave an appreciable advantage with respect to heat transfer as compared with isopentane and that, over a wide range, the velocity of immersion did not significantly affect the cooling rate. The employment of liquid helium II represents an innovation because of its thermal superconductivity and its superfluidity.

In general, it is advisable to place tissue specimens on a small piece of aluminum foil and drop this directly into the agitated quenching bath. Specific metal holders have also been devised for this purpose, but their use may entail considerable heat loss. Eränkö (1954a) recommended the use of the very high heat conductivity of copper by first cooling copper disks and freezing thin slices of tissue between the cold metal surfaces. He pointed out that under these conditions the same amount of heat is transferred about several thousand times more quickly through copper than through an organic liquid. The specimens which he used were less than a millimeter thick, and the metal temperature was $-192°C$. He reported that microscopic examination of the subsequently freeze-dried and stained specimens did not reveal ice-crystal artifacts even at very high optical magnification. It would seem, however, that fluids are more suitable for the freezing of specimens of irregular size where close apposition of the freezing solution is necessary.

According to Gersh (1932), $-20°C$ is below the freezing point of tissue fluids. However, due to concentration of inorganic substances which accompanies the drying process, a lower temperature must be used. Goodspeed and Uber (1934) found that dehydration at −32°C was more satisfactory than at −23°C, and also commented that dehydration time varies and must be arbitrarily determined. Hoerr (1936), Simpson (1941), G. H. Scott and Hoerr (1950), and Gersh and Stephenson (1954) are in agreement that drying temperatures above −30°C do not give as satisfactory results as the lower temperatures. Simpson (1941) found that tissues dehydrated at −40°C showed a more uniform quality of preservation than those dehydrated at −30°C or above. He reported, however, that there did not appear to be any advantage in employing temperatures below −40°C; G. H. Scott (1943), Copeland (1951), and Kulenkampff (1954) favor lower drying temperatures. With reference to preparation for electron microscopy, Gersh (1956) found that morphology was the same whether specimens were dried at −30°C or −78°C. On the other hand, Seno and Yoshizawa (1960) feel that a drying temperature of −55°C to −60°C is necessary. Of interest, however, is the fact that drying of pharmaceutical or other industrial products is usually carried out at −30°C or even higher (Flosdorf, 1954); but, of course, such specimens are not intended for morphological detail.

Salt (1961) has described the supercooling of water and of insect tissues at high temperatures, such as −10°C in an electrostatic field produced by parallel-plate electrodes. The voltage was approximately 15,000 and the current source was a tesla or automobile-type spark coil energized by a 4-V 60 cps source. One terminal led to the cold plate, the other to a 15-inch wire probe sheathed with glass tubing except for the terminal inch. The probe was held vertically 0.5 inch above each sample for 5 sec. The sample to be frozen is placed on or close to one electrode. The nature of the action of the electrostatic field in stimulating nucleation can only be surmised. It is possible that molecules of supercooled water, or the nucleating agents may be oriented by the electrostatic field in a manner favorable to nucleus formation.

Fernández-Morán (1960, 1962) has studied the formation of submicroscopic ice crystals by means of electron microscopy. With specialized techniques employing liquid helium II, tissues were frozen at −272°C (1°K). Recently a text dealing with low-temperature techniques employing liquid helium was published by Rose-Innes (1964); this deals not only with characteristics of liquid helium but with its application in cryostats and for refrigeration. Fernández-Morán (1960) has pointed out that many chemical reactions involving addition of hydrogen atoms, which diffuse readily through solid olefins and other hydrocarbons, can take place at liquid nitrogen temperature, and even at 20°K (−253°C). Many stable chemicals, such as free radicals, still show considerable reactivity at 70°K (−203°C). It has only recently been possible to trap these chemical fragments by freezing them into an inert solid at very low temperatures with liquid helium. The free radicals and other transient intermediates with unpaired electron-spin play an important role in enzymatic reactions and metabolic electron transfer. Moreover, the production of abundant free radicals is closely linked with all biological effects of ionizing radiation, and their study is therefore basic to an understanding of radiation damage. Electron-spin resonance as the primary tool for the study of free radicals in biological systems has important limitations and lacks the necessary sensitivity for adequate detection of the small, steady-state concentrations of free radicals in many biological processes. In addition to making possible temperatures below 15°K (−258°C), liquid helium possesses several unique properties that may be highly suitable for very rapid cooling of biological specimens. Two forms of liquid helium I and II are available. Atmospheric helium gas condenses into the *"quantum liquid state,"* which is so unusual that it has been referred to as the only representative of a fourth state of matter. At the temperature of 2.9°K (−270°C) helium undergoes the remarkable second-order transformation characterized by sharp discontinuities in specific heat, thermal conductivity, viscosity, and other physical properties. This spectacular nature is clearly discernible when liquid helium II is prepared. Liquid helium I (normal thermal conductivity of the order of 10^{-5} unit), when evaporated under reduced pressure, is boiled violently. However, as the temperature falls, all bubbling suddenly ceases and a limpid column of quiescent fluids fills the inner Dewar flask. In this bath there is no boiling because the million-times-greater thermal conductivity of liquid helium II prevents any temperature differences from arising between bottom and top of the bulk liquid that might be large enough to allow vapor bubble formation. This is in striking contrast to liquid nitrogen which bubbles violently when tissue is placed in it. Therefore thermal superconductivity is an outstanding property of liquid helium II and, under certain conditions, the liquid will conduct heat 10,000 times better than copper, achieving a high conductivity of 10^4 watt units. This transfer of heat does not conform to the usual low heat of conductivity and depends upon the temperature gradient. Although bulk liquid helium II is a superconductor of heat, it has been found that all solid surfaces immersed in the liquid behave as though they were covered by a thin, poorly conducting boundary layer.

The previously mentioned superfluidity of helium II enables the bulk liquid to flow so rapidly through the finest capillaries that it seems to have an almost zero viscosity. An additional property of helium II is the fact that it forms a film which migrates rapidly over contacted surfaces above the bath level. This practically frictionless transfer of liquid helium II is effected by a mobile film, which is approximately 100 atoms thick and creeps over all solid surfaces that have maintained their temperature below the (lambda) point. Fernández-Morán has employed a cryoelectron microscope which utilizes a liquid nitrogen or liquid helium cooled stage to cool the thermally insulated specimen support (1960, 1964b, 1965). This technical refinement, which minimizes specimen damage due to electron bombardment, utilizes a cooled stage with an electron microbeam of low intensity. Under such conditions submicroscopic ice crystals have been directly observed during various stages of formation. In addition, by oriented deposition of ice crystals on coherent-crystal films, characteristic electron-optical effects such as moiré patterns have been recorded. In this way, indirect resolution of the atom arrangement in ice crystals may eventually be achieved. Thus, by demonstrating that frozen water can be examined under extreme conditions of high vacuum and electron bombardment, which had previously severely limited the application range of electron microscopy, it now has become feasible to consider electron optical studies of biological systems in a form more closely approximating their native hydrated state.

Ultrathin frozen sections of fresh tissues can be examined directly without thawing by the electron microscope, by the use of a liquid nitrogen cooling device (Fernández-Morán, 1964a,b).

Van Harreveld and Crowell (1964) and Van Harreveld et al. (1965) froze tissue rapidly by placing specimens of brain onto a polished silver mirror maintained at a temperature of about $-207°C$ ($66°K$). The tissue was then freeze-substituted into acetone containing 2% osmium tetroxide at $-85°C$ ($188°K$) for 2 days, and then studied by means of electron microscopy. On the basis of impedance measurements in conjunction with submicroscopic observations, it is felt that these tissues were frozen in the vitreous state.

Sherman and Lim (1967) have made a comprehensive study of the ultrastructure of ascites tumor and kidney cortical cells before the cells are frozen, while frozen, and after thawing. In the tumor cells they conducted parallel experiments on some enzymatic changes that accompany these changes of state.

III. Frozen-Section Procedures and Related Embedding Techniques

Unfixed frozen sections were among the first to be employed for enzyme histochemistry because they were highly active and readily prepared. Their use, however, in enzyme histochemistry must be carefully evaluated in terms of the specific problem at hand because of the known disruptive effects of freezing and thawing as well as loss of soluble enzyme and co-factors. According to Gomori (1950, 1952), the diffusion of enzymes in unfixed frozen sections is a significant factor in the production of false localizations. Porter *et al.* (1953) have found that freezing results in a marked reduction in the capacity of rat liver homogenates to oxidize many substances. This effect is believed to be a purely mechanical one, in which the enzyme-bearing particles are altered by compression and shearing between ice crystals. Under optimal conditions, only seven out of fifteen oxidative activities of the liver showed recoveries of better than 50% after freezing. Freezing in the presence of sucrose prevented most of the inhibitory effects. The aforementioned experiment actually includes the effects of freezing and thawing, and it is possible that the deleterious effects were in no small part due to thawing.

Histologists and pathologists have encountered many difficulties with conventional methods of preparation of frozen sections. Technical skill is required to cut satisfactory sections less than 5 μ in thickness and friable tissues, especially those containing necrotic foci and fat, must be cut thicker than usual for satisfactory preparations. The most objectional feature of the conventional technique is the necessity for the transfer of tissues from the microtome knife to a container of water. Breakage and crumbling of the sections and loss of certain constituents such as mucus, colloid, blood clots, necrotic tissues, and soluble proteins are generally unavoidable. Sections prepared in such a manner obviously do not provide the maximal effectiveness for interpretations from a histopathological standpoint.

The freezing of tissues so that thin sections may be cut is one of the oldest histological techniques and was introduced by Raspail and by Stilling (Baker, 1950). Subsequently freezing microtomes in which the tissue holder was cooled by CO_2 gas were designed. In 1931, Schultz-Brauns reported the use of carbon dioxide to cool the knife as well as the tissue block. Adamstone and Taylor (1947, 1948) devised a "cold knife" technique which has subsequently influenced most frozen-section procedures. They were stimulated by the revival of the Altmann freeze-dry technique by Gersh (1932) and wished to modify the ordinary freezing methods so that a cut section, still frozen, could be manipulated onto a glass slide and immersed in a Coplin jar of the desired reagent just prior to melting. They suggested that with this technique sections showing a minimum of cellular distortion could be obtained and that they facilitated the application of enzymatic studies such as the Gomori technique. In this "cold-knife" procedure, carbon dioxide or liquid air is used for freezing the tissue and the microtome knife is cooled by taping blocks of

Dry Ice to its surface. The frozen cut sections are manipulated by a brush so that they lie flat on the knife and are then transferred to a glass slide by a special section lifter, which also contains Dry Ice, so that the section remains frozen while being transferred to a glass slide. This procedure constitutes a vast improvement over the usual frozen-section technique in which the section is floated on a water bath. Adamstone and Taylor (1948) have emphasized that melting of the ice in the section must be prevented until chemical tests are started or fixative applied to preserve the section for subsequent processing. Immersion of the slide containing the tissue section must be done at *exactly the right moment*, which is the instant at which the section begins to melt and flatten on the slide. If the section is allowed to melt completely, the cells are ruptured or distorted. They have also pointed out that it is not feasible to carry out the procedure in a warm or humid room and that certain tissues are inherently very difficult to section. They mentioned also that the technique may be modified so that the tissue is first fixed before frozen sections are cut. This method negates the advantage of working with unfixed tissue but does obviate the necessity for handling the sections with extreme care. In order to facilitate the immediate immersion in a fixative or other solution just as melting occurs, a mechanical system has been devised (Adamstone, 1951) in which the slide is held in a chute above the jar of fixative; as soon as the first frozen section is placed upon it the slide is released by a magnetic system and rapidly immersed into the solution by a spring-actuated mechanism.

Taft (1949) evaluated the Adamstone-Taylor frozen-section method for use in routine surgical pathology. He found that sections prepared according to this method could be fixed, stained, and mounted within 15 min from the time that the block of tissue was frozen. He also confirmed their observation that sections cannot be made if the room is too warm. Taft found that tissues containing a large amount of fat, and also those containing large amounts of dense collagen, were cut with difficulty. The most satisfactory sections were obtained from liver, brain, and kidney. White and Allen (1951) modified the Adamstone-Taylor method by using a Bausch and Lomb rotary freezing microtome. They provided a "fence" made from sheet copper or tin, which was packed with Dry Ice and placed upon the knife to keep it cold. They were able to obtain serial sections 6–8 μ in thickness. Wachstein and Meisel (1953) sectioned unfixed frozen tissues with a Sartorius freezing microtome provided with a system for the simultaneous cooling of the knife and freezing stage by carbon dioxide. They reported that with some experience the most favorable degree of cooling of the knife and of freezing of the specimen can be learned. The knife could be cooled below zero degrees within a few seconds and a temperature as low as $-30°C$ could be maintained. In contrast to the Adamstone-Taylor procedure, sections were directly immersed in the incubating solution or fixing fluid. They were subsequently placed on clean slides and dried for approximately 7 min at 56°C. From the standpoint of enzyme histochemistry, the work of Wachstein and Meisel is of interest because they used the frozen-section technique in the demonstration of alkaline phosphatase, acid phosphatase, and esterase in a number of tissues. A modified Adamstone-Taylor system with the knife cooled by Dry Ice held in place by a metal "fence" is shown in Fig. 8.

Enclosing the microtome in a refrigerated chamber whose temperature is near the optimal for cutting tissues has extended the usefulness of the cold-knife method (Figs. 9–12). These refrigerated chambers, or cryostats, maintain their low temperature by means of Dry Ice or mechanical refrigeration. The first of these devices was designed by Linderstrøm-Lang and Morgensen (1938). Coons et al. (1951) modified their technique

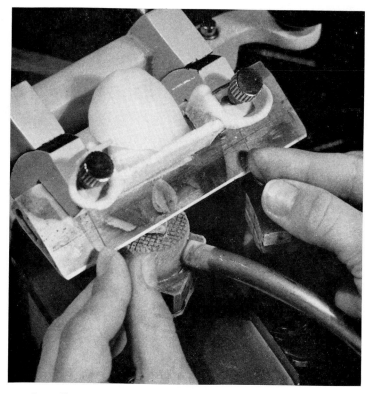

FIG. 8. A modified Adamstone-Taylor system with the knife cooled in Dry-Ice held in place by a metal "fence."

Fig. 9. Open-top cryostat containing International Minot Microtome as designed by Jeffrey Chang. (Courtesy of Dr. J. Chang.)

and cut sections in a cryostat chamber maintained at a temperature of around −16°C after which the sections were placed on glass slides, slowly thawed, and dried. Shimizu *et al.* (1956) used a sliding microtome in a refrigerated chamber and employed a device to prevent sections from curling that was a modification of the type originally introduced by Linderstrøm-Lang and Morgensen (1938). Shimizu *et al.* found that if curling of the sections adjacent to the cooled knife was prevented, refrigerated chamber could be maintained at higher temperature (0°). Cut sections were transferred to glass slides, allowed to dry at room temperature, and subjected to various histochemical methods. These authors reported satisfactory demonstration of succinic dehydrogenase, cytochrome oxidase, and adenosinetriphosphatase. The antiroll plate is also

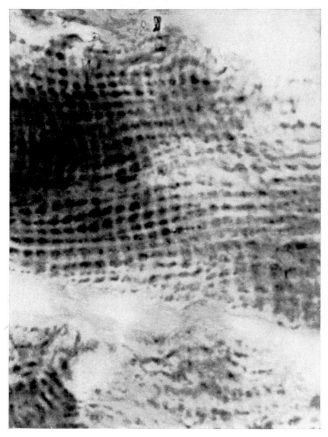

FIG. 10. Cytochrome oxidase activity of insect (bumble bee) leg muscle. *p*-Aminodiphenylamine methods. × 1800.

Fig. 11. Cytochrome oxidase activity of mitochondria of human heart. Fresh frozen section. p-Aminodiphenylamine method. × 700.

employed in the cryostat of Klionsky and Smith (1960), Pearse (1960, p. 19), and Chang et al. (1961a,b).

An analysis of frozen-section techniques was made by Thornburg and Mengers (1957), who ascertained optimal conditions for cutting thin sections from unfixed frozen tissues. They reported a set of optimal temperatures for the tissue block, knife, and refrigerated chamber and suggest that there is a zone of "micromelting" at the edge of the knife.

A variation of the frozen-section technique has been reported by Chang and Hori (1961), who immersed frozen sections directly into "substituting" fluids in a modified freeze-substitution procedure.

An excellent discussion dealing with the technical aspects of the preparation of frozen sections is described in a recent book by Steedman (1961). Jensen (1962) has discussed frozen sectioning with specific reference to plant tissue. In this text considerable detail is given to the preparation of frozen sections and their subsequent handling as well as freezing in gelatin.

The inherent difficulty with routine frozen-section or cryostat technique is that tissues must usually be thawed before being treated with appropriate histochemical reagents. This thawing may exert a serious disruptive effect upon cellular organelles including those containing sites of enzyme activity. Some structures, however, such as the mitochondria of the human heart, are fairly resistant to freezing and thawing so that

FIG. 12. Distribution of cytochrome oxidase in human myocardial infarction showing disruption of sarcosomal pattern in damaged fiber. p-Aminodiphenylamine method. Fresh frozen section. × 310.

useful mitochondrial localizations may be obtained with fresh frozen sections mounted on glass slides (Figs. 11 and 12). As previously mentioned, thawing is also believed to occur during sectioning owing to the pressure of the knife passing across the block (Thornburg and Mengers, 1957), so that thawing damage to cells may occur even before the sections are immersed in the substrate solution.

From both histological and cytological standpoints it is obvious that unfixed frozen sections (relatively slow freezing and thawing) do not usually exhibit as much quality of detail as are seen in frozen-dried and freeze-substituted specimens. Thus enzyme localizations in frozen sections may be variable and not always reproducible. Some improvement in the quality of preparations may be obtained by briefly fixing unfixed frozen

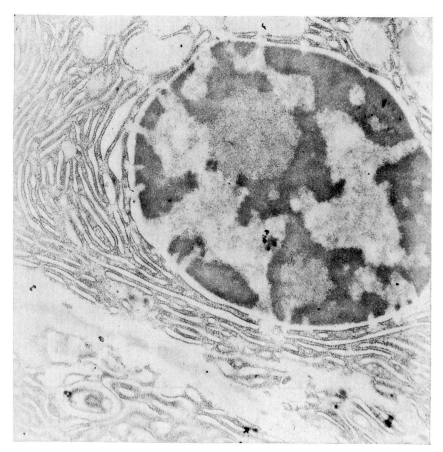

FIG. 13. Nucleus of pancreatic cell (rat) frozen after 15 sec in glycerol and substituted with acetone alone. Note nuclear pores, chromatin, nucleoli, and interchromatin areas. Final staining with lead ions. × 32,000. (Courtesy of Dr. L. I. Rebhun.)

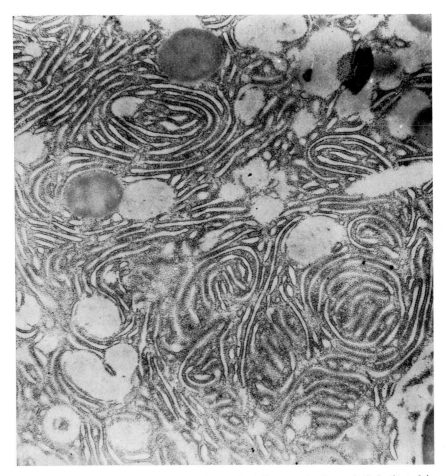

Fig. 14. Rat pancreas frozen after 15 sec in full-strength glycerol. Substituted in acetone without osmium. Note endoplasmic reticulum and ribosomes. Mitochondria often stain poorly in glycerol-dehydrated cell if osmium is not included in the substituted fluid. However, with long staining times (several hours), the typical negative image is seen as spaces, although most other components are overstained. × 32,000. (Courtesy of Dr. L. I. Rebhun.)

sections mounted on glass slides with acetone or other solvents. This procedure has been used in the demonstration of aminopeptidase (Willighagen and Planteydt, 1959) and alkaline and acid phosphatases (Burstone, 1961). On the other hand, newer techniques utilizing ultrarapid cooling with Freons, propane, other hydrocarbons, or helium in conjunction with suitable substitution or vacuum dehydration will give good morphological detail at the ultrastructure level (Figs. 13–16).

A great advance in frozen section technique was made by Chang *et al.*

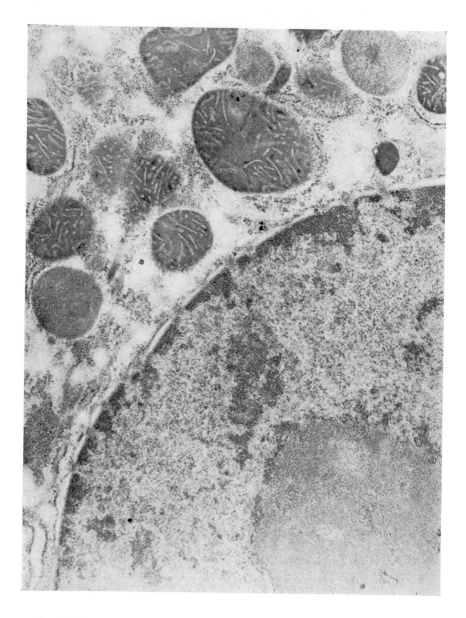

FIG. 15. Freeze-substituted rat liver showing details of nucleus and endoplasmic reticulum. × 45,000. (Courtesy of Dr. L. I. Rebhun.)

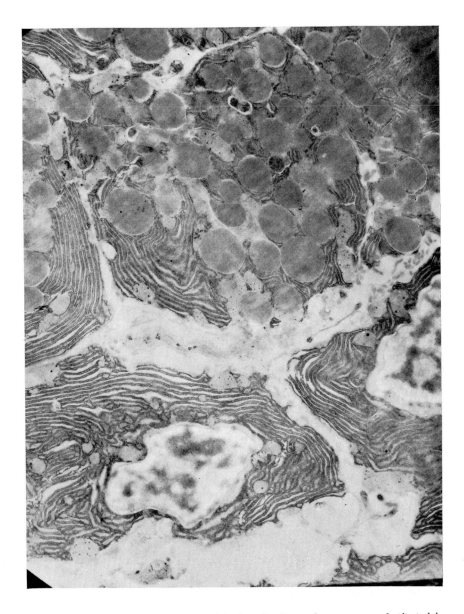

Fig. 16. Mouse pancreas, treated with glycerin, frozen in propane, substituted in ethanol, embedded in Epon, and stained with lead hydroxide. In Epon embedding, the zymogen granules do not shrink away from the cytoplasm as in methacrylate. There is some separation of the cells. × 15,000. (Courtesy of Dr. S. Bullivant.)

(1961a,b) and associates, who developed the open-top type of cryostat. This open-top cryostat is relatively small and the operator is not required to wear gloves while manipulating the tissues. The use of this cryostat with freeze-substitution procedures has also been developed by Chang and will be described in the section dealing with this subject (Figs. 9 and 17).

With reference to specific technique, the antiroll plate has received considerable attention as a means of obtaining serial sections (Pearse, 1960; Chang *et al.*, 1961b; Burstone, 1962a). Chang (1965) prefers the brush technique to the antiroll device. The frozen cut sections are manipulated by a brush onto a section platform of simple construction (Fig. 17).

Concerning the preparation of cryostat sections, the microtomecryostat handbook published by the International Equipment Company (Baker, 1961, 1964) may also be of value. The second, revised, edition of the

FIG. 17. Interior detail of open-top cryostat showing knife and adjacent thick metal platform. (Courtesy of Dr. J. Chang.)

handbook was based upon the original first edition written by John R. Baker. The manual discusses not only adjustments and maintainence of the International stainless steel microtome (Minot rotary microtome), but also freezing and related procedures for use with this specific cryostat. In addition, the mounting of sections on slides and their subsequent staining with routine stains such as hematoxylin and eosin as well as application of cryostat sections for fluorescent microscopy are described.

Batsakis (1963) reports a cold-knife technique employing Freon 12 and the principle of thermal conduction through the knife and freezing head. This modification employs a standard tissue-freeze unit with the freezing microtome stage cooled by a braided flexible tube which carries the refrigerant also to a brass clamp attached to the microtome blade.

Stumpf and Roth (1964) have described frozen-sectioning below $-60°C$ with a refrigerated microtome in a modified two-stage refrigerator (Harris Mfg. Co., Cambridge, Massachusetts, Model 3L-2-075). With such low temperatures recrystallization phenomena should be avoided. Temperatures below $-85°C$ were obtained by addition of liquid nitrogen to the refrigerating chamber. Special lubrication with a commerically available compound, molykote Z powder (Alpha-Molykote Corp., Stamford, Connecticut) suspended in absolute ethenol was used. Stumpf and Roth have suggested that sectioning at very low temperatures reduces ice crystal formation and provides thin frozen sections for high resolution optical microscopy.

An important aspect of the preparation of cryostat sections is the knife angle, including the clearance angle. The latter should be at least 5 degrees according to the manuals of both the Spencer Microtome (American Optical Co.) and Minot Rotary Microtome (International Equipment Co.). In publications of Bush and Hewitt (1952), a clearance angle of 5 degrees is specifically recommended.

Alginate gels have been employed as an embedding medium for facilitating the cutting and handling of frozen sections (Lewis and Shute, 1963). Small pieces of formalin-fixed tissues are infiltrated first with a 1% and then with a 2% low-viscosity, sodium alginate, which is a polymannuronic acid obtained from seaweed. The tissue is transferred to a solution of high molecular weight sodium alginate, containing colloidally dispersed tricalcium phosphate. When a freshly prepared solution of gluconolactone is added, a calcium gel is gradually formed; the lactone slowly hydrolyzes to produce the free acid which liberates calcium ions from the colloidal phosphate. Subsequently, a block of gel containing the tissue is removed. If desired this block can be hardened in a buffered calcium acetate solution, and its cutting properties improved further by treatment in 20% ethanol. According to Lewis and Shute, enzymes such as cholinesterases and phosphatases are not affected and the procedure can be carried out at 0°C, if necessary. It is reported that this gel does not crack and makes possible the cutting of coherent, serial frozen sections.

Many investigators have partially infiltrated tissues with gelatin prior to sectioning within a cryostat. This gelatin matrix tends to support the tissues and make sectioning more uniform. In a recent modification, small specimens are placed face down on a 5-mm thick layer of solidified 7.5% gelatin in the bottom of a cardboard box 2¼ by 1¼ by ⅝ inches in size. Additional gelatin, cooled to temperature slightly above the gelling point, is carefully poured into the box to just cover the piece of tissue. Floating of the tissue can be prevented by allowing a small amount of gelatin to solidify around the base of the tissue before the pouring is complete. The box of embedded tissue is kept in a refrigerator until the gelatin has solidified firmly. The embedded block may be stored in Dry Ice prior to sectioning. The cardboard box and frozen gelatin are trimmed to leave margins of frozen gelatin 1–2 mm on each side of the block. The bottom of the box is peeled off and the block is placed in a small pool of water on the specimen carrier of the freezing microtome.

Diethylene glycol distearate embedding has been reported for ultra-microtome sectioning for light microscopy by Salazar (1964). Frozen-dried tissues may also be placed in the melted wax for infiltration. Earlier work in this field has been reported by Sidman et al. (1961), who employed polyethylene glycol 400 distearate, and Chesterman and Leach (1956), who used diethylene glycol monostearate and distearate.

A water-soluble embedding medium referred to as Aquon, which is obtained by water extraction of Epon has been described by Gibbons (1959), Mishima et al. (1962b), and Loud and Mishima (1963). Tissues may be transferred directly to 50% aqueous Aquon. At hourly intervals they may be changed to 70%, 95%, and 100% Aquon. The tissues may then be kept for three successive 12-hour periods in fresh changes of the embedding medium in a desiccator containing phosphorus pentoxide. The last two changes are composed of 10 parts of Aquon, 25 parts of dodecanolsuccinic anhydride, and 0.3 part of benzol-dimethylamine. Final polymerization is carried out at 60° for 3 days.

The use of water-soluble methacrylates as embedding media after formalin fixation, as well as other types of fixation, has been reported (Wichterle et al., 1960; Bernhard et al., 1961). Two water-soluble mono-mers were employed, glycol monomethacrylate and triethyleneglycol dimethacrylate. In the presence of suitable catalysts, the polymerization reaction was found to proceed at a relatively low temperature. Although the techniques have been primarily applied to the study of ultrastructure at the electron microscope level, modifications of the procedure should make it adaptable for routine tissue sectioning. Recently Feder (1960) employed acrolein and other aldehydes which gave excellent morphological preservation. These, when used at low temperature, may be useful histochemical fixatives. Sabitini *et al.* (1961) have found that a number of aldehyde compounds may be successfully employed as fixatives in conjunction with histochemical methods for both the light and electron microscope. Among the fixatives is glutaraldehyde which is buffered with phosphate or cacodylate buffers. Of interest is hydroxyadiapaldehyde which permits preservation of a number of oxidative enzymes including cytochrome oxidase, succinic dehydrogenase, and DPN diaphorase.

The preparation of thin sections in the $5–50 \mu$ range by the use of the McIlwain Chopper has been reported by Smith and Farquhar (1965). Although this device was primarily designed for the preparation of gluteraldehyde nonfrozen sections, such sections may be subsequently frozen and dried under cryogenic conditions. The original McIlwain Tissue Chopper (McIlwain *et al.*, 1953) was designed to prepare specimens from irregular tissue fragments or those that would be difficult to cut by ordinary techniques and is presently available from Brinkmann Instruments, Westbury, New York.

Techniques for the preparation of calcified tissues are based upon grinding, cutting with an abrasive wheel, or sawing (Burstone, 1962b; Gray and Opdyke, 1962; Opdyke, 1962). With the technique of Gray and Opdyke, routinely cut sections $40–50 \mu$ in thickness from whole undecalcified teeth can be prepared. In specific instances, $10-\mu$ sections of dentine can be cut. The application of such cutting devices in conjunction with low-temperature technique would be of great value in the study of enzyme systems in hard tissues.

IV. Freeze-Drying

The various freeze-dry systems may be grouped into three types:

(1) Vacuum chambers usually cooled by mechanical refrigeration and characterized by a long mean free path to the vapor trap.

(2) Vacuum chambers cooled by liquid and/or solid refrigerants with a short mean free path to the vapor trap.

(3) Refrigerated drying tube through which passes a stream of dry air or gas.

Further details of design and general application of freeze-drying in histochemistry may be referred to in the original papers and reviews by Kanehira (1953), Gersh and Stephenson (1954), Neumann (1958), and Burstone (1962a).

The fundamental concepts of freezing, sublimation, secondary drying and dehydration phases and reviews have been indicated in the studies and reviews by Harris (1954), Grauman and Neumann (1958), Meryman (1960, 1961, 1963), Parkes and Smith (1960), Burstone (1962a), Greaves (1962), Jensen (1962), Rey (1962), and Greaves *et al.* (1963). In a low temperature, freeze-drying preservation technique, the initial freezing of the material is followed by dehydration from the frozen state. After it has been frozen, the tissue is placed in a vacuum chamber for dehydration, which occurs first by the sublimation of ice. When all the ice has been removed, the product is allowed to warm in a positive temperature in order to eliminate, as fast as possible, nonfrozen water. Thus far, it has not been possible to use the endocellular cryophylactic agents (ECA's), in freeze-drying since these liquids remain in the tissues during sublimation because they have a low vapor pressure. The problem of freezing the tissues in the presence of ECA's may be overcome by freeze-substitution of glycerol. It is possible to dissolve glycerol in a frozen tissue in another liquid solvent maintained at low temperature. This solvent can be frozen by further cooling and eliminated by sublimation. Freeze-drying of nonaqueous solvents has been reported by Simatos and Rey (1965).

Freezing and drying as a histological procedure was first described by Altmann (1890). It was reported that this technique eliminated shrinkage of histological specimens, and furthermore offered a means of studying intravital dyes. Of historical interest is the work of Mann (1902), Kossel (1913), Bayliss (1924), and Behrens (1932). Modern freeze-drying for histological and histochemical purposes was developed by Gersh (1932), who pointed out that the freeze-dry procedure facilitated the retention of tissue constitutents in a reactive state. It is apparent that the use of routine fixatives for histochemical studies represents a compromise, if not somewhat equivocal, procedure. Although the exact details of tissue changes that occur during freezing and drying are not completely known, the fact that various frozen and dried biological and pharmaceutical products retain their native protein and other characteristics recommends this process as an optimal type of histochemical fixation for enzyme preservation, since initial fixation and dehydration are carried out at low temperature. Hoerr, in 1936, noted that the "glycolytic enzyme" of the liver was not destroyed by freeze-drying. Gomori (1952) suggested that freeze-drying is useful for enzyme histochemistry but felt at the time that the equipment was too bulky and expensive for routine use.

Once dried, tissues exhibit considerable resistance to denaturation by heat and to some extent by chemical agents. In spite of the fact that frozen-dried tissues are usually embedded in paraffin, the heat encountered does not appear to be detrimental, provided the specimens are sufficiently dehydrated. Greaves (1954) has pointed out that when the water content of frozen-dried products is very low they exhibit remarkable resistance to high temperature. He stated that water seems to be the "catalyst" that is necessary for marked denaturation to occur. Of course, from a traditional as well as modern industrial standpoint, drying has been used for the preservation of biological substances as well as pharmaceutical products (Flosdorf, 1954; Rowe, 1960).

It is erroneous to equate frozen-dried tissues with unfixed frozen sections. Freeze-drying is the removal of water from a tissue specimen after it has been frozen. Thus the disruptive effects of thawing which are encountered in the use of unfixed frozen sections are avoided. In addition, the techniques employed in the freeze-dry procedure usually result in a smaller ice-crystal size than those employed in the preparation of frozen sections. Some components of frozen-dried tissues also appear to exhibit a mild state of denaturation. For example, Sylvén (1951) points out that freezing and drying results in some decrease in aqueous solubility and has been observed in the case of frozen dried serum lipoproteins (Potthoff, 1949; Oncley et al., 1950). Of course, any decrease in the solubility of cytoplasmic constituents would be of advantage in conjunction with histochemical procedures. It is of interest that zymograms of fresh and frozen-dried liver are essentially identical whereas those of cold formalin-fixed liver show suppression of certain bands.

The freeze-dry procedure may be divided into the following phases: (a) freezing (quenching); (b) dehydration or drying (usually *in vasuo);* and (c) embedding and subsequent processing for histochemical study (Burstone, 1962a).

The sublimation of water vapor from the frozen eutectic mixtures in tissues occurs when the partial pressure of water vapor at the frozen surface exceeds that of the atmosphere adjacent to it. The eutectic or lowest temperature at which a liquid phase is present in tissues is not known. Thus many workers have felt that it would be desirable to dehydrate at the lowest temperature possible. At very low temperatures (e.g., below −40°C), the vapor pressure of ice falls rapidly so that excessively long drying times are required. In general −30° to −40°C is employed for the drying of tissues. Packer and Scott (1942), in a study of the location of inorganic salts, used a temperature below −55°C, which is the eutectic point of calcium chloride and is the lowest of any salt that may be present. It is known, however, that in tissues complex systems exist that have very low eutectic points, and it is not possible at present to determine what the eutectic point of living tissue may be (G. H. Scott and Hoerr, 1950).

On the other hand, Greaves (1954) found that conductivity tests showed that serum was not completely frozen at temperatures above −60°C; this indicates that tissues should be dried at temperatures below this point. More recently other evidence, as described in the sections dealing with low temperature techniques, has indicated the advisability of using much lower temperatures than those previously employed for freeze-drying.

Greaves (1962) has reviewed aspects of thermal analysis and automatic control of frying temperature, and the design of freeze-dry systems. The latter systems are of interest and may be further explored.

At atmospheric pressure and pressures down to a few millimeters of mercury, collisions between evaporating water molecules and those of the surrounding air retard evaporation. Under higher vacuum, the partial pressure of the air, not only immediately above the surface but throughout the entire system, is kept to a value at most one-tenth the local pressure of the water vapor. It has been previously mentioned that, when tissue is frozen, ice crystals form and separate from the organic matrix compressing it, so that a network or wall is formed around each ice crystal. Tissue dries from the exterior inward. As water molecules arising from sublimation traverse the specimen, they must pass through dried areas previously occupied by ice crystals in order to be removed by the vacuum system. Thus the dry organic shell, which increases in thickness as drying proceeds, offers resistance to water molecules attempting to pass through it to the outside chamber. By interruption of the drying of a large tissue block, the sharp interface between the dried shell and the frozen interior is easily discernible (Gustafsson, 1954). The wide temperature range encountered in tissue during freezing and drying is shown in Fig. 18. Drying occurs because heat is supplied to ice crystals in the tissue, thus causing water molecules to vaporize from their free surfaces. According to Stephenson (1953), after a water molecule sublimes it either passes through the dried shell to the drying chamber and eventually reaches the vapor trap, or else it may be returned to the interface between the dried shell and frozen interior and be recaptured by an ice crystal. He suggested that both paths may have variations. For example, a molecule that escapes from an ice crystal may enter a tissue space partially occupied by another ice crystal. After making an indeterminate number of collisions, it is recaptured by the ice crystal or passes through one of the holes in the walls to a neighboring space. In general, a molecule that reaches the surface does so only after having made a large number of collisions within the dried shell. Once a water molecule is free of the dry shell it may be readily removed by means of the trap or vacuum system. It has been shown that for a given temperature of subliming ice crystals, the minimum drying time of guinea pig liver is greater than the minimum sublimation time of a piece of ice of the same size by a factor of the order of one thousand (Stephenson, 1953). This was also demonstrated by the

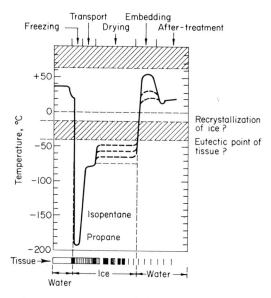

FIG. 18. Temperature ranges encountered during the various stages of freeze-drying and subsequent processing of tissues for histological application. (After Gustafsson, 1954.)

work of Jansen (1954), who constructed an ingenious vacuum-tight torsion balance in which variations in the weights of various drying materials could be accurately determined. He compared the drying rates of pure water (ice), pure water absorbed by filter paper, and rat liver. It was found that the drying rates of rat liver and filter paper were longer than that of the pure water. Of interest is the fact that water frozen after being absorbed by filter paper dries at a different rate than that of ice itself. Yamida (1953) has also studied dehydration rates in a vacuum system at low temperatures.

The change from the solid to vapor state requires energy in the form of heat which must be constantly supplied to the frozen surface of the drying specimen. As each molecule changes from ice to vapor a discrete amount of heat is removed from the environment and unless it is replaced the temperature of the environment will fall. A temperature reduction in turn reduces the degree of sublimation. Thus, heat transfer to the drying specimen must be constant and reasonably efficient if the drying process is to proceed at an appreciable rate. Heat transfer is brought about by radiation and to some extent by conduction. A drying object will receive the maximum amount of heat through radiation if it is surrounded as completely as possible by a radiating shield of the temperature selected. Consequently, freeze-dry devices in which the tissue is exposed at close proximity to the very low temperature of a cold trap may be less efficient with regard to drying rate than those in which the cold trap is placed at some distance from the specimen.

Once water molecules have left the dried shell, they must be removed by the adjacent vapor trap. The vapor trap may consist of a chamber cooled by alcohol–Dry Ice, or liquid nitrogen. A trap containing phosphorus pentoxide at room temperature has proved to be very satisfactory in many systems. At atmospheric pressure, the mean free path of a water molecule is about 0.05 μ. However, when the partial pressure of air is 10^{-4} mm Hg, this corresponds to a mean free path of approximately 50 cm. Thus, the collision of water molecules with air molecules should be relatively infrequent. Mathematical analysis of this and other factors, as well as practical experience, indicates that the mean free path distance is not critical (Goodspeed and Uber, 1934; Stephenson, 1954; Gersh and Stephenson, 1954).

As early as 1934, Goodspeed and Uber evaluated the physical and mathematical aspects of the dehydration of frozen tissue. The rate of loss of water vapor from a surface into a complete vacuum, according to kinetic theory, is given by

$$m = \alpha P \left(\frac{M}{2RT} \right)^{1/2} \text{grams/cm}^2/\text{sec}$$

where m is the mass in grams, M the gram molecular weight, R the gas constant, T the absolute temperature, P the saturated vapor pressure in dynes per square centimeter, and α a constant. If vapor is present above an ice surface at a pressure of Pv, the resultant loss of ice is given by

$$m = 1.463\alpha \frac{Ps - Pv}{T^{1/2}} \text{grams/cm}^2/\text{min}$$

where α represents the fraction of vapor molecules that recondense on the ice surface and both Pv and the saturated vapor pressure Ps are measured in millimeters of mercury. For a water surface, α is approximately 0.01, but its value for ice is unknown. If Ps is 292 μ (its value at $-30°C$), then nothing significant is gained by having Pv less than 1 μ, for their difference would not appreciably increase even though Pv were equal to zero. At a pressure of 1 μ, attainable with a rotary oil pump, the mean free path of water molecule is over 5 cm. More recently Roberts and St. Pierre (1965) have discussed mean free path and collision of molecules as related to pressure (Table I).

Attempts to radically decrease the drying time have met with limited

TABLE I

CLASSIFICATIONS OF VACUUM: THE VARIATION OF GAS DENSITY,
MEAN FREE PATH, AND COLLISION FREQUENCY WITH PRESSURE[a]

Property	Vacuum				
	←Rough→	←Medium→	←High→	←Ultrahigh→	
Pressure (torr)	760	1	10^{-3}	10^{-8}	10^{-13}
Density (mole/cm³)	2.5×10^{19}	3.2×10^{16}	3.2×10^{13}	3.2×10^{8}	3.2×10^{3}
Mean free path[b] (cm)	6.6×10^{-6}	5×10^{-3}	5	5×10^{5}	5×10^{10}
Collisions with surface[b] (mole sec⁻¹ cm⁻²)	2.9×10^{23}	3.8×10^{20}	3.8×10^{17}	3.8×10^{12}	3.8×10^{7}

[a] By courtesy of Drs. Roberts and St. Pierre (1965).
[b] For air at 25°C.

success for the following reasons:

(1) The major impediment to fast drying lies in the object itself, namely in the resistance of the drying shell.

(2) It is difficult to prevent drying tissues from cooling too much below the optimal temperature because of withdrawal of latent heat of evaporation, although heat can be supplied to the drying tissue through conduction or radiation.

It is apparent that tissues are rather poor thermal conductors, and that when a slice of tissue is placed upon a heated flat surface, the surface available for evaporation is immediately decreased by half. In recent years several innovations have been suggested that may facilitate more rapid drying. It was suggested that heat could be supplied to the drying object by filling the drying tube with a heat-conducting gas at an appropriate pressure. Jansen (1954) found that this type of system was workable with reference to sublimation of ice. Treffenberg (1953), Jensen (1954), and Meryman (1959) employed systems that removed water from the specimen surface by a stream of cold dry air. Such systems may operate at atmospheric pressure or under a partial vacuum. These studies tend to show that the passage of water vapor from the interface between the frozen center and dried shell is facilitated by the vapor pressure gradient rather than by the absolute pressure of the system.

Another method of providing heat is the application of high-frequency electromagnetic radiation in the microwave range (Copson, 1958). Copson was able to dry large samples of dense structure, including bone, in a short period of time because of the heat energy applied directly to the inner frozen core of the specimen. As yet, this approach has not been applied to histological specimens.

Kaesberg (1964) described freeze-dry methods to perserve ultra-structure. This author primarily describes the Williams' method (Williams, 1953; Rice *et al.*, 1955). This system contains a sublimation chamber and a cold trap attached to a vacuum system (Fig. 19). In freeze-drying a collodion film is prepared on the smooth surface of a copper support which is placed on the bottom of the sublimation tube and is attached there with vacuum grease which also serves as a thermal conductor. The sublimation chamber is then sealed and under vacuum the chamber and its contents are cooled by liquid nitrogen or Dry Ice–alcohol mixture. The cold trap is kept at liquid nitrogen temperature for about 20 min at this time the copper support has reached an equilibrium temperature. Then Dry Ice is admitted to the chamber and the cover is removed. The spraying tube is inserted (which minimizes the amount of moisture that will remain in the chamber) and a few hundredths of a milliliter of the suspension are sprayed onto the collodion surface. The spraying tube is withdrawn, the system is closed and evacuated. The bath surrounding the sublimation chamber is replaced with one at a temperature approximately that of the sublimation point. With delicate specimens the operating temperature may be maintained as low as −65°C. More commonly, however, the sublimation temperature is −50°C. When the sublimation is complete, the chamber and the block are warmed slightly above room temperature to avoid condensation, and air is admitted to the system. Subsequently the specimen and its support are removed and shadowed according to standard techniques. After shadowing, the

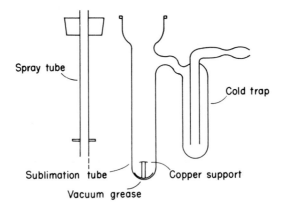

FIG. 19. Freeze-dry apparatus in which spray droplets are frozen onto a sublimation chamber which is attached to a cold trap and vacuum system. With this system only a few 1/100's of suspension may be sprayed onto a collodion surface. (After Williams, 1953.)

collodion is removed from the copper surface with the aid of cellulose tape which has several holes punched in it slightly larger than the diameter of the specimen grids. The areas of the collodion film covering these holes are then easily mounted onto a specimen grid. When very rapid freezing of the droplet suspension is not essential, this time-consuming mounting step may be avoided by placing the collodion-covered screens directly on the copper block.

The vacuum freeze-drying of frozen sections for dry-mounting, high resolution autoradiography has been described by Stumpf and Roth (1964). In this technique the specimen is coated with Santocel powder (Monsanto Chemical Co.) to improve heat transfer and the specimen is quickly immersed in liquid nitrogen. These authors indicate that tissues should be held at a range below $-30°C$ since the possibility of ice crystals formation still exists at this low temperature. After sectioning the specimens are transferred to a vacuum container at $-30°C$ ($253°K$) and dried for a period of 5 or 6 hours. Subsequently the sections are mounted directly on the emulsion.

V. Refrigerant Systems for Cryostats and for Freeze-Drying Equipment

These chambers are designed to maintain the tissue at an appropriate temperature so that no thawing or solution of tissue components occurs. According to Gersh (1932), $-20°C$ is below the freezing point of tissue fluids; however, owing to concentration of organic and inorganic substances during the drying process, a lower temperature must be employed. Goodspeed and Uber (1934) found that dehydration at $-32°C$ was more satisfactory than at $-23°C$ and also commented that dehydration time varies and must be empirically determined. Hoerr (1936), Simpson (1941), G. H. Scott and Hoerr (1950), Gersh and Stephenson (1954), and L. G. E. Bell (1956) are in agreement that drying above $-30°C$ does not give as satisfactory results as the lower temperatures. Simpson (1941) found that tissues dehydrated at $-40°C$ exhibited a more uniform quality of preservation than those dehydrated at $-30°C$ or above. He reported, however, that there did not appear to be any advantage in applying temperatures below $-40°C$. On the other hand, G. H. Scott (1943), Copeland (1951), and Kulenkampff (1954) favor lower drying temperatures. With recent developments in electron microscopy lower temperatures have been favored. Specifically Seno and Yoshizawa (1960) indicated that a drying temperature of $-55°C$ to $-60°C$ is necessary.

The insulation of refrigerated systems is of importance especially in those devices that require special cryogenic insulation. The high degree of effectiveness of such systems, for example, those that employ liquid helium, is important since the heat of vaporization of water at the boiling point is approximately 517,000 cal per liter, of liquid nitrogen 38,600 cal per liter, and of helium ca. 610 cal per liter. Since the usual types of insulation are unsatisfactory without some method of preventing atmospheric air from contacting the cold surface, cryogenic vessels often take the form of double-walled containers with a space between the walls, sealed from the atmosphere. It is between these walls, within the jacket, that various insulating materials are placed to inhibit the flow of thermal energy into the enclosed chamber. One of the best examples of this type of enclosure is the well-known Dewar flask. More detailed discussions of insulation are described in the texts by McClintock (1964) and Rose-Innes (1964) and include refrigerated radiation shields and powder insulations. Among these powders are Alumina, silica aerogel, and Santocel (Monsanto Chemical Co.). Another type of insulating material is the so-called foam insulation, as examplified by silica aerogel containing aluminum flakes or aluminum powder. Foam polystyrene, epoxy resins, polyisocyanate, rubber, and glass have also been applied.

Modified freeze-dry systems have also been reported by A. Taylor (1944), Wang and Grossman (1949a), and J. E. Harris *et al.* (1950). Mendelow and Hamilton (1950) used a metal system in which the liquid nitrogen vapor trap was close to the tissue. They employed ethyl oxalate kept frozen at $-40°C$ by Dry Ice. The vapor trap or cold finger contained liquid nitrogen and was the forerunner of systems based on a short mean free path between drying tissue and vapor trap. Dried tissues were removed and embedded in a vacuum oven. The design of Stowell (1951) employed a drying chamber that was entirely surrounded by liquid nitrogen, which acted as both a refrigerant and a vapor trap. The temperature of the drying tissue was maintained by a thermostatically controlled heating element; this system likewise was characterized by a very short mean free path. Dry ice or other mixtures may also be used as the refrigerant. Glick and Malmström (1952) described a freeze-dry apparatus that embodied a similar principle. A liquid nitrogen vapor trap was employed while Dry Ice–acetone mixtures were used to maintain the temperature of the frozen tissue. It was pointed out that the very low temperature of the frozen specimen would result in prolonged dehydration time, and therefore a mixture of a number of ethers and Dry Ice was suggested. The aforementioned system was modified by Moberger *et al.* (1954). A vacuum of approximately 10^{-5} mm Hg was obtained in 15 min. Glick and Malmström reported that dehydration could be accomplished at a temperature below $-60°C$ in 6–12 hours, depending upon the size and nature of the tissue specimens. As with most systems of this type, the tissues were embedded in the drying tube. Glick and Bloom (1956) subsequently reported another modification in which they pointed out that elaborate high vacuum systems were not necessary.

Butler and Bell (1953), Gustafsson (1953), Danielli (1953), and Lacy and Blundell (1955) have reported devices characterized by a short mean free path and a drying chamber partly or completely surrounded by a cold trap. Eränkö (1954b) described a relatively simple inexpensive system that consisted of an inner glass tube connected by a ground joint to an outer tube, and a two-stage mechanical pump for evacuating the space between the tubes. This design, too, was based on the principle of short path condensation. Diethyl oxalate and solid carbon dioxide were used to produce a temperature of −44°C in the drying chamber. The trap was cooled either with liquid air or a mixture of Dry Ice and ethanol or acetone. A somewhat similar system with an exceedingly short mean free path was described by Freed in 1955. A simplified apparatus based on the design of Gersh was introduced by Arcadi and Tesar (1954). The refrigerated chamber consisted of an insulated box made of plywood packed with rock wool. Dry Ice was employed to maintain a temperature of −30°C in the refrigerated chamber. Phosphorus pentoxide was employed as the drying agent, and the vacuum system consisted of a single rotary oil pump which maintained a pressure of 10^{-3} mm Hg. An interesting innovation in simplified designs was reported by Jansen (1954) (Fig. 20). The apparatus consisted of a U-shaped glass tube, one leg of which is connected to a vacuum jacket. A piece of movable copper tubing surrounds this jacket from about the middle to well below the lower end. The lower part of the tube is cooled by a Dry Ice–acetone mixture in the Dewar flask. The portion of the tube immersed in the Dry Ice–acetone mixture will, of course, be at a temperature of approximately −70°C; but the temperature of the drying tube which is isolated by the vacuum jacket can be varied between −70°C and room temperature by adjusting the relative heights of both copper tubes. A temperature of −40°C to −45°C is obtained within the drying tube. Jansen reports that once set, the temperature remains within this range in spite of changes in room temperature and pressure in the drying tube. Naidoo and Pratt (1956) described multiple drying tubes with a phosphorus pentoxide drying trap. Temperature was maintained by a mixture of Dry Ice and ethyl phenyl ether (−34°).

Clements (1962) described a freeze-dry system employing a stainless steel 2000-ml beaker, surrounded by a bell jar and cooled by a Dry-Ice, ethanol mixture. The coolant is placed in the beaker. For drying times over 24 hours, the beaker is filled and a Dewar flask also filled with Dry Ice is inverted over the beaker. This system is reported to have high capacity and very efficient effectiveness in trapping water vapor.

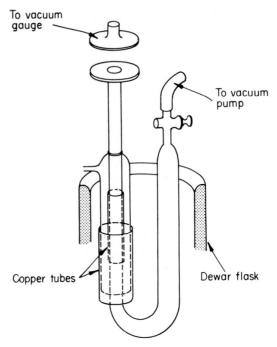

To vacuum gauge

To vacuum pump

Copper tubes

Dewar flask

FIG. 20. Freeze-dry apparatus of Jansen (1954). The temperature range is varied by adjusting the height of the external copper tube.

As previously indicated, in many types of freeze-dry machines, liquid nitrogen is employed as the cooling agent and the tissues are warmed to approximately −40°C by means of a heating coil. A combination of both mechnical refrigeration employing a Freon-type gas in conjunction with liquid nitrogen has been reported by Thermovac Industries Corporation, Copiague, Long Island, New York. This system is designated as the Thermovac Model FD-1 Freeze Dryer and has a large tissue capacity.

The principle of expansion of a gas (e.g., Freon) which is employed in household refrigerators either as a single-stage or two-stage compressor has been the basis for refrigeration of a number of freeze-dry devices as well as cryostat units. All mechanical or cyclic refrigeration processes are based on fact that they involve the extraction of heat from some quantity of matter at temperatures lower than its environment, and the transmission of this heat to a substance capable of accepting it. To effect this process, work must be done. If the object refrigerated is considered to be a reservoir of heat at some low temperature and the object to which the heat is rejected is a high-temperature reservoir, a continuously operating refrigeration cycle is utilized. If the only work on the medium were that necessary to cause its circulation, an effect opposite to refrigeration would occur. One would therefore cool only the warm reservoir since heat flows in the direction of a decreasing temperature gradient. This principle has come to be accepted as the zeroth law of thermodynamics (McClintock, 1964).

In the review by McClintock (1964), a compact refrigerator which operates at 4.2°K (−268.95°C) and maintains a temperature stability of the object refrigerated within ±0.06°K as shown. This unit is based upon application of newer superconductors and may be of use in production of small freeze-dry units employing close-cycle refrigeration at very low temperatures.

Refrigerating chambers of this general type have been applied by Chang and others (Pearse, 1960) in cryostat units (Figs. 9 and 17). Frozen sectioning below −60°C with a refrigerated microtome by Stumpf and Roth (1965) has already been described (see page 39).

The first and pioneering modern approach to the freeze-drying of tissues for histological purposes was reported by Gersh in 1932. Since that time a variety of freeze-dry devices have been described that in large part derive from the original design. In the Gersh apparatus the temperature inside the chamber was found to be close to −22°C, the temperature of liquid ammonia. Phosphorus pentoxide was employed as a drying agent and the vacuum pumps consisted of a mechanical and mercury vapor diffusion pump. Incorporated in the system was a special chamber for vacuum embedding. In 1934, Goodspeed and Uber reported the design of a freeze-dry system which is very similar to many modern counterparts (Fig. 21). It consisted of a drying tube inserted vertically in a mechanically refrigerated chamber (−22°C to −32°C). A single mechanical vacuum pump was used in conjunction with a phosphorus pentoxide drying chamber. A glow discharge tube was built into the system in order to check the approximate vapor pressure. Goodspeed and Uber stated that there is no advantage in using high-vacuum systems and that a good rotary pump is adequate. They were among the very first to offer a mathematical analysis of drying mechanisms, and they pointed out that the mean free path of water molecules in their vacuum system was over 5 cm. As contrasted with other systems, they removed dried tissues from the vacuum chamber and embedded them in a small vacuum bell jar in a paraffin oven. In 1936, G. H. Scott and Williams reported on a system with a very short mean free path. It contained a variable temperature control and permitted embedding in the dehydrating chambers. Packer and Scott (1942) also employed a variable temperature control. In addition, they utilized two vacuum gauges in order to help ascertain drying time. Two drying traps were also employed: (1)

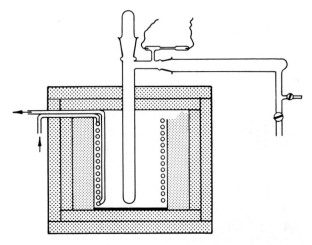

FIG. 21. Design of freeze-dry system of Goodspeed and Uber (1934).

phosphorus pentoxide; (2) liquid nitrogen. Sjöstrand (1944) used a number of dehydrating chambers with a permanent refrigeration system operating at −47°C. In 1948, Gersh published a design in which fixed refrigeration and multiple drying chambers were used. A drying temperature of −32°C to −40°C was recommended. Other developments were made by Pease and Baker (1949), who used a drying chamber of wide diameter connected to a vacuum pump with no vapor trap intervening.

A system based on the design of Goodspeed and Uber (1934) and Gersh (1948) (Fig. 22) has been in operation in the author's laboratory for many years (Burstone, 1962a). The unit utilizes mechanical refrigeration and the drying tubes are of large capacity. Ball joints are used throughout to relieve strain on the glass. This type of system has proved to be of use in processing large numbers of surgical pathology specimens (Fig. 23). Each of the drying tubes is surrounded by a loosely fitting copper well one-eighth inch thick in the refrigerated chamber. Figure 24 shows the details of one of the combined drying tubes and phosphorus pentoxide trap. One of these tubes inserted into a suitable refrigerating unit constitutes a rugged and inexpensive drying unit of fairly large capacity. A rebuilt vacuum oven is employed for the simultaneous embedding of a large number of thick specimens (Fig. 25). Benditt et al. (1961) have also described a somewhat similar system consisting of a three-barreled glass vacuum unit which fits into a refrigerated chamber. A 1/3 h.p. refrigerating unit using Freon 22 is capable of maintaining a temperature of −40°C. Provision is made for infiltration of the tissue in the apparatus if desired. Systems such as this are advantageous to the pathologist in that large numbers of specimens may be dried simultaneously.

Another principle which is applied in cryogenics and may be used for freeze-drying is the Joule-Thompson effect. With this type of system, air, or a gas, is compressed to approximately 2000 psi and then it is allowed to expand through a throttling valve, thereby reducing its temperature.

Fig. 22. Freeze-dry system as employed by the author. Note the large-diameter glass tubing and ball joints. The drying agent is phosphorus pentoxide.

FIG. 23. Different view of system shown in Fig. 22.

Such units are presently available from Air Products and Chemicals Incorporated, Allentown, Pennsylvania, and are referred to as Cryo-Tip Refrigerators. In these units nitrogen at normal ambient temperature will provide cooling by direct Joule-Thompson expansion. Hydrogen, however, must be precooled below ambient temperature before it will act as a refrigerant. If hydrogen is used, it is precooled by an auxiliary nitrogen circuit as shown in Fig. 26. Once cooled to approximately 77°K, hydrogen gas applies Joule-Thompson refrigeration to temperatures as low as 15°. Refrigeration is conserved by countercurrent heat exchange between the high and low pressure gases. Temperature may be varied between 21°K to 32°K by changing the setting of the dome-loaded regulator shown in the schematic flow diagram (Fig. 26). Since temperature increases with pressure, for operating temperatures below 21°K a vacuum pump is required. Temperatures above 32°K are varied by changing the pressure of the inlet gas. It is reported that precise temperature control, ±0.1°K between 15°K (−258°C) and 32°K (−241°C), ±3°K can be maintained between 32°K (−241°C; −402°F) and 200°K (−72°C; −100°F). In these units there is no frost buildup since all gas lines are at ambient temperatures. According to present day freeze-dry devices, these are exceedingly low temperatures far below what is usually

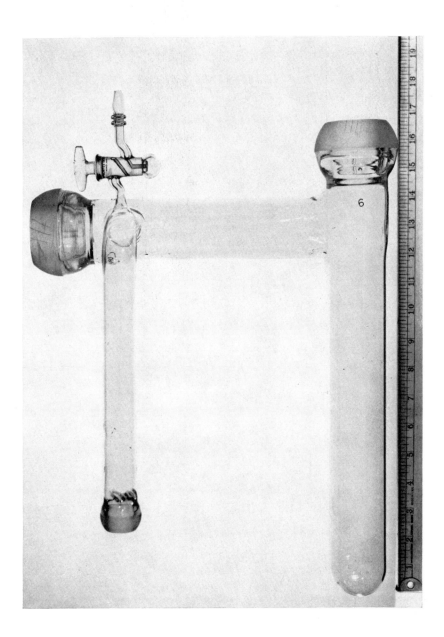

FIG. 24. Drying tube and manifold as employed in Figs. 22 and 23.

Fig. 25. Vacuum oven for embedding of frozen-dried tissues in paraffin.

considered necessary. However, in conjunction with very high vacuum systems and specially designed drying systems, these low temperatures may be advantageous in maintaining stability of tissue components.

The so-called Peltier effect was originally observed by the French physicist Peltier, who found that upon passing a current through a circuit containing junctions of two dissimilar metals, heat was released or absorbed at the junctions depending upon the polarity of the current. Thus, either cooling or heating may be obtained with semiconductor materials or thermoelectric elements presently available in electronic technology.

Utilization of the Peltier effect has been described in several articles (Wolfe, 1963; Hardy and Rutherford, 1962; Rutherford et al., 1964). The application of the Peltier effect in the preparation of frozen histological specimens has already been studied by Ioffe (1957) and Brown and Dilly (1962), who cooled the microtome stage by means of thermoelements containing semiconductor materials. Rutherford et al. (1964) have utilized thermoelectric cooling units (Frigistor thermoelements) to replace CO_2 gas and solid CO_2 for microtome stage and knife cooling (Figs. 27–29). These units consist of assemblies of series-connected thermoelements, functioning by the Peltier effect. Cooling is controlled by the direct current applied to the units; and this current is supplied by a double powerpack giving 15 A at 4.8 V for the cooling unit, and 15 A

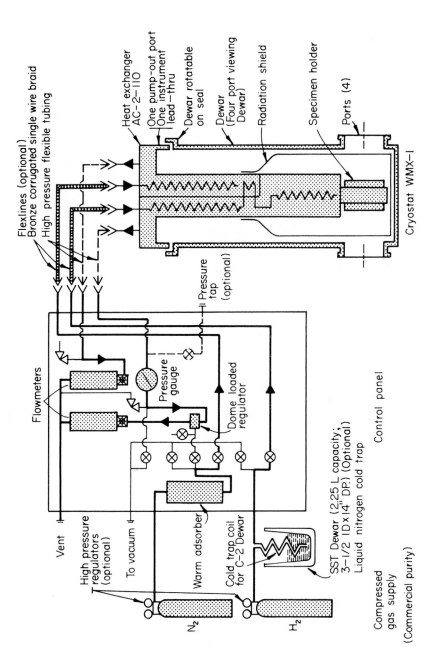

FIG. 26. Flow diagram for Cryo-Tip refrigerators. (Courtesy of Air Products and Chemicals, Inc.)

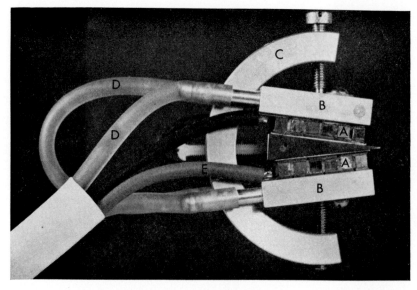

FIG. 27. Details of thermoelectrically cooled microtome of Rutherford *et al.* *A*, Thermoelements or thermistors; *B*, heat transfer sink; *C*, knife clamps; *D*, inlet and outlet water tubing; *E*, electrical leads. (Courtesy of Dr. Rutherford and associates.)

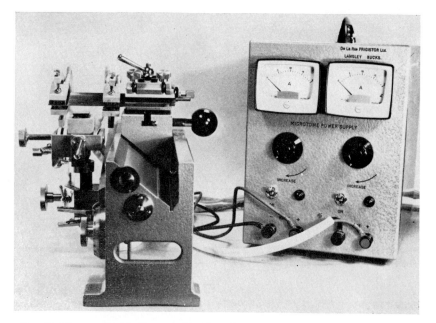

FIG. 28. Thermoelectrically cooled knife and stage attached to a sledge microtome. Note the dual power supply. (Courtesy of Dr. Rutherford and associates.)

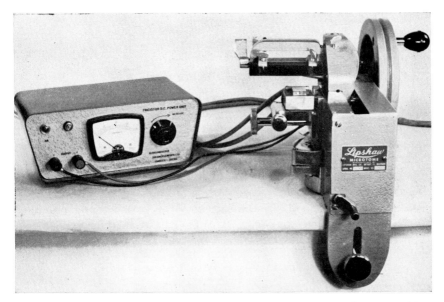

Fig. 29. Thermoelectrically cooled stage attached to a rotary microtome with a single power supply. (Courtesy of Dr. Rutherford, and associates.)

at 1 V for the stage. By varying the current flow, the optimum cutting temperature can be obtained and held indefinitely. Thus an 8-coupled Frigistor unit replaces CO_2 stage of a Lipshaw freezing microtome. The stage temperature may be lowered to $-36°C$ in 40–60 sec, and at the optimum temperature 5-μ serial sections of frozen tissues can be obtained.

Recently, Lotke and Dolan (1965) have utilized thermoelectric cooling for whole-organ freezing and thawing. The cooler consisted of a thermoelectric system sandwiched between a cold plate and heat sink. The function of the cold plate was to furnish a path for thermal conduction from the whole organ to the cold surface of the thermoelectric elements. Heat was then pumped from the cold side of the semiconductor elements and dissipated at the hot junction by a water-cooled heat sink. The cold plate was made of brass with kidney-shaped depressions that could hold a large number of dog kidneys. The semiconductor elements were four ceramic thermoelectric modules with 30 couples in each module. These can be obtained from Material Electronic Products Corporation (Melcor), Trenton, New Jersey. They were connected in series to a direct-current power supply consisting of a full-wave, bridge-type, capacity-filtered rectifier system for converting a 115-V, 60-cycle alternating current to a direct current 15 A. The heat sink consisted of a hollow copper plate soldered to the thermoelectric elements. Water flows through this heat sink at the rate of 2 liters per minute. For actual use, two identical units with the eight thermoelectric modules results in a rapid exchange of heat. When the polarity of the current is reversed, the cold plates then become heated and may be employed to thaw the organ (Figs. 30 and 31).

VI. Specialized Drying Systems

A few designs of drying devices based on the use of a dry gas to remove water evaporating from the tissue specimen have been reported (Treffenberg, 1953; Jansen, 1954; Kramer and Hill, 1956). However, high-vacuum equipment is needed for drying the air and maintaining the necessary low temperature of the air in specimens during the dehydration. The system of Kramer and Hill appears to circumvent some of the aforementioned difficulties. A mixture of carbon dioxide snow and Cellosolve contained in a Dewar flask serves to cool the chamber and provide a stream of dry gas. Drying time of 10–24 hours is claimed for tissue blocks of small size.

VII. Vacuum Systems in Freeze-Drying

The text by Guthrie (1963) on vacuum technology is a valuable reference dealing with various aspects of vacuum technology including the design and characteristics of various types of pumps, measurement of pressure, measurement of pumping speed, properties of vacuum materials, and the characteristics of ultrahigh vacuum systems. The last category covers pressure below 10^{-6} mm Hg.

On the basis of experience it would appear that a vacuum at 10^{-3} to 10^{-4} mm Hg is adequate for freeze-drying. Although such pressures can be obtained with a good mechanical pump under optimal conditions, it is best to have a diffusion pump included in the system in order to compen-

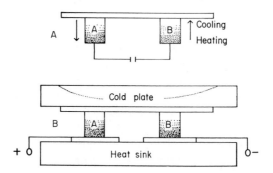

Fig. 30. Peltier effect showing that passing a current through two dissimilar metals, *A* and *B*, results in a cooling effect at the junction. Cold plate attached to the junction, *B* (lower part of diagram) utilizes the cooling effect for organ preservation. (Courtesy of Drs. Lotke and Dolan.)

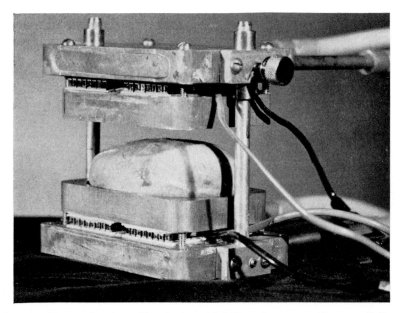

Fig. 31. Thermoelectric cooling device with kidney in system. The overall dimensions are 4 × 3 × 4 inches. (Courtesy of Drs. Lotke and Dolan.)

sate for minor leaks or slight contamination of pump oil. On the other hand, newer ultrahigh vacuum systems employing triode ion and zeolite (molecular sieve) pumps may accelerate the drying process. The determination of end point of drying can be made by various types of vacuum gauges and also on the basis of experience with the particular freeze-dry system in use (Fig. 32). A McLeod gauge may be used to measure the partial pressure of the system, but this gauge of course does not measure water vapor. Gauges employing hot filaments may be employed in the detection and measurement of water vapor, but contamination of the filament may result in inaccurate readings. The use of a tesla coil may be of value to ascertain the final stages of drying. At pressures below 0.001 mm Hg, the glow discharge will disappear from the interior of the system. The maintenance of pressures, this low or lower, coupled with what appears to be a reasonable drying time, as determined by trial and error for a particular apparatus, should serve as an adequate indicator for the end point of drying. Recent advances in ultrahigh vacuum instrumentation and technology have been described by Vanderslice (1963) and Roberts and St. Pierre (1965).

Liquid nitrogen traps have been used in many freeze-dry systems to remove water vapor from the vacuum systems. The advantage of this

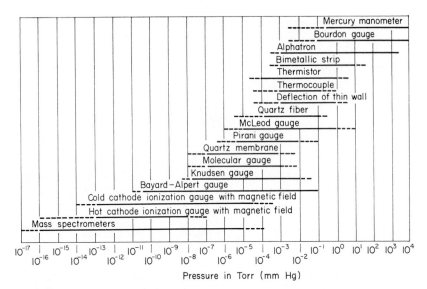

FIG. 32. Pressure ranges for a number of vacuum gauges. (From Roberts and St. Pierre, 1965.)

approach to gas pumping lies in its simplicity and enormous pumping speeds. For example, a 1-cm² surface of liquid nitrogen (77°K) will pump water vapor at a rate of approximately 15 liters per second. The pumping speed of 1 ft² would be 13,900 liters per second. The temperature of liquid nitrogen is not low enough to pump all the components of air, but liquid hydrogen (20°K) and liquid helium (4.2°K) (−268.8°C) are satisfactory. Despite the effectiveness of liquid nitrogen or helium, their practical use has not been great because of the vaporization of these liquefied gases from the freeze-dry system. Recently, however, Linde Cryogenic Equipment made by Union Carbide has been reported to control such temperatures for extended periods. In spectrography, micrography and other cooling systems operating at 15°–200°K, so-called Cryo-Tip refrigerators, use standard nitrogen and hydrogen gas cylinders and require no electricity or other power sources. A schematic diagram of the Cryo-Tip refrigerator is shown in Fig. 26.

VIII. Applications of Freeze-Drying in General Histochemistry

Implicit in the processing of frozen-dried tissue is its proper embedding and handling. This is particularly true for the demonstration of enzyme systems. Although tissues may now be embedded in methacrylate, polymerized at low temperature by ultraviolet light, this technique still results in some inactivation of enzyme systems. However, new techniques employing water-soluble embedding media may be employed. Leduc and Barnhard (1962) have described a number of water-soluble embedding media for ultrastructural cytochemistry. These include Durcupan, which is an aliphatic polyepoxide; Aquon, the water-soluble component of the epoxy resin called Epon (see Frozen Section Procedures, Section III); and glycol methacrylate, the ethylene-glycol ester of methacrylic acid. The structural formula of these three compounds is indicated in Fig. 33. From a chemical standpoint it should be mentioned that an epoxide is a triangular configuration of an oxygen atom bridging two carbons of an organic molecule. Thus ethylene oxide is the simplest epoxy. Two or more of these epoxy groups on the same molecule give a product with a potential for forming resins as well as plastics. Epoxy resins frequently have been produced by the reaction of epichlorohydrin with a polyol, usually the bisphenol from phenol and acetone.

Under specialized conditions, frozen-dried sections containing paraffin may be incubated in substrate solution or small pieces of tissue may be treated with appropriate substrates followed by freeze-drying, embedding in paraffin, and staining without removal of the wax (Glenner *et al.*, 1959) (Fig. 34).

Dried specimens are usually warmed to room temperature and directly embedded in paraffin. Many freeze-dry systems have provision for paraffin infiltration within the vacuum chamber (Scott and Williams, 1936; Stowell, 1951; Moberger *et al.*, 1954; Freed, 1955). Infiltration within the vacuum chamber is apt to be a cumbersome procedure in that

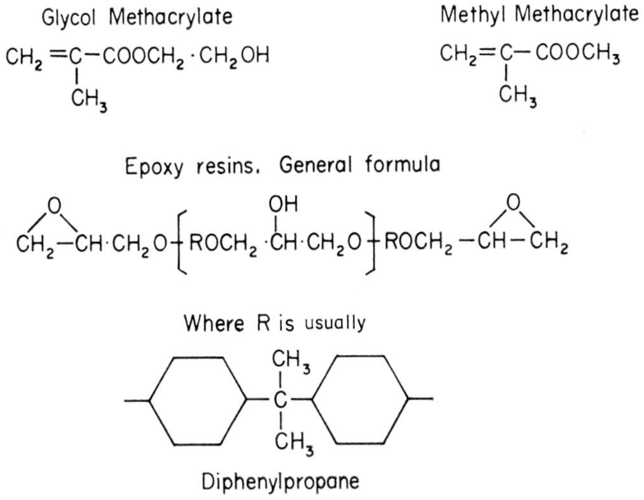

Glycol Methacrylate

$$CH_2=C-COOCH_2 \cdot CH_2OH$$
$$\quad\quad |$$
$$\quad\quad CH_3$$

Methyl Methacrylate

$$CH_2=C-COOCH_3$$
$$\quad\quad |$$
$$\quad\quad CH_3$$

Epoxy resins. General formula

$$CH_2-CH \cdot CH_2O \left[ROCH_2 \cdot CH \cdot CH_2O \right] ROCH_2 -CH-CH_2$$

Where R is usually

$$-\bigcirc-\underset{\underset{CH_3}{|}}{\overset{\overset{CH_3}{|}}{C}}-\bigcirc-$$

Diphenylpropane

FIG. 33. Structural formulas of embedding media.

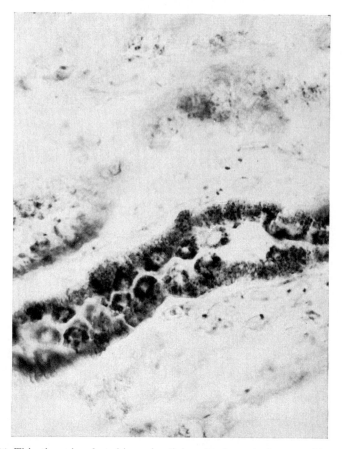

FIG. 34. Thin tissue incubated in aminodiphenylamine cytochrome oxidase reagent, frozen and dried, and embedded in paraffin and sectioned. Note localization of oxidase to mitochondria of kidney tubule. × 835.

the specimens usually must be reoriented and reembedded. In most cases it is entirely satisfactory to remove the dried specimens and embed them in a vacuum oven or suitable chamber. Figure 25 illustrates a modified vacuum oven that is used to infiltrate large numbers of frozen-dried specimens. Glass high-vacuum stopcocks have been used to replace the original metal ones, and the inlet tube has been rebored. With this chamber an internal pressure of less than 10×10^{-3} mm Hg can be obtained. Dried tissues are known to be difficult to infiltrate unless a suitable vacuum is present. At atmospheric pressure specimens tend to float on the surface of the melted paraffin for a long time. Although dried specimens are hygroscopic to some extent, they are sufficiently stable to allow exposure to the atmosphere and further treatment outside of the drying tube. If specimens removed from the drying tube and exposed to the atmosphere become wet in appearance, it indicates that the tissue was not dried, not that atmospheric moisture was absorbed. Fat, which is very difficult to dry, often shows this characteristic. Frozen-dried specimens briefly infiltrated and embedded in paraffin are highly suitable for use with a number of enzyme techniques including those for amino-peptidase. The latter enzyme is markedly sensitive to aqueous fixation followed by routine embedding procedures. Some of the oxidative enzyme systems (e.g., succinic dehydrogenase) withstand freezing, drying, and paraffin embedding. Subsequent dewaxing with paraffin solvents results in very low activity, probably due to the loss of cofactors. When adequately infiltrated and embedded, frozen-dried specimens generally section fairly easily. Because of their hygroscopic nature the sections cannot be floated on a water bath to remove wrinkles but must be dry mounted on a clean glass slide. Following dry mounting, the paraffin is melted for a short period of time on a thermostatically controlled hot plate in order to assure close approximation between the tissue section and the glass slide. On the other hand, the double embedding technique is a useful adjunct in that it enables frozen-dried sections to be floated out on water without the loss of enzyme activity (Burstone, 1958c, 1960c, 1962a). Double embedding in celloidin at low temperature followed by paraffin also facilitates the sectioning of larger and more brittle dried specimens.

Although methacrylate embedding is primarily employed with relation to electron microscopy it can also be utilized in light microscopy (Flax and Caulfield, 1962). These investigators reported that methacrylate embedding following osmium tetroxide or neutral formalin fixation for histological preparation of thin sections resulted in marked improvement in morphology as compared with paraffin embedding. Their schedule for tissue preparation embedding and sectioning is given as follows:

The two primary fixatives employed were osmium tetroxide and 10% formalin.

Osmium tetroxide method. This method is a standard technique in tissue preparation for electron microscopy. Tissue samples are cut into blocks 1–2 mm in thickness and treated as follows:

1. Fix for 1.5–2 hours in barbital–acetate-buffered osmium tetroxide (pH 7.2–7.4), with sucrose added (45 mg/ml).

2. Dehydrate in a graded series of ethanol (25%, 50%, 70% for 15 min each, 95% for 0.5 hour, and 3 changes of one-half each in absolute alcohol).

3. Transfer to 50/50 mixture of absolute ethanol and n-butyl methacrylate for 0.5 hour.

4. Transfer to butyl methacrylate monomer—2 changes of one-half hour each.

5. Transfer to monomeric *n*-butyl methacrylate containing catalyst (1% benzoyl peroxide) for 0.5 hour.

6. Infiltration is completed with partially polymerized methacrylate overnight at 4°C.

7. Transfer to gelatin capsules where final polymerization is carried out in a 45-degree oven for 12–24 hours.

Primary fixation in formalin with postfixation in osmium tetroxide. This method employs either fresh or formalin-fixed tissue and is used when relatively large pieces of tissue are to be embedded (the maximal thickness employed is 3–4 mm). Tissue is fixed in 10% formalin for 12 hours or longer. The subsequent processing is as follows:

1. Wash for one-half hour in barbital–acetate buffer with sucrose identical to that used in the fixative above.

2. Transfer to buffered osmium tetroxide fixative with sucrose for 1.5–2 hours.

3. Dehydrate stepwise in graded series of ethanol (25%, 50%, 70% for 15 min each, 95% for 0.5 hour, and 3 changes of 0.5 hour each in absolute alcohol).

4. Transfer to 50/50 mixture of absolute ethanol and *n*-butyl methacrylate for 0.5 hour.

5. Transfer to *n*-butyl methacrylate monomer—2 changes of 0.5 hour each.

6. Infiltrate with *n*-butyl methacrylate plus 1% benzoyl peroxide catalyst for 1–2 days, depending on the size of tissue.

7. Transfer to partially polymerized methacrylate for 1–2 days at 4°C.

8. Transfer to gelatin capsule for polymerization. The capsules are first kept for a half day each at room temperature and 37°C and finally for 1 day of 48°C (slow polymerization is carried out to reduce the incidence of bubbles).

Postfixation with osmium (steps 1 and 2) may be eliminated with little apparent structural alteration at the light microscope level.

Sectioning. The methacrylate-embedded tissue may be sectioned with a Porter-Blum microtome at 0.5–2 μ thickness using either glass or diamond knives. The sections are floated onto the water surface of the attached trough, transferred to albumin-coated slides, and dried on a warming plate. Spreading of the section can be accomplished by passing an applicator stick, previously dipped in xylene, close to the surface of the sections, while the sections are floating freely on the liquid. Block faces 2–3 mm in diameter can be cut conveniently on the Porter-Blum microtome, but larger ones may be cut with an ordinary steel microtome knife utilizing a Minot microtome modified for thin sectioning.

Pioneering work in applied histochemistry of frozen-dried tissues was done by Gersh and Catchpole (1949). These studies describe changes in ground substance in physiological and pathological conditions and suggest a corresponding change in the aggregation of components of the ground substance. Subsequently, electrochemical studies by Joseph et al. (1952, 1954) and Catchpole et al. (1952, 1956) have been conducted. These studies provide data on the concentration of immobile negatively charged colloids in connective tissue. From a thermodynamic standpoint, the colloids were regarded to be organized as a two-phase system; a colloid-rich (water-poor) and a colloid-poor (water-rich phase). This type of system provides the minimum, but sufficient, equilibrium for any connective tissue to be in equilibrium with the blood. The two phases themselves are also in thermodynamic equilibrium.

The application of frozen-dried, oral hard and soft tissues, including neoplasms, is reviewed and described in several works (Burstone, 1962a,b; Gersh, 1950, 1960).

The distribution of ferrocyanide in the connective tissue of mouse diaphragm has been studied by freeze-drying in conjunction with the Prussian-Blue reactions (Chase, 1959a). These findings indicate that ferrocyanide is not uniformly distributed in a ground substance, but occurs as small aggregations or droplets at the submicroscopic level. The droplets were resolved into still smaller vacuoles measuring 600–1200 Å in diameter.

Freezing-drying, as applied to plant materials, has been studied by Goodspeed and Uber (1934) and more recently by Jensen (1954). Jensen found that there was a greater difference between types of tissues that between species and that, regardless of species, leaf tissue was easiest and root tissue the most difficult to freeze and dry. Leaf segments required 1 or 2 days to dry, while root materials required 6 days or more. In all tissues except leaf, 1- or 2-mm segments were optimal for freezing and drying although 4-mm segments could occasionally be used. The system which they used was similar in design to the one described by Glick and Malmström (1952) in which the temperatures of the tissues were maintained below −30°C.

IX. Application of Freeze-Drying in Enzyme Histochemistry

The vast experience of the pharmaceutical and food industries has demonstrated the good state of preservation of proteins, including enzymes in frozen-dried tissues (Sizer and Josephson, 1942; Joslyn, 1949; R. J. C. Harris, 1954). The elegant preservation of histological and cytological structures in properly processed frozen-dried material has been demonstrated over the years by the work of Gersh and others (Gersh and Stephenson, 1954). Mucin and zymogen granules, thyroid colloid, and mitochondria (Fig. 35) exhibit a good state of preservation. Phase constrast and ultraviolet microscopy have shown close similarities between frozen-dried and living cells (Danielli, 1953; Caspersson, 1950).

Until very recent years frozen-dried tissues have been applied to either quantitative studies or, in the case of microscopic histochemistry, to the demonstration of enzymes by the older metal-salt techniques. Dounce (1950) and Mirsky (1951) used frozen-dried tissues in quantitative studies of serveral enzymes including catalase, arginase, esterase, and lipase. Lowry et al. (1954) employed frozen-dried specimens in their microquantitative techniques for the study of a number of enzymes in the centeral nervous system. Doyle (1950, 1954, 1955) and Doyle and Liebelt (1955) studied the preservation of phosphatase, esterase, and peptidase in frozen-dried paraffin-embedded blocks by quantitative techniques and observed that these enzymes are well preserved in paraffin for an indefinite period of time. It was found that freeze-drying in liquid nitrogen, followed by vacuum dehydration at −28°C and paraffin embedding, resulted in preservation of essentially the full activity of labile as well as more stable peptidases (Doyle, 1950). With reference to esterase, Doyle

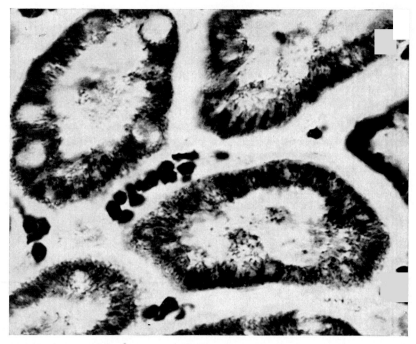

Fig. 35. Frozen-dried section of rat kidney. Regaud iron hematoxylin mitochondrial stain. × 1100.

(1954) found that gastric tissue could be frozen and dried and embedded in paraffin with negligible loss of activity. It was also observed that lymphatic tissue fixed for 1 hour in cold formalin exhibited only 5–8% of the activity of frozen-dried specimens (Doyle and Liebelt, 1954).

The earlier attempts to apply frozen-dried material to microscopic enzyme histochemistry dealt almost exclusively with the demonstration of phosphatases by the glycerophosphate technique (Bevelander and Johnson, 1946, 1950; Emmel, 1946; Wang and Grossman, 1949b; Yokoyama and Stowell, 1951; Neumann, 1952; Firket and Michel, 1954; Reale, 1956). It should be pointed out that the metal-salt methods are in many instances not entirely ideal for application with paraffin embedded tissues, so that frozen-dried specimens may not exhibit their optimal qualities with such techniques. Naidoo and Pratt (1951, 1952) studied, in addition to acid and alkaline phosphatases, ATPase, 5-nucleotidase, and thiamine pyrophosphatase of the central nervous system. Comparison of frozen-dried material with homogenates revealed no loss of enzyme activity. Demonstration of other enzymes in frozen-dried tissue include cholinesterase (Shen *et al.*, 1952), polyphenol oxidase (Smyth, 1954), phosphamidase (Neumann *et al.*, 1954), phosphorylase (Cobb, 1953), and DOPA oxidase (Rappaport, 1955).

More recently, newer azo-dye procedures have been used to study extensively the distribution of a number of hydrolytic enzyme systems in frozen-dried tissues (Burstone, 1956, 1957a,b,c, 1958a,b,c, 1959a,b, 1960a,b,c, 1962a; Burstone and Folk, 1956; Burstone and Keyes, 1957; Glenner and Burstone, 1958; Glenner *et al.*, 1959) (Figs. 36–38).

Melnick (1965) has studied the effects of freezing rates on the histochemical identification of enzyme activity including acid and alkaline phosphatases, other hydrolytic enzyme systems, and oxidative enzymes.

Quantitative alkaline phosphate activity of frozen-dried rat kidney glomeruli has been described by O'Brien and Chase (1964). The glomeruli were weighed employing a quartz, fiber balance. Phosphatase activity was ascertained by employing nitrophenyl phosphate as a substrate, after which the optical density of the release nitrophenol was measured in a spectrophotometer.

X. Applications of Freeze-Drying in Electron Microscopy

Modern concepts of the ultrastructure of animal cells and tissues are based mainly on electron microscopic observations of osmium tetroxide-fixed specimens. In a few cases it has been possible to verify the ultrastructure revealed by the electron microscope as compared with the intact living cell. Thus the existence of layering of myelin sheath in the chloroplast was confirmed by X-ray diffraction and polarization micros-

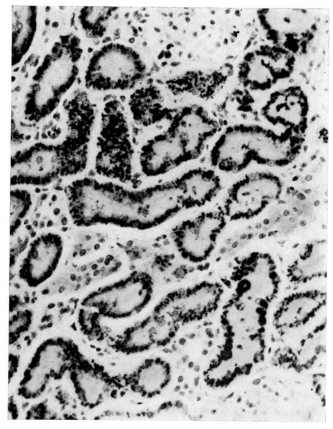

FIG. 36. Acid phosphatase activity of frozen-dried kidney. Note activity localized in "droplets" or lysosomes. Azo-dye method employing naphthol AS-BI phosphate. × 285.

copy (Reimer, 1959). The application of tissues frozen and sectioned or frozen-dried under cryogenic conditions should be of great value in realizing the nature of the ultrastructure of cells.

An advance, with reference to the fixation of enzyme systems to be studied at the submicroscopic level, has been made by several investigators (Sabitini *et al.*, 1961, 1963, 1964; Barrnett and Tice, 1963; Torack and Barrnett, 1964; Tice and Barrnett, 1965), who have employed aldehyde fixatives, some of which facilitate preservation of oxidative enzymes.

The application of physical fixation procedures such as the imaginative freeze-dry techniques of Gersh *et al.* (1957, 1960) and the freeze substitution methods of Fernández-Morán (1959, 1960) represent pioneering studies in the development of new methods for the preservation of both the enzymatic activity and the integrity of the submicroscopic structure of tissue. A significant requirement in submicroscopic histochemistry is the extreme thinness of the specimens employed, the most useful range being 200–600 Å. This requirement of necessity limits the morphological information, in effect, to a two-dimensional level. Furthermore, it is apparent that the quantity of precipitate or dye in these thin sections is extremely low. At the present time, in order to obtain such thin sections, tissues are usually embedded in a hard plastic such as methacrylate. This type of processing subjects the tissue specimens to a fairly strong solvent action (methacrylate monomer) which readily removes many azo-dyes. Fortunately, however, water-soluble plastic embedding procedures are being developed that may obviate this difficulty (see Section VIII). With reference to this approach, Craig *et al.* (1962) have found that a commercially available water-miscible plastic, Epon, is a useful embedding medium in the preparation of ultrathin sections for electron microscopy.

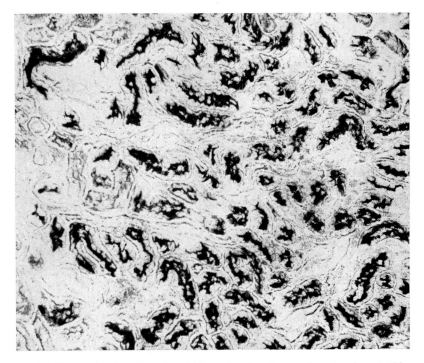

Fig. 37. Frozen-dried section of rat kidney showing distribution of amino peptidase. *dl*-Alanyl-β-naphthylamide substrate.

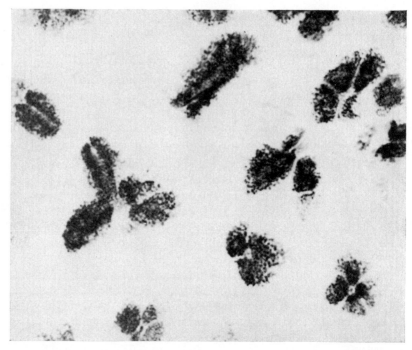

FIG. 38. Frozen-dried rat pancreas showing esterase activity of zymogen granules. Naphthol AS-LC acetate method. × 1000.

Burstone (1962a, p. 533 et seq.) has proposed the application in electron microscopy of dyes derived from naphthol-AS and analogs. Specific naphthol-AS dyes are of large molecular size and are capable of forming metal complexes. Among the metal complexes that may be of value are those containing lead, tungsten, molybdenum, and uranium. The application of salts of these metals as electron microscope stains has been considered by Watson (1958a,b).

With reference to the utilization of simultaneous coupling azo-dye procedures for electron microscopy, it should be pointed out that in such techniques the finite coupling time that occurs as the naphthol is released from its corresponding ester may result in diffusion artifacts, as may be readily seen at the routine optical level when simpler naphtholic substrates are used. The fact that diffusion artifacts may be less readily evaluated at the submicroscopic level may be the result of several factors. First, the diffused dye, which may be less tightly bound to tissue protein is readily removed by the solvents employed in the methacrylate embedding and thus the section may contain only sharply defined foci of dye deposits. Second, the nature and type of diffusion artifacts at the submicroscopic level have not been definitively evaluated at the present time.

From a theoretical standpoint it would appear that the most desirable type of azo-dye or naphtholic substrate procedure would be a postcoupling or noncoupling method. Thus, a suitable tissue specimen could simply be incubated in the presence of a naphtholic ester, which upon enzymatic hydrolysis would leave an insoluble precipitate *in situ*. Substrates of this type have been illustrated (Burstone, 1962a). If the released naphthol were sufficiently dense to the electron beam, the specimen could be studied without further treatment. However, such a naphthol may be readily coupled with a variety of diazonium salts, including slow couplers of large molecular size, diazo components containing metals, and those containing coordinating groups for metal chelation. Diazonium salts of this type have been described in a recent paper by Burstone and Weisburger (1961a).

Included in this general type of approach is the application of a substrate containing the 1-hydroxyanthraquinone residue which is capable of forming intermolecular chelates with a number of metals (Fig. 39). In this instance, the metal complexing procedure would follow the incubation of tissue specimen. Another potential approach involves the formation of "lakes" of 1-nitroso derivatives of 3-hydroxy-2-naphthoic acid arylamides. According to Venkataraman (1952), naphthol-AS and its analogs, when treated in ethanolic solution with different molecular proportions of ferric salt in the presence of nitrous acid, yield two types

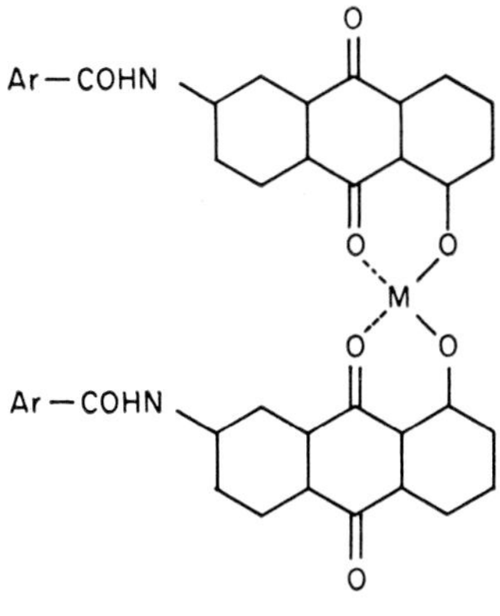

Fig. 39. Intermolecular chelation of aromatic compound containing alizarin grouping (M = metal). Ar represents the aryl grouping containing the ester that is hydrolyzed by enzymatic activity.

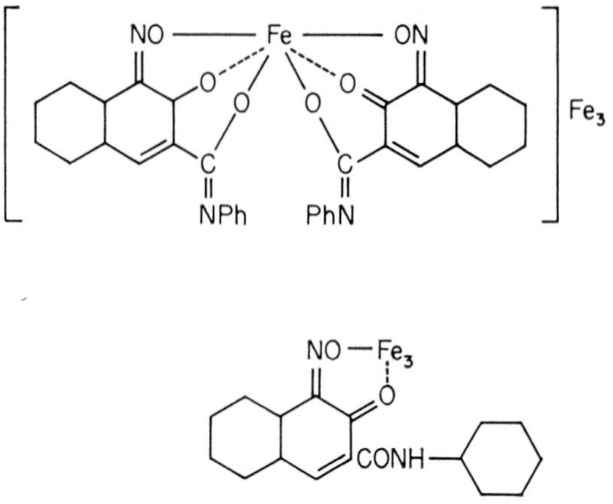

FIG. 40. Types of iron complexes formed from naphthol AS compound after enzymatic hydrolysis of esterified hydroxyl groupings.

of iron complexes that are represented in Fig. 40. Iron or other metallic complexes of naphthol-AS derivatives deposited *in situ* following enzymatic hydrolysis should offer a novel approach to the demonstration of a variety of hydrolytic enzymes at the submicroscopic level. Several new aminopeptidase substrates that contain coordinating groups for metal chelation have been reported by Burstone and Weisburger (1961b), but as yet these compounds have not been applied to electron microscopy.

There have been studies on the application of frozen-dried material to electron microscopy in a few of those related to the histochemical demonstration of enzymes. The possibility of preserving tissues by purely physical techniques involving almost instantaneous fixation should facilitate the study of the localization of enzymes at the submicroscopic level. Sjöstrand and Baker (1958) were among the first to use freeze-drying for electron microscopy of cells. They observed vacuolization due to ice crystal formation but found that it did not interfere in a critical way with the observation of certain submicroscopic structures, such as mitochondria and α-cytomembranes. It was found that serious artifacts were produced when the dried tissue was infiltrated with plastic monomer according to routine procedures. Artifacts were minimized by infiltration and polymerization with plastic at low temperatures according to the technique of Müller (1957). Müller also pointed out the value of propane as a quenching medium, as well as the significance of low temperature dehydration. Hanson and Hermodsson (1960) extended and confirmed the aforementioned work of Sjöstrand and Baker and also stressed the importance of very low temperature dehydration in order to avoid artifacts (vacuoles) due to ice crystal formation. Exocrine pancreas was used as a test object, and morphological structures observed with conventional osmium-fixed material could be confirmed to a great extent.

Hanson and Hermodsson (1960) described the equipment and technique for fixation of tissues by freeze-drying at the electron microscope level. In many of the specimens, damage to the ultrastructure was impossible to avoid and analysis was made of the cause of these artifacts. It was felt that the critical stage was the infiltration of the dry specimens with fluid plastic. The frequency of occurrence of damage may be decreased by treating the dried specimens with osmium tetroxide vapor. Thus it is important to note that freeze-drying in itself is not the primary cause of damage; and the development of new embedding media will probably resolve the artifact problems. These workers noted that it is important to maintain the specimens below $-70°C$ until they are dry in order to avoid ice crystal formation. Exocrine pancreas was used as a test specimen when studying the preservation of ultrastructure. Although observations upon conventionally fixed material could be confirmed to a great extent, there was one important exception: no 150-Å particles (RNA) were found in the cryoplasm of the frozen dry cells.

Gersh et al. (1957, 1960) employed freeze-dry techniques in conjunction with electron microscope stains, some of which were capable of demonstrating protein groups. Seno and Yoshizawa (1960) employing the basic techniques of Müller (1957) studied the submicroscopic structure of frozen-dried liver and pancreas. These authors concluded that routine osmium fixation gives satisfactory preservation of a number of cell structures that are clearly delineated in carefully processed frozen-dried specimens. Grunbaum and Wellings (1960a,b) have also investigated frozen-dried material for the study of cellular ultrastructure. With reference to enzyme systems, Nelson (1958, 1959) has studied adenosinetriphosphatase and succinic dehydrogenase in frozen-dried rat sperm. Yaeger (1961) applied a tetrazole method to localize succinic dehydrogenase in muscle cells of mouse diaphragm. The widespread application of frozen-dried tissue to definitive enzyme histochemistry awaits the development and synthesis of new substrates and new embedding techniques and modifications.

Chase (1959c) has described the fine structure of rat adipose tissue which was frozen and dried and then postfixed in aqueous osmium tetroxide. He found a large number of mitochondria and small very dense granules concentrated in the cytoplasm near the fat vacuole. The internal structure of mitochondria was similar to that described after routine fixation in aqueous osmium tetroxide, but a characteristic negative image was found. Chase also studied, employing similar techniques, the basement membranes of fat cells and has employed freeze-dry techniques in the study of elastic fibers in mouse lung tissue. Elastic fibers stained with orcein showed increased density in the electron microscope, which served to delineate them from the surrounding tissue.

Chase (1963) has also frozen and dried fragments of mouse gut mucosa and embedded them in methacrylate. Serial sections were studied with both light and electron microscopic methods following staining with the Gomori alkaline phosphatase method. With the electron microscope, deposits of calcium phosphate were seen in the brush border and the Golgi area of the epithelial cells, and in large and small apical granules.

An interesting recent variant of application of freeze-drying to electron microscopy of cells is the freezer-fracture replication method (Moor, 1966; Bullivant and Burke, 1966; Leake and Burke, 1967). In the last study, a pellet of cells (blue-green alga, *Anabaena*) obtained by centrifuging was fractured, in the frozen state, with a razor-blade under liquid nitrogen. After vacuum dehydration, a platinum-carbon replica of a fractured surface was made; the thawed specimen was removed by dissolution in nitric acid; and the cleaned and washed replica was mounted on the grid for study. The result is a visualization in face view and at various angles of fracture of many cell structures (e.g., lamellae) commonly seen in sections of fixed material.

XI. Freeze-Substitution

The freeze-substitution technique was originated by Simpson (1941) in the course of an analysis of the Altmann-Gersh freeze-dry procedure. In an attempt to isolate the effects of freezing from the effect of subsequent vacuum dehydration, he froze tissues and placed them in organic solvents at low temperatures from $-40°C$ to $-78°C$. Included among the solvents were methyl Cellosolve, ethanol, diethyl ether, and chloroform. Lison (1949) employed the technique in the study of glycogen, and Blank *et al.* (1951) used freeze-substitution as a means of studying radioactive P^{32} and referred to their method as nonvacuum freeze-drying. Blank and associates found that by using propylene-glycol followed by polyethylene-glycol embedding (Blank, 1949), losses of radioactive material were minimized as compared with the ordinary paraffin technique. Various modifications as well as applications of the procedure have been employed by a number of investigators (Russell *et al.*, 1949; Lillie and Lasky, 1951; Taft, 1951; Baud, 1952; Persson, 1952; Gourévitch, 1953; Davies, 1954; Pollister and Ornstein, 1959; Deitch and Godman, 1955; Chang, 1956; J. H. Taylor, 1956; Davies *et al.*, 1957; Hancox, 1957; Fernández-Morán, 1957, 1959; McMaster-Kaye and Taylor, 1958; Nair, 1958; Patten and Brown, 1958; Davis *et al.*, 1959).

The physical mechanisms involved in freeze-substitution have received little attention. Persson (1952) studied the dehydration time of cylinders of gelatin frozen at different temperatures and found that the shortest drying time was correlated with the lowest initial freezing temperature. Hancox (1957) found that protein denaturation was minimal in rat tissues dehydrated in butanol at $-38°C$. Johnson (1959) compared substitution rates using a number of anhydrous solvents at $-45°C$. Acetone and ethanol-acetone showed the most rapid dehydration action, while isoamyl alcohol, butanol, and tetrahydrofuran were very slow. Less than half of a 5-μl sample of frozen synthetic tissue fluid could be dehydrated in 10 ml of the aforementioned solvents in 12 days. None of the solvents causes as rapid dehydration as that obtained at $-30°C$ with a simple freeze-dry apparatus. The advantage claimed for freeze-substitution is that, after quenching, the solvents employed for dehydration dissolve the ice out of the specimen and the tissue thus retains its relatively undenatured state. L. G. E. Bell (1952a) has pointed out that it is not certain at what stage the substitution of solvent for water occurs. It may well take place to some degree during the warming-up state. This suggests that diffusion artifacts may occur and that the fixation may in part be chemical and similar to the cold acetone technique of Gomori (1952).

The most recent extensive consideration of methods and principles of fixation by freeze-substitution has been reported by Feder and Sidman (1958). They rapidly froze tissues in propane-isopentane cooled by liquid nitrogen. The frozen tissue was placed in a substituting fluid at $-70°C$ (for approximately one week) consisting of 1% mercuric chloride or picric acid in ethanol or 1% osmium tetroxide or chromic acid in acetone. After substitution, the specimens were washed for 12 hours or more followed by three changes of ethanol or other solvents and placed in chloroform for 6–12 hours. They were then brought up to room temperature, transferred to xylene, and embedded in paraffin. Their findings confirmed the original observations of Lison (1949), who found that the quality of preservation was vastly improved by incorporation of a fixative with the dehydrating solvent. Feder and Sidman (1958) point out that most investigators have used nonaqueous solvents as substituting fluids and that the relatively unfixed specimens were subject to distortion during subsequent processing and embedding. They believe that the fixing agent in the substituting fluid actually exerts its effect at $-70°C$ and not when the specimen is warmed prior to embedding. This contention is supported by several model experiments. These authors did not report any studies on the use of their technique for enzyme histochemistry.

Davis and Ornstein (1959) have reported the histochemical demonstration of esterase and alkaline phosphatase at both routine optical and electron microscope levels in freeze-substituted tissues using azo-dye methods. Although their results were satisfactory from cytological standpoint, it is not known how much inactivation of the enzymes studied had occurred. Bullivant (1960) froze mouse pancreas in liquid helium II, and substituted the tissue ice with methanol at −75°C. Specimens were substituted for 2 weeks at low temperature and then embedded and polymerized in methacrylate plastic at low temperature. Sections were treated to reveal acid phosphatase according to the Gomori glycerophosphate-lead nitrate method. It was pointed out that although the resulting precipitate may not reveal the true site of the enzyme, this type of histochemical approach is feasible for the resolution of sites of enzyme activity at the electron microscope level.

Protagonists of the freeze-substitution technique stress that the procedure should be as effective as freeze-drying and that freeze-substitution requires no vacuum system. However, it should be pointed out that freeze-substitution (just as with most freeze-dry systems) requires a low temperature relatively expensive to maintain over a period of time. In addition, substitution of rather small pieces of tissue requires considerable solvent and is very time consuming. In view of the prolonged periods during which freeze-substituted tissues are subjected to organic solvents at low and at room temperatures, as well as of the potential hazard of inactivation of enzymes due to the presence of residual fixatives, it would appear that at the present time freeze-drying is a superior technique for enzyme histochemistry.

Persijn et al. (1964) have described a freeze-substitution apparatus for the processing of temperatures down to −130°C. Their system does not employ mechanical cooling, but uses liquid air. These authors indicate that the conditions of substitution are more critical for morphological preservation than are the conditions of freezing and that for electron microscopy frozen sections can probably be utilized instead of frozen blocks to reduce the time of substitution.

Fernández-Morán (1961a,b, 1962) has developed several approaches for freeze-substitution of tissues in conjunction with electron microscopy. These employ freezing in helium II or liquid nitrogen–Freon mixtures followed by substitution in heavy metal salt-containing solvents at temperatures between −130°C and −80°C. This is followed by infiltration with methacrylate below −75°C and subsequent ultraviolet initiated polymerization below −20°C. Prior to freezing the tissues were protected by infiltration with glycerol solutions at low temperatures.

Bullivant (1965a) reported that liquid helium II was an only slightly better coolant than helium I and not as rapid as propane cooled in liquid nitrogen. In this study Bullivant used mouse pancreas impregnated in varying concentrations of glycerol ranging from 3 to 60% in isotonic Veronal acetate buffer (pH 7.2). The glycerinated tissue was frozen in liquid propane, cooled by liquid nitrogen and then transferred in a refrigerator at −75°C into dried ethanol at the same temperature. The tissues were substituted in three changes of ethanol at this low temperature over a 3-week period and then transferred into butyl/methyl methacrylate or butyl/methyl methacrylate + 1% Lucidol. Polymerization took place under the influence of ultraviolet light at −25°C and was accomplished in 3 days. Bullivant also applied Durcupan mixture (Stäubli, 1960) as well as the Epon mixture of Luft (1961).

Post (1965) has described a technique for cutting thin sections from solvent-substituted, paraffin-embedded tissues. Reagent grade acetone cooled to −65°C was used as previously employed by Patten and Brown (1958) and Feder and Sidman (1958). The acetone is changed at least twice during the first 48-hour period, replacing it with previously cooled acetone and minimizing the possibility of water condensation in the tube by carrying out the procedure in the −65°C freezer employed for tissue storage. Post primarily employed this technique to study immunofluorescent procedures but was unable to demonstrate the injected protein with sufficient clarity. Several possible explanations for the limitations were evident. He found that freezing and thawing artifacts were consistently encountered and routine standing revealed extensive cellular destruction. It is interesting that he reported that relatively slow drying applied to cryostat sections offered the possibility for lateral diffusion of soluble proteins such as bovine serum albumin. Despite the above mentioned artifacts good photomicrographs were shown of kidney stained with either a periodic acid-Schiff and iron hematoxylin stains. However, the best photographs were obtained with tissues fixed in osmium tetroxide. It is noted that the organic solvents employed in the substituting and embedding procedures probably resulted in alteration of some proteins. However, the use of organic solvents alone does not yield sections in which cell structure is adequately preserved. Therefore a 0.5% solution of osmium tetroxide in acetone (w/v) at −65°C was employed. This solution was allowed to stand at −65°C in order to ensure solution for several hours or overnight prior to use. For embedding, the tissues were drained of acetone which was replaced by tetrahydrofuran (THF); fixation is carried out by decanting the substituting acetone, transferring the tissues to cooled, glass-stoppered tubes, and adding the osmium–acetone to the test tube containing the tissues. Tissues are fixed at −65°C for at least 72 hours. After fixation the tissues are washed several times with acetone at −65°C and then allowed to remain overnight in cold acetone. They may be stored at −65°C in acetone after fixation. For embedding, Post employed the following schedule:

A. Embedding schedule for fixed tissue:
Overnight in THF, −65°C
To room temperature in a fresh change of THF
15 min in one-half THF–one-half paraffin-beeswax, 60°C (213°K)
Two 15-min periods in paraffin-beeswax, 60°C
Two 30-min periods in paraffin-beeswax, 60°C
30 min in paraffin-beeswax, 40 mm Hg vacuum, 60°C
15 min in paraffin-beeswax, in base mold, 40 mm Hg vacuum, 60°C

B. Embedding schedule for unfixed tissue:
THF, −65°C, 2 hours
To room temperature in a fresh change of THF
5 min in one-half THF–one-half paraffin-beeswax, 60°C
Three 5-min periods in paraffin-beeswax 60°C
15 min in paraffin-beeswax, 40 mm Hg vacuum, 60°C
5 min in paraffin-beeswax, in base mold, 40 mm Hg vacuum, 60°C

C. Schedule for basic fuchsin staining:
Deparaffinize in THF
Place slide directly in 0.025% basic fuchsin in water, 30 sec
Transfer slide directly to THF, two changes of 1–2 min each
To xylene and mount

D. Potassium chrome-alum for dipping slides to ensure section adherence:
Heat 200 ml of water containing 1 g of gelatin (Knox) to 56°C and stir until clear
Dissolve 0.1 g of chromium potassium sulfate ($CrK(SO_4)_2 \cdot 12H_2O$)
Dip each slide individually (precleaned) and dry vertically, protected from dust

E. Preparation of sections for fluorescein-conjugated antibody reaction:
Deparaffinize sections in THF, briefest possible time (1–2 min)
Wash in isotonic saline buffered to pH 7.45 with phosphate buffer, 5–10 min
Allow to react with conjugate for a suitable time, wash 10–20 min in buffered saline, and mount in buffered glycerin

Rebhun (1965) has employed a number of substituting fluids for freeze-substitution for application in electron microscope. Among the hydrocarbons investigated were isopentane, isobutane 3-methyl-1-butene, 2-methyl-1-pentane, and butene-1, as well as propane, propylene, ethane, ethylene, the boiling points of which are well below room temperature. The halogenated hydrocarbons employed were Freons 12, 13, 14, 22, 13 B-1 and Genetron 23 (Fluoroform). Azotropic Freon 22–propane mixtures (68 parts Freon 22 to 32 parts propane) as well as various other mixtures were employed. A variety of nucleating powders were used, including alumina of various grades, a variety of cellulose powders, rosins, metallic powders, and Santocel. The fastest cooling velocities were obtained in propane or propylene. Ethane or ethylene gave virtually identical results with a variety of nucleating powders, but not without them. Freon 22–propane mixture were inferior to propane although better than Freon 22. The nucleating powders greatly increased cooling rates in liquid nitrogen and Freons, but these rates were still slower than those obtained with the first group mentioned.

Water was removed by solvents substituted with a variety of reagents at temperatures of $-79°$ to $-108°C$. Most of this work is a result of substitution with acetone or ethanol at $-79°C$ to $-85°C$, using either Dry Ice or a low-temperature freezer. Substitution periods varied from 2 to 4 weeks, after which specimens were embedded in a variety of embedding media including cross-linked methacrylates. Araldite 502, Epon 812, and a special Araldite 506–Unox-206 medium. The tissue was warmed to room temperature, then handled as ordinary tissue in absolute solvent. Gersh (1965), Feder and Sidman (1958), and Fernández-Morán (1960) studied the dissolution of dye solutions in capillaries by various substitution fluids at different temperatures. Their result suggest that a period of 2–3 weeks at $-80°C$ with tissue blocks of small size is sufficient to remove the water. Also, osmium dissolved in alcohol or acetone reduces and turns black at room temperature. However, in solutions at low temperatures it may keep for many months without reduction.

Bullivant (1960, 1965a) evolved a freeze-substitution technique employing helium II of unprotected materials for the electron microscope. Membranous organelles appeared in negative contrast, particularly after heavy metal staining. The ribosomes were not so easily visible in unstained material but were revealed by heavy metal staining and were found to be somewhat variable in size and in more intimate contact with a dense layer on the membrane surface than is seen with the usual osmium-fixed material.

Of interest is the work of Bartl (1962), who substituted directly in water-soluble embedding glycol methacrylate.

Afzelius (1962) employed the well-known fixative acrolein as a substituting fluid at low temperature. He also has reviewed other chemical fixatives for electron microscopy of rat liver tissue. These, however, were not used in conjunction with freeze-substitution, but it is interesting that he reports that, contrary to the common belief, formaldehyde may be used as a fixative for electron microscopy and its use results in electron micrographs of good contrast. The limitation of formaldehyde appears to be the lack of adequate stabilization of the tissue structure in the electron beam rather then a lack of contrast. The mitochondria are elongated, and their matrix is electron dense. The cristae are visible because of their lower electron density and thus appear in reversed contrast as a light, double line in a grayish background. This type of reverse image is also seen in frozen-dried material.

Pease (1964) has reviewed freeze-substitution for electron microscopy in his recent text and emphasized the usefulness of freeze-substituted material which can be polymerized easily with ultraviolet light at low temperature ($-72°$C).

Gersh (1965) has found that when specimens are frozen at an ultra-rapid rate of about 5000°C/sec and suitably dried no empty spaces or negative images can be seen. Instead, every part of the cell seems to contain solid components, some regions being denser than others. This kind of "complete" structure can be observed after a variety of specimen treatments, including heat denaturation of the dried specimen *in vacuo*, treatment of the specimens in ethanol and treatment of the specimens with protein reagents such as dinitrofluorobenzene. The latter acts as a cross-linking agent and tends to make insoluble and to stain even amino acids. This observation is interesting in that it appears to verify the application of routine biochemical and histochemical reagents for electron microscopy.

The freeze-substitution of individual sections has been developed by Chang and associates (1961a,b, 1962). For this technique, sections 8–10 μ thick are guided by an artist's camel-hair brush onto a platform (Fig. 17). The sections are then swept into a screw-cap vial containing absolute acetone which has been prechilled by crushed Dry Ice in a Dewar flask (approximately 1 ml of acetone is required for a section 5 mm square). The free sections should be transferred to the acetone solution within 1 min after sectioning. This is adequate time for an experienced operator to cut five to seven good sections. If the sections are left in the cryostat longer than 1 min, their morphology may be altered as a result of partial dehydration and possibly of ice crystal formation. After transfer of the tissues, the vial is quickly capped, returned to the Dewar flask, and covered with Dry Ice to complete the freeze-substitution process. Dehydration is usually completed within 12 hours. According to Chang and Hori (1961) the free sections may be kept in acetone at Dry Ice temperature for 4 weeks or more without detectable loss of enzymes or alteration of cellular morphology. After completion of the dehydration in acetone, the sections can be mounted on coverslips with or without celloidin coating, depending upon the specific histochemical or staining method employed. For localization of oxidative enzymes and for 5'-nucleotidase, celloidin coating is required; it is not required for localization of other enzymes or histochemical substances. For the celloidin mounting process, a metal box is employed. This box is 23 × 23 × 9 cm deep, and its floor walls are insulated with Styrofoam 25 mm (1 inch) in thickness. It is partially filled with Dry Ice packed around a 250-ml beaker containing absolute acetone which has been prechilled in Dry Ice. The vial containing the frozen-substituted sections is quickly transferred from the Dewar flask into the beaker, and the top of the vial is removed. A chemically clean coverslip 22 mm square is held with forceps and dipped first into the acetone in the beaker for a few seconds, then into the vial. By a gentle stir of the coverslip, the sections are momentarily suspended in the acetone solution. While they are in suspension, the coverslip is slipped beneath a section which, in turn, is guided onto the coverslip by a dissecting needle held with the other hand. The sections will adhere to the coverslip as it is lifted out of the acetone and quickly placed in a small, shallow dish containing celloidin solution. After a few seconds in the celloidin solution, the coverslip with the mounted tissue section is removed and dried at room temperature on a coverslip rack. The dried sections are kept at room temperature until stained. As a substitute for celloidin, USP collodion diluted to halfstrength by ethanol–ether may be readily employed. Chang and Hori (1961) have indicated that celloidin coating is necessary in the localization of oxidative enzymes and 5′-nucleotidase because without this coating the enzymes may diffuse and a weak stain be produced. The celloidin solution is 1% in 30 parts of ether, 30 of ethanol, and 40 of acetone. A higher concentration of celloidin would produce an uneven and weaker staining while a lower concentration would result in diffuse staining. Freshly made celloidin solutions are recommended, and these solutions should be kept at Dry Ice temperature during coating.

When celloidin coating is not employed, the vial containing the tissue sections is transferred to an empty Dewar flask or into the freezing compartment of the refrigerator for gradual warming. The cap of the vial should be loosened to permit the escape of gas. Three hours later the vial is brought to room temperature. The sections are then transferred to 95% ethanol at room temperature and, after 2 min, are mounted on coverslips. In this process the sections are manipulated with coverslip, a dissecting needle, and a pair of forceps according to the previously outlined procedure for celloidin coating. To prevent the sections from curling, which may occur during prolonged immersion in ethanol, they should be treated individually or a few at a time. Among the more sensitive enzymes localized by this freeze-substitution technique were di- and triphosphopyridine nucleotide diaphorases, succinic dehydrogenase and choline dehydrogenase, hydrolytic enzymes, including alkaline and acid phosphatases, esterase, amylophosphorylase, and β-glucuronidase; other components, including nucleic acids, carbohydrates, protein and amino groups, inorganic elements, and soluble isotopes, have also been described. The freeze-substitution frozen section technique has also been used to demonstrate lipids in mitochondria and other cellular elements, including lipid-dependent oxidative enzymes (Hori and Chang, 1963). Therefore, newer modifications of the freeze-substitution technique have been shown to have considerable usefulness not only with complete blocks of tissue, but also with cryostat sections.

REFERENCES

Adamstone, F. B. (1951). *Stain Technol.* **26**, 157–161.
Adamstone, F. B., and Taylor, A. B. (1947). *Anat. Record* **99**, 639.
Adamstone, F. B., and Taylor, A. B. (1948). *Stain Technol.* **23**, 109–116.
Afzelius, B. A. (1962). *In* "The Interpretation of Ultrastructure" (R. J. C. Harris, ed.), pp. 1–19. Academic Press, New York.
Altmann, R. (1890). "Die Elementarorganismen und ihre Beziehungen zu den Zellen." Veit, Leipzig.
Andrews, S., and Levitt, J. (1967). *Cryobiology* **4**, 85–89.
Arcadi, J. A., and Tesar, C. (1954). *J. Lab. Clin. Med.* **43**, 479–481.
Asahiana, E. (1965). *Federation Proc.* **24**, Suppl. 15, S183–S187.
Baker, J. R. (1950). "Cytological Technique," 3rd Ed. Methuen, London.
Baker, J. R. (1961). "Handbook on the Microtome-cryostat." Bio-research Consultants, International Equipment Co., Boston, Massachusetts.
Baker, J. R. (1964). "Microtome-cryostat Handbook," 2nd Ed. International Equipment Co., Needham Heights, Massachusetts.
Barrnett, R. J., and Tice, L. W. (1963). *In* "Histochemistry and Cytochemistry," Proc. 1st Intern. Congr. (R. Wegmann, ed.), pp. 139–180. Macmillan (Pergamon), New York.
Bartl, P. (1962). *In* "Electron Microscopy" (S. S. Breese, Jr., ed.), p. 4. Academic Press, New York.
Batsakis, J. G. (1963). *Stain. Technol.* **38**, 51–54.
Baud, C. A. (1952). *Bull. Microscop. Appl.* **2**, 158–160.
Bayliss, W. M. (1924). "Principles of General Physiology." Longmans, Green, London.
Becker, N. H., Goldfischer, S., Shin, W. Y., and Novikoff, A. B. (1960). *J. Biophys. Biochem. Cytol.* **8**, 649–663.
Behrens, M. (1932). *Z. Physiol. Chem. Hoppe-Seylers* **209**, 59–74.
Bell, J. H., Jr. (1963). "Cryogenic Engineering." Prentice-Hall, Englewood Cliffs, New Jersey.
Bell, L. G. E. (1952a). *Intern. Rev. Cytol.* **1**, 35–63.
Bell, L. G. E. (1952b). *Nature* **170**, 719.
Bell, L. G. E. (1956). *Phys. Tech. Biol. Res.* **3**, 1–27.
Benditt, E., Lagunoff, D., and Johnson, F. B. (1961). *Arch. Pathol.* **72**, 546–549.
Bernhard, W., Yokoyama, H. O., and Stowell, R. E. (1952). *Proc. Soc. Exptl. Biol. Med.* **81**, 125–128.
Bernhard, W., Granboulan, N., Barski, G., and Tournier, P. (1961). *Compt. Rend.* **252**, 202–204.
Bevelander, G., and Johnson, P. L. (1946). *J. Dental Res.* **25**, 381–385.
Bevelander, G., and Johnson, P. L. (1950). *Anat. Record* **108**, 1–21.
Blank, H. (1949). *J. Invest. Dermatol.* **12**, 95–99.
Blank, H., McCarthy, P. L., and DeLamater, E. D. (1951). *Stain Technol.* **26**, 194–197.
Bourne, G. H., and Danielli, J. F. (1957). *Intern. Rev. Cytol.* **6**.
Brown, R., and Dilly, N. (1962). *J. Physiol. (London)* **161**, 1–4.
Bullivant, S. (1960). *J. Biophys. Biochem. Cytol.* **8**, 639–647.

Bullivant, S. (1965a). *Lab. Invest.* **14:** 1178–1195.

Bullivant, S. (1965b). "Subcellular Pathology." Harper & Row (Hoeber), New York.

Bullivant, S., and Burke, J. F. (1966). *J. Cell Biol.* **29**, 435–447.

Burstone, M. S. (1956). *J. Histochem. Cytochem.* **4**, 130–139.

Burstone, M. S. (1957a). *A.M.A. Arch. Pathol.* **63**, 164–167.

Burstone, M. S. (1957b). *J. Natl. Cancer Inst.* **18**, 167–173.

Burstone, M. S. (1957c). *Oral Surg. Oral Med. Oral Pathol.* **10**, 296–303.

Burstone, M. S. (1958a). *J. Natl. Cancer Inst.* **20**, 601–614.

Burstone, M. S. (1958b). *J. Natl. Cancer Inst.* **21**, 523–539.

Burstone, M. S. (1958c). *J. Histochem. Cytochem.* **6**, 322–339.

Burstone, M. S. (1959a). *J. Histochem. Cytochem.* **7**, 39–41.

Burstone, M. S. (1959b). *J. Histochem. Cytochem.* **7**, 147–148.

Burstone, M. S. (1960a). *J. Natl. Cancer Inst.* **24**, 1199–1217.

Burstone, M. S. (1960b). *Ann. N.Y. Acad. Sci.* **85**, 431–444.

Burstone, M. S. (1960c). *In* "Calcification in Biological Systems" (R. F. Sognnaes, ed.), pp. 213–243. Am. Assoc. Advance. Sci., Washington, D.C.

Burstone, M. S. (1961). *J. Histochem. Cytochem.* **9**, 146–153.

Burstone, M. S. (1962a). "Enzyme Histochemistry and Its Application in the Study of Neoplasms." Academic Press, New York.

Burstone, M. S. (1962b). *In* "Orban's Oral Histology and Embryology" (H. Sicher, ed.), 5th Ed., pp. 352–376. Mosby, St. Louis, Missouri.

Burstone, M. S., and Folk, J. E. (1956). *J. Histochem. Cytochem.* **4**, 217–226.

Burstone, M. S., and Keyes, P. H. (1957). *Am. J. Pathol.* **33**, 1229–1235.

Burstone, M. S., and Weisburger, E. K. (1961a). *J. Histochem. Cytochem.* **9**, 349–355.

Burstone, M. S., and Weisburger, E. K. (1961b). *J. Histochem. Cytochem.* **9**, 712–713.

Bush, V., and Hewitt, R. E. (1952). *Am. J. Pathol.* **28**, 863–873.

Butler, L. O., and Bell, L. G. (1953). *Nature* **171**, 971–972.

Caspersson, T. O. (1950). "Cell Growth and Cell Function, A Cytological Study." Norton, New York.

Catchpole, H. R., Joseph, N. R., and Engel, M. B. (1952). *J. Endocrinol.* **8**, 377–385.

Catchpole, H. R., Joseph, N. R., and Engel, M. B. (1956). *A.M.A. Arch. Pathol.* **61**, 503–511.

Chang, J. P. (1956). *Exptl. Cell Res.* **11**, 643–646.

Chang, J. P. (1965). Personal communication.

Chang, J. P., and Hori, S. H. (1961). *J. Histochem. Cytochem.* **9**, 292–300.

Chang, J. P., Russell, W. O., Moore, E. B., and Sinclair, W. K. (1961a). *Am. J. Clin. Pathol.* **35**, 14–19.

Chang, J. P., Russell, W. O., and Moore, E. B. (1961b). *J. Histochem. Cytochem.* **9**, 208.

Chase, W. H. (1959a). *A.M.A. Arch. Pathol.* **67**, 550–555.

Chase, W. H. (1959b). *J. Ultrastruct. Res.* **2**, 283–287.

Chase, W. H. (1963). *J. Histochem. Cytochem.* **11**, 96–101.

Chesterman, W., and Leach, E. H. (1956). *Quart. J. Microscop. Sci.* **97**, 593–597.

Chilson, O. P., Costello, L. A., and Kaplan, N. D. (1965). *Federation Proc.* **24**, Suppl. 15, S55–S65.

Clements, R. L. (1962). *Anal. Biochem.* **3**, 87–90.

Cobb, J. D. (1953). *A.M.A. Arch. Pathol.* **55**, 496–502.

Coons, A. H., Leduc, E. H., and Kaplan, M. H. (1951). *J. Exptl. Med.* **93**, 173–188.

Cooper, I. S. (1965). *Federation Proc.* **24**, Suppl. 15, S237–S240.

Copeland, D. E. (1951). *J. Natl. Cancer Inst.* **12**, 224–225.

Copson, D. A. (1958). *Food Technol.* **12,** 270–272.
Coriell, L. L., Green, A. E., and Silver, R. K. (1964). *Cryobiology* **1,** 72–79.
Cowley, C. W. (1964). *Cryobiology* **1,** 40–43.
Cowley, C. W., and Rinfret, A. P. (1963). *In* "Culture Collections: Perspectives and Problems" (S. M. Martin, ed.). Univ. of Toronto Press, Toronto.
Cowley, C. W., Timson, W. J., and Sawdye, J. A. (1961). *Biodynamica* **8,** 317–329.
Cowley, C. W., Timson, W. J., and Sawdye, J. A. (1962). *Ind. Eng. Chem. Process Design Develop.* **1,** 81–84.
Craig, E. L., Frajola, W. G., and Greider, M. H. (1962). *J. Cell Biol.* **12,** 190–194.
Danielli, J. F. (1953). "Cytochemistry—A Critical Approach." Wiley, New York.
Davies, H. G. (1954). *Quart. J. Microscop. Sci.* **95,** 433–457.
Davies, H. G., Deeley, E. M., and Denby, E. F. (1957). *Exptl. Cell Res. Suppl.* **4,** 136–149.
Davis, B. J., and Ornstein, L. (1959). *J. Histochem. Cytochem.* **7,** 297–298.
Davis, B. J., Ornstein, L., Taleporos, P., and Koulish, S. (1959). *J. Histochem. Cytochem.* **7,** 290–292.
Deitch, A. D., and Godman, G. C. (1955). *Anat. Record* **123,** 1–18.
Doebbler, G. F., and Cowley, C. W. (1964). *Intern. Sci. Technol.* June, pp. 58–71.
Doebbler, G. F., and Rinfret, A. P. (1962). *Biochim. Biophys. Acta* **58,** 449–458.
Dounce, A. L. (1950). *In* "The Enzymes" (J. B. Sumner and K. Myrbäck, eds.), Vol. I, Pt. I, pp. 187–266. Academic Press, New York.
Doyle, W. L. (1950). *Federation Proc.* **9,** 34.
Doyle, W. L. (1954). *J. Gen. Physiol.* **38,** 141–144.
Doyle, W. L. (1955). *J. Biophys. Biochem. Cytol.* **1,** 221–236.
Doyle, W. L., and Liebelt, R. (1954). *Anat. Record* **118,** 384.
Doyle, W. L., and Liebelt, R. (1955). *J. Histochem. Cytochem.* **3,** 50–60.
Emmel, V. M. (1946). *Anat. Record* **95,** 159–175.
Eränkö, O. (1954a). *Acta Pathol. Scand.* **35,** 426–432.
Eränkö, O. (1954b). *Acta Pathol. Scand.* **35,** 426–432.
Feder, N. (1960). *J. Histochem. Cytochem.* **8,** 309–310.
Feder, N., and Sidman, R. L. (1958). *J. Biophys. Biochem. Cytol.* **4,** 593–600.
Fernández-Morán, H. (1957). *In* "Metabolism of the Nervous System" (D. Richter, ed.), pp. 1–34. Macmillan (Pergamon), New York.
Fernández-Morán, H. (1959). *Science* **129,** 1284–1285.
Fernández-Morán, H. (1960). *Ann. N.Y. Acad. Sci.* **85,** 689–713.
Fernández-Morán, H. (1961a). *In* "The Structure of the Eye" (G. K. Smelser, ed.), p. 521. Academic Press, New York.
Fernández-Morán, H. (1961b). *In* "Macromolecular Complexes" (M. V. Edds, Jr., ed.), p. 113. Ronald Press, New York.
Fernández-Morán, H. (1962). *In* "The Interpretation of Ultrastructure" (R. J. C. Harris, ed.), Vol. I, pp. 411–427. Academic Press, New York.
Fernández-Morán, H. (1964a). *In* "The Interpretation of Ultrastructure" (R. J. C. Harris, ed.), pp. 411–427. Academic Press, New York.
Fernández-Morán, H. (1964b). *J. Am. Med. Assoc.* **189,** 31–33.
Fernández-Morán, H. (1965). *Proc. Natl. Acad. Sci. U.S.* **53,** 445–451.
Firket, H., and Michel, J. P. (1954). *Bull. Microscop. Appl.* **4,** 1–5.
Fisher, J. C., Hollomon, J. H., and Turnbull, D. (1949). *Science* **109,** 168–169.
Flax, M. H., and Caulfield, J. B. (1962). *Arch. Pathol.* **74,** 387–395.
Flosdorf, E. W. (1954). *In* "Biological Application of Freezing and Drying" (R. J. C. Harris, ed.), pp. 63–86. Academic Press, New York.

Freed, J. J. (1955). *Lab. Invest.* **4**, 106–121.

Gersh, I. (1932). *Anat. Record* **53**, 309–337.

Gersh, I. (1948). *Bull. Intern. Assoc. Med. Museums* **28**, 179–185.

Gersh, I. (1950). *Harvey Lectures Ser.* **45**, 221.

Gersh, I. (1956). *J. Biophys. Biochem. Cytol.* **2**, 37–43.

Gersh, I. (1960). *In* "Bone as a Tissue" (K. Rodahl, J. T. Nicholson, and E. M. Brown, eds.), pp. 128–143. McGraw-Hill, New York.

Gersh, I. (1965). *Federation Proc.* **24**, Suppl. 15, S233–S234.

Gersh, I., and Catchpole, H. R. (1949). *Am. J. Anat.* **85**, 457–521.

Gersh, I., and Stephenson, J. L. (1954). *In* "Biological Applications of Freezing and Drying" (R. J. C. Harris, ed.), pp. 329–384. Academic Press, New York.

Gersh, I., Isenberg, I., Stephenson, J. L., and Bondareff, W. (1957). *Anat. Record* **128**, 91–112.

Gersh, I., Vergara, J., and Rossi, G. I. (1960). *Anat. Record* **138**, 445–459.

Gibbons, I. R. (1959). *Nature* **184**, 375–376.

Glenner, G. G., and Burstone, M. S. (1958). *Anat. Record* **130**, 243–252.

Glenner, G. G., Meyer, D. B., and Burstone, M. S. (1959). *J. Histochem. Cytochem.* **7**, 297.

Glick, D., and Bloom, D. (1956). *Exptl. Cell Res.* **10**, 687–696.

Glick, D., and Malmström, B. G. (1952). *Exptl. Cell Res.* **3**, 125–135.

Gomori, G. (1950). *J. Lab. Clin. Med.* **35**, 802–809.

Gomori, G. (1952). "Microscopic Histochemistry; Principles and Practice." Univ. of Chicago Press, Chicago, Illinois.

Goodspeed, T. H., and Uber, F. M. (1934). *Proc. Natl. Acad. Sci. U.S.* **20**, 495–501.

Goodspeed, T. H., and Uber, F. M. (1935). *Univ. Calif. (Berkeley) Publ. Botany* **18**, 23–44.

Gourévitch, A. (1953). *Bull. Microscop. Appl.* **3**, 130–137.

Grauman, W., and Neumann, K., eds. (1958). "Handbuch Der Histochemi," Vol. 1. Fischer, Stuttgart.

Gray, J. A., and Opdyke, D. L. (1962). *J. Dental Res.* **41**, 172–181.

Greaves, R. I. N. (1954). *In* "Biological Applications of Freezing and Drying" (R. J. C. Harris, ed.), pp. 87–127. Academic Press, Incorporated, New York.

Greaves, R. I. N. (1962). *J. Pharm. Pharmacol.* **14**, 621–640.

Greaves, R. I. N., Nagington, J., and Kellaway, T. D. (1963). *Federation Proc.* **22**, 90–93.

Grunbaum, B. W., and Wellings, S. R. (1960a). *J. Ultrastruct. Res.* **4**, 73–80.

Grunbaum, B. W., and Wellings, S. R. (1960b). *J. Ultrastruct. Res.* **4**, 117–126.

Gustafsson, B. E. (1953). *Lunds Univ. Arsskr., Avd. 2* **49**, 1–9.

Gustafsson, B. E. (1954). *Kgl. Fysiograf. Sallskap. Lund, Forh.* **24**, 12–20.

Guthrie, A. (1963). "Vacuum Technology." Wiley, New York.

Hancox, N. M. (1957). *Exptl. Cell Res.* **13**, 263–275.

Hanson, V., and Hermodsson, L. H. (1960). *J. Ultrastruct. Res.* **4**, 332–348.

Hardy, W. S., and Rutherford, T. (1962). *Nature* **196**, 785–786.

Harris, J. E., Sloane, J. F., and King, D. T. (1950). *Nature* **166**, 25–26.

Harris, R. J. C., ed. (1954). "Biological Applications of Freezing and Drying." Academic Press, New York.

Heide, H. G. (1962). *Intern. Congr. Electron Microscopy, 5th, Philadelphia J. Cell Biol.* **13**: 147–152.

Hoerr, N. L. (1936). *Anat. Record* **65**, 293–317.

Holland, L., Laurenson, L., and Delville, J. P. (1965). *Nature* **206**, 883–884.

Hori, S. H., and Chang, J. P. (1962). *J. Histochem. Cytochem.* **11**, 115–116.

Hori, S. H., and Chang, J. P. (1963). *J. Histochem. Cytochem.* **11**, 71–79.

Huggins, C. E. (1965). *Federation Proc.* **24**, Suppl. 15, S190–S195.

Ioffe, A. F. (1957). "Semiconductor Thermoelements and Thermoelectric Cooling." Infosearch, London.

Jacob, S. W. (1964). *Cryobiology* **1**, 176–180.

Jansen, M. T. (1954). *Exptl. Cell Res.* **7**, 318–326.

Jensen, W. A. (1954). *Exptl. Cell Res.* **7**, 572–574.

Jensen, W. A. (1962). "Botanical Histochemistry—Principles and Practice." Freeman, San Francisco, California.

Johnson, F. B. (1959). *J. Histochem. Cytochem.* **7**, 293.

Joseph, N. R., Engel, M. B., and Catchpole, H. R. (1952). *Biochim. Biophys. Acta* **8**, 575–587.

Joseph, N. R., Engel, M. B., and Catchpole, H. R. (1954). *A.M.A. Arch. Pathol.* **58**, 40–58.

Joslyn, M. A. (1949). *Advan. Enzymol.* **9**, 613–652.

Kaesberg, P. (1964). *In* "Modern Developments in Electron Microscopy" (B. M. Siegel, ed.), pp. 99–117. Academic Press, New York.

Kanehira, S. (1953). *Teion Kagaku* **A10**, 137–156.

Klionsky, B., and Smith, O. D. (1960). *Am. J. Clin. Pathol.* **33**, 144–151.

Kossel, A. (1913). *Z. Physiol. Chem. Hoppe-Seylers* **84**, 354–358.

Kramer, H., and Hill, R. G. (1956). *J. Roy. Microscop. Soc.* **75**, 48–57.

Kulenkampff, H. (1954). *Verhandl. Anat. Ges.* **101**, 166–169.

Lacy, D., and Blundell, M. (1955). *J. Roy. Microscop. Soc.* **75**(3), 48–57.

Leake, L. V., and Burke, J. F. (1967). *Exptl. Cell Res.* **48**, 300–306.

Leduc, E. H., and Barnhard, W. (1962). *In* "The Interpretation of Ultrastructure" (R. J. C. Harris, ed.), Vol. I, pp. 21–45. Academic Press, New York.

Lewis, P. R., and Shute, C. C. D. (1963). *Stain Technol.* **38**, 307–310.

Liebow, A. A. (1963). *Federation Proc.* **22**, 80.

Lillie, R. D., and Lasky, A. (1951). *Bull. Intern. Assoc. Med. Museums.* **32**, 80–82.

Linderstrøm-Lang, K., and Morgensen, K. R. (1938). *Compt. Rend. Trav. Lab. Carlsberg, Ser. Chim.* **23**, 27–34.

Lison, L. (1949). *Compt. Rend. Soc. Biol.* **143**, 115–116.

Lotke, P. A., and Dolan, M. F. (1965). *Cryobiology* **1**, 289–291.

Loud, A. V., and Mishima, Y. (1963). *J. Cell Biol.* **18**, 181–194.

Lovelock, J. E. (1954). *Biochem. J.* **56**, 265–270.

Lowry, O. H., Roberts, N. R., Wu, M. L., Hixon, W. S., and Crawford, E. J. (1954). *J. Biol. Chem.* **207**, 19–37.

Lozina-Lozinsky, L. K. (1965). *Federation Proc.* **24**, Suppl. 15, S206–S211.

Luft, J. H. (1961). *J. Biophys. Biochem. Cytol.* **9**, 409–414.

Luft, J. H., and Hechter, O. (1957). *J. Biophys. Biochem. Cytol.* **3**, 615–618.

Luyet, B. J. (1951). *In* "International Symposium on Freezing and Drying" (R. J. C. Harris, ed.), pp. 77–96. Hafner, New York.

Luyet, B. J. (1960). *Ann. N.Y. Acad. Sci.* **85**, 549–569.

Luyet, B. (1961). *Biodynamica* **8**, 331–352.

Luyet, B. J., and Gonzales, F. (1951). *Biodynamica* **7**, 61–66.

McClintock, M. (1964). "Cryogenics." Reinhold, New York.

McIlwain, H., and Buddle, H. L. (1953). *Biochem. J.* **53**, 412–420.

McMaster-Kaye, R., and Taylor, J. H. (1958). *J. Biophys. Biochem. Cytol.* **4**, 5–11.

Mann, G. (1902). "Physiological Histology Methods and Theory." Oxford Univ. Press (Clarendon), London and New York.

Mazur, P. (1965). *Federation Proc.* **24,** Suppl. 15, S175–S182.

Meckel, A. H., Griebstein, W. J., and Neal, R. J. (1965). *Arch. Oral Biol.* **10:** 585–597.

Melnick, P. J. (1965). *Federation Proc.* **24,** Suppl. 15, S259–S267.

Mendelow, H., and Hamilton, J. B. (1950). *Anat. Record* **107,** 443–451.

Mendelssohn, K. (1960). "Cryophysics." Wiley (Interscience), New York.

Mendelssohn, K. (1961). "Progress in Cryogenics," Vol. 3. Heywood, London.

Meryman, H. T. (1959). *Science* **130,** 628–629.

Meryman, H. T. (1960). *U.S. Naval Med. Res. Inst., Res. Rept.* **MR 005.02–0001.07,** 1–19.

Meryman, H. T. (1961). *U.S. Naval Med. Res. Inst., Res. Rept.* **MR 005.02–0002.07,** 153–174.

Meryman, H. T. (1963). *Federation Proc.* **22,** 80–89.

Meryman, H. T. (1964). *Cryobiology* **1,** 52–56.

Mirsky, A. E. (1951). *Cold Spring Harbor Symp. Quant. Biol.* **16,** 481–482.

Mishima, Y., Loud, A. V., and Schaub, F. F., Jr. (1962a). *J. Invest. Dermatol.* **39,** 55–62.

Mishima, Y., Mevorah, B. L., and Schaub, F. F., Jr. (1962b). *J. Invest. Dermatol.* **39,** 369–372.

Moberger, G., Lindström, B., and Andresson, L. (1954). *Expt. Cell Res.* **6,** 228–237.

Moline, S. W., and Glenner, G. G. (1964). *J. Histochem. Cytochem.* **12,** 777–783.

Mommaerts, W. F. H. M. (1965). *Federation Proc.* **24,** Suppl. 15, S169–S172.

Moor, H. (1966). *Intern. Rev. Exptl. Pathol.* **5,** 179–216.

Morichi, T. (1964). *Hakko Kogaku Zasshi* **42,** 56–61.

Müller, H. R. (1957). *J. Ultrastruct. Res.* **1,** 109–137.

Naidoo, D., and Pratt, O. E. (1951). *J. Neurol. Psychiat.* **14,** 287–294.

Naidoo, D., and Pratt, O. E. (1952). *J. Neurol. Psychiat.* **15,** 164–168.

Naidoo, D., and Pratt, O. E. (1956). *Acta Histochem.* **3,** 85–103.

Nair, K. K. (1958). *Experientia* **14,** 172–173.

Nei, T. (1964). *Cryobiology* **1,** 87–93.

Nelson, L. (1958). *Biochim. Biophys. Acta* **27,** 634–641.

Nelson, L. (1959). *Exptl. Cell Res.* **16,** 403–410.

Neumann, K. (1952). *Z. Wiss. Mikroskopie* **60,** 449–462.

Neumann, K. (1958). *In* "Handbuch der Histochemie" (W. Graumann and K. Neumann, eds.), Vol. 1, pp. 1–77. Fischer, Stuttgart.

Neumann, K., Oehlert, G., and Hansmann, H. (1954). *Z. Geburtshilfe Gynaekol.* **141,** 109–130.

O'Brien, M., and Chase, W. H. (1964). *Nature* **202,** 304–305.

Oncley, J. L., Gurd, F., and Melin, M. (1950). *J. Am. Chem. Soc.* **72,** 458–465.

Opdyke, D. L. J. (1962). *Arch. Oral Biol.* **7,** 207–219.

Packer, D. M., and Scott, G. H. (1942). *J. Tech. Math.* **22,** 85–96.

Parkes, A. S. (1964). *Cryobiology* **1,** 3.

Parkes, A. S., and Smith, A. U. (1960). "Recent Research in Freezing and Drying." Blackwell, Oxford.

Patten, S. F., and Brown, K. A. (1958). *Lab. Invest.* **7,** 209–223.

Pearse, A. G. E. (1960). "Histochemistry. Theoretical and Applied." Little, Brown, Boston, Massachusetts.

Pease, D. C. (1964). "Histological Techniques for Electron Microscopy." Academic Press, New York.

Pease, D. C., and Baker, R. F. (1949). *Am. J. Anat.* **84,** 175–200.

Persijn, J. P., DeVries, G., and Daems, W. T. (1964). *Histochemie* **4,** 35–42.

Persson, B. H. (1952). *Acta Soc. Med. Upsalien.* **57,** 8–18.

Pollister, A. W., and Ornstein, L. (1959). *In* "Analytical Cytology" (R. C. Mellors, ed.), pp. 431–510. McGraw-Hill, New York.
Porter, V. S., Deming, N. P., Wright, R. C., and Scott, E. M. (1953). *J. Biol. Chem.* **205**, 883–891.
Post, R. S. (1965). *Cryobiology* **1**, 261–265.
Potthoff, C. J., ed. (1949). "Preservation of the Formed Elements and of the Proteins of the Blood." Harvard Med. School, Boston, Massachusetts.
Pryde, J. A., and Jones, G. O. (1952). *Nature* **170**, 685–688.
Rappaport, B. Z. (1955). *A.M.A. Arch. Pathol.* **60**, 1–9.
Read, P. L. (1963). *Vacuum* **13**, 271–275.
Reale, E. (1956). *Monit. Zool. Ital.* **63**, 188–196.
Rebhun, L. I. (1965). *Federation Proc.* **24**, Suppl. 15, S217–S232.
Reimer, L. (1959). "Elektronenmikroskopische Untersuchungs und Praparations-metheden." Springer, Berlin.
Rey, L. (1961). *Biodynamica* **8**, 241–260.
Rice, R. V., Kaesberg, P., and Stahmann, M. A. (1955). *Arch. Biochem. Biophys.* **59**, 332–340.
Rinfret, A. P., Cowley, C. W., Doebbler, G. F., and Schreiner, H. R. (1962). *Proc. 9th Congr. Intern. Soc. Blood Transfusion, Mexico, D. F.,* pp. 80–88. Karger, Basel.
Roberts, R. W., and St. Pierre, L. E. (1965). *Science* **147**, 1529–1542.
Rose-Innes, A. C. (1964). "Low Temperature Techniques—The Use of Liquid Helium in the Laboratory." Van Nostrand, Princeton, New Jersey.
Rowe, T. W. G. (1960). *Ann. N.Y. Acad. Sci.* **85**, 641–681.
Russell, R. S., Sanders, F. K., and Bishop, O. N. (1949). *Nature* **163**, 639–640.
Rutherford, T., Hardy, W. S., and Isherwood, P. A. (1964). *Stain Technol.* **39**, 185–190.
Sabitini, D. D., Bensch, K., and Barrnett, R. J. (1961). *Anat. Record* **142**, 274.
Sabitini, D. D., Bensch, K., and Barrnett, R. J. (1963). *J. Cell Biol.* **17**, 19–58.
Sabitini, D. D., Miller, F., and Barrnett, R. J. (1964). *J. Histochem. Cytochem.* **12**, 57–71.
Salazar, H. (1964). *Stain Technol.* **39**, 13–17.
Salt, R. W. (1961). *Science* **133**, 458–459.
Scott, G. H. (1943). *Biol. Symp.* **10**, 277–289.
Scott, G. H., and Hoerr, N. L. (1950). *In* "Medical Physics" (O. Glasser, ed.), Vol. 2, pp. 292–296. Yearbook Publ., Chicago, Illinois.
Scott, G. H., and Williams, P. S. (1936). *Anat. Record* **66**, 475–481.
Scott, R. B. (1959). "Cryogenic Engineering." Van Nostrand, Princeton, New Jersey.
Seno, S., and Yoshizawa, K. (1960). *J. Biophys. Biochem. Cytol.* **8**, 617–638.
Shen, S. C., Greenfield, P., and Sippel, T. (1952). *Proc. Soc. Exptl. Biol. Med.* **81**, 452–455.
Sherman, J. K. (1962). *Anat. Record* **144**, 171–177.
Sherman, J. K. (1964a). *Anat. Record* **149**, 591–604.
Sherman, J. K. (1964b). *Cryobiology* **1**, 103–129.
Sherman, J. K. (1965). *Cryobiology* **1**, 298–299.
Sherman, J. K., and Lim, K. S. (1967). *Cryobiology* **4**, 61–74.
Shimizu, N., Kubo, Z., and Morikawa, N. (1956). *Stain Technol.* **31**, 105–109.
Sicher, H., ed. (1962). "Orban's Oral Histology and Embryology," 5th Ed. Mosby, St. Louis, Missouri.
Sidman, R. L., Mottla, P. A., and Feder, N. (1961). *Stain Technol.* **36**, 279–284.
Simatos, D., and Rey, L. (1965). *Federation Proc.* **24**, Suppl. 15, S213–S215.

Simpson, W. L. (1941). *Anat. Record* **80,** 173–189.
Sittig, M., and Kidd, S. (1963). "Cryogenics—Research and Applications." Van Nostrand, Princeton, New Jersey.
Sizer, I. W., and Josephson, E. S. (1942). *Food Res.* **7,** 201–209.
Sjöstrand, F. S. (1944). *Acta. Anat.* **1,** Suppl. 1, 1–63.
Sjöstrand, F. S., and Baker, R. F. (1958). *J. Ultrastruct. Res.* **1,** 239–246.
Smith, A. U. (1961). "Biological Effects of Freezing and Supercooling." Williams & Wilkins, Baltimore, Maryland.
Smith, A. U. (1965). *Federation Proc.* **24,** Suppl. 15, S196–S203.
Smith, R. E., and Farquhar, M. G. (1965). *R C A Sci. Instr. News* **10,** 13–18.
Smyth, J. D. (1954). *Quart. J. Microscop. Sci.* **95,** 139–152.
Stäubli, W. (1960). *Compt. Rend.* **250,** 1137–1139.
Steedman, H. F. (1961). "Section Cutting in Microscopy." Thomas, Springfield, Illinois.
Stephenson, J. L. (1953). *Bull. Math. Biophys.* **15,** 411–429.
Stephenson, J. L. (1954). *Bull. Math. Biophys.* **16,** 23–43.
Stephenson, J. L. (1956). *J. Biophys. Biochem. Cytol.* **2,** 45–52.
Stephenson, J. L. (1960). *Ann. N.Y. Acad. Sci.* **85,** 535–540.
Stowell, R. E. (1951). *Stain Technol.* **26,** 105–108.
Stowell, R. E., ed. (1965). *Federation Proc.* **24,** No. 2, Suppl. 15, 324 pp.
Stowell, R. E., Young, D. E., Arnold, E. A., and Trump, B. F. (1965). *Federation Proc.* **24,** Suppl. 15, S115–S141.
Stumpf, W. E., and Roth, L. J. (1964). *Stain Technol.* **39,** 219–223.
Stumpf, W. E., and Roth, L. J. (1965). *Cryobiology* **1,** 227–232.
Sylvén, B. (1951). *Acta, Unio Intern. Contra Cancrum* **7,** 708–712.
Taft, E. B. (1949). *Am. J. Pathol.* **25,** 824–825.
Taft, E. B. (1951). *Stain Technol.* **26,** 205–212.
Taylor, A. (1944). *J. Lab. Clin. Med.* **29,** 657–663.
Taylor, J. H. (1956). *Phys. Tech. Biol. Res.* **3,** 545–576.
Thornburg, W., and Mengers, P. E. (1957). *J. Histochem. Cytochem.* **5,** 47–52.
Tice, L. W., and Barrnett, R. J. (1965). *J. Cell Biol.* **25,** 23–42.
Torack, R. M., and Barrnett, R. J. (1964). *J. Neuropathol. Exptl. Neurol.* **23,** 46–59.
Treffenberg, L. (1953). *Arkiv. Zool.* **4,** 295–296.
Trump, B. F., Young, D. E., Arnold, E. A., and Stowell, R. E. (1965). *Federation Proc.* **24,** Suppl. 15, S144–S168.
Turchini, J., and Malet, P. (1965). *J. Histochem. Cytochem.* **13,** 405–406.
Vanderslice, T. A. (1963). *Science* **142,** 178–184.
Van Harreveld, A., and Crowell, J. (1964). *Anat. Record* **149,** 381–385.
Van Harreveld, A., Crowell, J., and Malhotra, S. K. (1965). *J. Cell Biol.* **25,** 117–137.
Venkataraman, K. (1952). "The Chemistry of Synthetic Dyes," Vol. 2. Academic Press, New York.
Vos, O., and Kaalen, M. C. A. (1965). *Cryobiology* **1,** 249–260.
Wachstein, M., and Meisel, E. (1953). *Stain Technol.* **28,** 135–139.
Wang, K. J., and Grossman, M. I. (1949a). *J. Lab. Clin. Med.* **34,** 292–296.
Wang, K. J., and Grossman, M. I. (1949b). *Anat. Record* **104,** 79–87.
Watson, M. L. (1958a). *J Biophys. Biochem. Cytol.* **4,** 475–478.
Watson, M. L. (1958b). *J. Biophys. Biochem. Cytol.* **4,** 727–729.
White, R. T., and Allen, R. A. (1951). *Stain Technol.* **26,** 137–138.
Wichterle, O., Bartl, P., and Rosenberg, M. (1960). *Nature* **186,** 494–495.
Williams, R. C. (1953). *Exptl. Cell Res.* **4,** 188–201.

Williams, R. C. (1957). *Intern. Rev. Cytol.* **6,** 129–191.
Willighagen, R. G., and Planteydt, H. T. (1959). *Nature* **183,** 263–264.
Wolfe, R. (1963). *Semicond. Prod.* **6,** 23–28.
Woods, P. S., and Pollister, A. (1955). *Stain Technol.* **30,** 123–131.
Yaeger, J. A. (1961). *Exptl. Cell Res.* **22,** 493–502.
Yamida, M. (1953). *Chem. Abstr.* **47,** 8814.
Yokoyama, H. O., and Stowell, R. E. (1951). *J. Natl. Cancer Inst.* **12,** 211–213.
Zlotnik I. (1960). *Quart. J. Microscop. Sci.* **101,** 251–254.

CHAPTER 2

Microspectrophotometry in the Ultraviolet Spectrum

JEROME J. FREED[1]

[1] Research Career Development Awardee of the National Cancer Institute (K3-CA-3401). Support of the author's work during preparation of this chapter was provided by grants CA-05959 and CA-06927 from the National Cancer Institute and by contract AT(30-1)2356 with the U.S. Atomic Energy Commission (Report NYO-2356-27) and an appropriation from the Commonwealth of Pennsylvania. The author is indebted to Dr. G. T. Rudkin for access to unpublished data and helpful discussions of UV cytophotometry over many years, and further indebted to him and to Dr. R. P. Perry for their criticism of this manuscript.

I. Introduction

The ultraviolet (UV) microscope, first used as an absorption micro-spectrophotometer by Caspersson (1936, 1950), played a central role in revealing the distribution of nucleic acids in cellular systems and thus in providing the foundation for that concern with nucleoprotein function which today dominates biological thought. Complete microscope equipment for the spectral region from 230 to 280 mμ had been developed by Köhler (1904). The air-spaced quartz objective lenses were monochromats, i.e., they were intended for use at specific design wavelengths. The image was detected photographically after approximate focusing with the aid of a fluorescent eyepiece attachment. The required monochromatic illumination was obtained from a powerful metallic arc, and the objectives were computed for use at lines of particularly high intensity in the Cd and Mg spectra. Through the use of UV radiation, it was intended to take advantage of the increased resolving power for a given numerical aperture associated with the reduced wavelength. In the hands of Köhler and others, the UV microscope not only provided the expected greater resolution but revealed an unexpected contrast in biological structures transparent to visible light (Köhler, 1904; Lucas, 1930; Lucas and Stark, 1931; Wyckoff et al., 1932; Wyckoff and Ter Louw, 1931; Wyckoff and Ebeling, 1933; Wyckoff, 1934). That the strong UV absorption of nucleic acid might account for this effect was suspected, and Caspersson, in his classic work (1936), undertook to define the conditions under which the microscope could function as an absorption microspectrophotometer. His studies clearly demonstrated that the high absorption by chromosomes, nuclei, and the cytoplasm of many cell types resulted from the presence of high concentrations of nucleic acids and protein. In subsequent studies with J. Schultz and others, the involvement of the nucleic acids in cell growth, protein synthesis, and the transmission of genetic information was inferred (see Caspersson, 1950, for review). Together with the observations of Brachet (1940, 1944), who demonstrated nucleic acid distribution in embryos with basic dyes and nuclease digestion, this work showed that high concentrations of nucleic acid were present and presumably important in a number of biological processes. These experiments stimulated the further studies that have revealed the biological functions of the nucleic acids.

Caspersson and his co-workers in Stockholm extended their studies to a variety of biological problems and at the same time set about to develop improved instruments. These were designed for UV microspectrophotometry of intracellular structures and included specialized instruments to investigate the optical problems posed by inhomogeneous biological materials. This work has been summarized in Caspersson's monograph of 1950, which remains a valuable summary of the fundamentals involved in this work. It and Caspersson's thesis of 1936 should be consulted if possible by anyone undertaking work in this field for the first time.

After 1950, workers in a number of laboratories began to develop precise instruments for UV absorption measurements on the subcellular scale. To facilitate the scanning procedures required to estimate amounts of absorbing compounds, a variety of photoelectric recording instruments were developed (Caspersson et al., 1951; Caspersson, 1955; Lomakka, 1955; Exner, 1959). The construction of achromatic reflecting objectives allowed instruments to be designed for direct recording of absorption spectra at a chosen point in the cell (Wyckoff, 1952; Walker and Deeley, 1956). With precise and convenient recording densitometers, the older photographic method was extended to detailed studies of the composition of biological objects. The studies of Walker and Yates (1952) and of Davies (1954) on the nucleic acids in living and fixed cultured cells and of Rudkin et al. (1955) on the quantitative distribution of nucleoproteins in dipteran giant chromosomes are indicative of the precision attained in photographic work.

Since 1960, remarkable improvements in optical apparatus and other components have been made. This period has seen the construction of quartz-fluorite refracting achromatic objectives, and the general availability of powerful discharge lamps, excellent monochromators and photomultiplier tubes of increased quantum efficiency. Excellent reflecting objectives have also been put on the market, while the UV image converter tube has greatly increased the feasibility of focusing accurately at the wavelength used for measurement. It is also noteworthy that instruments for UV microspectrophotometry have now been adapted to commercial manufacture.

The problems faced by UV microspectrophotometry today are thus, more than ever, those posed by the nature of the biological material rather than those of adequate instrumental recording. At present, investigations of the organization and function of nucleoprotein structures within the cell are being pursued at levels below the resolving power of the UV microscope, employing techniques of chemical analysis and centrifugal separation not directly applicable in UV microspectrophotometry.[2] However, in connection with these techniques, microspectrophotometry retains its value for verifying the homogeneity of a cell population; i.e., it allows the experimenter to determine whether a decrease of 5% in some measured quantity represents a 5% change in each cell or a 100% change in 5% of the population. Further, studies of cell differentiation demand methods capable of dealing with biochemical events in single cells or small aggregations of cells; in studies of this kind analytic microscopic methods remain indispensable. Similarly, questions of chromosomal fine structure and of chromosomal differentiation require the spatial resolution of the microspectrophotometric method.

The high sensitivity of modern photoelectric detectors has in recent years stimulated the construction of television instruments capable of examining the absorbance properties of intact living cells in greater detail than was previously possible (Montgomery and Bonner, 1959; Williams and Neuhauser, 1962; Zworykin and Hatke, 1957; Freed and Engle, 1962). Kinetic quantitative studies of living systems by the UV method have for the first time become feasible (e.g., Freed and Benner, 1964). The image output of television microscope systems also lends itself well to recording for subsequent computer processing; research in the computer analysis of microscope images is presently being pursued in several laboratories (Ledley, 1964; Mendelsohn et al., 1964), although at present most of this work is restricted to visible light microscopy.

A fruitful extension of the microspectrophotometric technique to today's problems in cell biology has come from its use in conjunction with biochemical separations carried out on the cytological scale with the aid of a micromanipulator. Edström (1964) has developed microextraction procedures for the determination of DNA and of RNA and for the estimation, after microelectrophoresis, of base ratios of RNA extracted from different parts of the cell. While the spatial resolution of these methods is

---

[2] Methods and results in this field have been reviewed (inter alia) in recent volumes of Progress in Nucleic Acid Research and Molecular Biology (Academic Press, New York) and Progress in Biophysics and Molecular Biology (Pergamon Press).

limited by the precision with which the microdissection can be carried out, they allow a considerably extended range of biochemical characterization of intracellular structures at the microscopic level. Since the samples involved in microextraction work are inherently microscopic in volume, photometric methods are most conveniently employed. UV microspectrophotometry may find its widest future use in such micromanipulative chemical studies rather than the cytophotometric investigation of intact biological structures *in situ*.

It is the plan of this chapter to review the methods available for recording UV absorbance information from small biological specimens and especially to consider their application to studies of fixed cells. The same considerations apply in work with living cells, but the extensive use of television techniques and the problems posed by the sensitivity of living material suggests a separate consideration of this work. The application of UV methods to determine the absorption of samples extracted by micromanipulative chemical procedures will also be separately described. The intention is to present enough information on the methods and apparatus in current use to enable an investigator to choose appropriate procedures. Since recently designed instruments of the automatic recording type are necessarily complex, some older procedures that employ simpler equipment will be reviewed; these methods remain valuable for studies of many kinds. Many of the theoretical aspects of UV microspectrophotometry have been discussed in considerable detail in the classic papers in this field and in prior reviews. These papers and the proceedings of conferences held in recent years (see general references) contain valuable discussions of measurement procedures and specific types of apparatus.

II. Basic Requirements for Microspectrophotometry

A. GENERAL

The fundamental assumption made in microspectrophotometry is that the distribution of energy in an enlarged image is purely a function of molecular interaction of the object with light of specific wavelength. Thus, the fraction of energy emerging from the object is directly related to the amount of absorbing compound, as is the case in the spectrophotometry of ideal solutions. Then, if the energy in free space adjacent to the microscopic object is I_0 and that at an infinitesimal measuring point in the object is I, the absorbance at that point (see Fig. 1) is given by

$$E = \log \frac{I_0}{I}$$

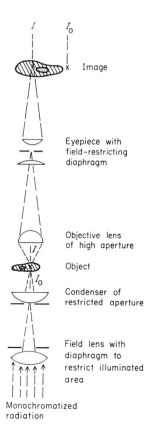

FIG. 1. General conditions required for operation of a microscope for spectrophotometry. Condenser aperture restriction is required to reduce errors due to nonparallel illumination and glare. Restriction of the area illuminated in the object plane
and of the image area at the eyepiece further reduces glare. Immersion lenses give
less glare than dry systems; an objective aperture diaphragm (not shown) is effective
in further reducing glare arising at objective lens mounts.

If E is measured at a series of wavelengths an absorption spectrum for
the point in question may be plotted. While the area measured in this
fashion should be infinitesimally small, in order to reduce the distortions
in absorption produced by inhomogeneities in the object, the findings of
Caspersson (1936) and Wilkins (1950) suggest that it is not possible to
obtain valid absorption data from objects of dimensions much less than
three times the wavelength.

Adequate correspondence of energy distribution in the image plane to
that in the object plane can be expected if the microscope system used
fulfills certain conditions, diagrammed in Fig. 1. For an object in which

refractive index differences are small (less than 0.01), errors originating in the specimen and microscope system should be less than 5% when the objective lens aperture is greater than 0.5 and the condenser aperture is less than 0.3 (Caspersson, 1950).

Microspectrophotometry on the cytological scale is frequently employed to estimate the mass of absorbing material in a biological unit structure, e.g., a whole cell, a cell nucleus. Since the distribution of absorbing materials in such structures is rarely homogeneous, the Bouger-Beer law cannot be applied directly, as is done in the spectrophotometry of solutions. Rather, it becomes necessary to sum, by scanning and integrating, the absorbances of all infinitesimal absorbing elements over the biologically defined structure, to yield the integrated absorbance (E_t), which is proportional to the weight of absorbing material present. The incremental mass of absorbing material dM in incremental area dA may be expressed:

$$dM = K \, dA \, \log \frac{I}{I_0}$$

where, as in Fig. 1, I_0 is a measure of the incident radiation intensity and I is that transmitted by the specimen. Over the total area of interest A:

$$M = K \int_0^A \log \frac{I}{I_0} \, dA = KE_t$$

K is a coefficient specifying the absorbance of a unit mass of chromophore uniformly distributed in unit projected area. The quantity E_t is thus a product of mean absorbance and total area; it has the dimensions of area. The scanning procedures used to perform the integration introduce restrictions and errors to be discussed in Section V, E.

The operation of a microscope as a microspectrophotometer is more critical than its use for normal observations both in regard to the original design of the optical elements and in the precautions to be observed in the actual operation of the instrument. The design of microscope elements and the factors governing their use will be considered below.

B. MICROSCOPE OPTICS

In producing the newer microscope objectives for use in the UV, the designers have attempted to provide the high apertures and good corrections necessary to meet the conditions stated above and further to produce lenses with achromatic characteristics as opposed to the severe wavelength restrictions of the older quartz monochromats. Achromatic optics not only facilitate focusing the microscope at a wavelength to which the eye is sensitive, but allow the employment of a broader spectral bandwidth without introduction of severe aberrations. It should be noted that

images of the best quality can only be obtained from the quartz monochromats when they are illuminated by the extremely narrow lines of the
metallic arc illuminator: they rarely give their best performance when
illuminated via a monochromator and continuous source.

Since reflecting surfaces are inherently achromatic, a number of
objectives have been produced over the years in which spherical or
aspheric aluminized reflectors serve as the magnifying elements (Burch,
1947; Grey, 1950; Norris *et al.*, 1951; Blaisse *et al.*, 1952; see review by
Blout, 1953). At the present time, reflecting objectives useful in spectrophotometry are available from E. Leitz, R. and J. Beck, and Bausch and
Lomb Inc. (see Fig. 2). The Leitz objectives (after Blaisse *et al.*, 1952; see
Thaer, 1965) are Schwartzchild mirror systems using two concentric
spherical reflecting surfaces arranged so that both reflecting layers are
placed between cemented quartz elements. In this way, the reflecting
surface is protected from atmospheric oxidation and mechanical shock.
The lower convex reflecting element, which would otherwise obscure a
large part of the central portion of the lens, is made as a partially reflecting mirror; this reduces somewhat the transmission of radiation through
the system but improves contrast and resolving power. Achromacy is
claimed in the wavelength range between 220 and 700 mμ. A glycerin-
immersion objective of numerical aperture 0.85 yields a primary magnification of 300× so that no ocular is required and the problem of providing
an achromatic ocular system is avoided.

R. and J. Beck manufacture a two-component solid quartz objective

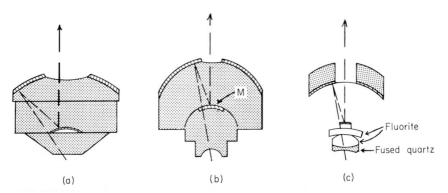

(a)   (b)   (c)

Fig. 2. Diagrammatic sections of reflecting objectives for UV microscopy. Stippling
indicates solid fused quartz elements, hatching shows aluminized reflecting surfaces.
(a) R. and J. Beck, N.A. 0.9 (after Walker, 1956). (b) E. Leitz, N.A. 0.85 (after
Thaer, 1965). *M*, partially transmitting convex mirror to reduce effect of central
obscuration. (c) Bausch and Lomb, N.A. 0.72 (after Grey, 1952). Catadioptric design:
quartz-fluorite refracting elements precede the reflector system.

(Wilkins, 1953). This system, with numerical aperture 0.9, is arranged for water immersion and has been employed successfully for spectrophotometric work (Walker *et al.*, 1963). Since UV radiation in this design must traverse a considerable path length through quartz, it is interesting to note that the transmission of these lenses appears to be better than that of comparable achromatic refractors (Wagener and Grand, 1963). It has been noted by Walker (1956) that although the Beck objective remains in focus from 250 to 550 mμ there is a variation in magnification over this range so that it must in any case be used with relatively monochromatic light.

Catadioptric immersion objectives employing both reflecting and refracting elements are produced by Bausch and Lomb (Grey, 1950). These are available as dry systems of N.A. 0.72, or as water immersion systems of N.A. 1.00. They are readily adaptable to microspectrophotometric uses which do not demand a well-corrected field greater than 100 μ in diameter. When employed with the quartz oculars supplied by Bausch and Lomb they are not fully achromatic from visible to UV but require final focusing in the UV, facilitated by the image converter system supplied by the same firm.

It should be pointed out that immersion systems are not only required to increase numerical aperture but also tend to reduce glare in the microspectrophotometric system to a substantial extent.

The reflecting objectives described above have certain disadvantages in their performance which are inherent in the reflecting design. The use of the central rays which are most important for image formation is not possible and this restriction leads to some degradation of image quality or severe limitation of the well-corrected field. These problems, as users of ordinary light microscopes are aware, are more readily solved in achromatic refracting systems. From this point of view, the series of fully achromatic optics (Ultrafluars) for the range from 240 mμ to 700 mμ produced by Zeiss as part of their commercial microspectrophotometer has been a welcome development. These objectives are offered as immersion systems with magnifications of 32 or 100× and with numerical aperture up to 1.25. Their properties are discussed by Trapp (1966). Corresponding achromatic UV projective lenses, functioning as ocular lenses in the microscope, have also been produced. The achromatic UV condenser used with all the objectives has a maximum numerical aperture of 0.8. These objectives have been employed in a variety of microspectrophotometric investigations and probably present the fewest problems in designing a measuring instrument. They are, for example, relatively insensitive to variations in slide and coverslip thickness. However, it should be noted that Chamberlain and Walker (1965a) have reported that scanning errors are greater in their system with a Zeiss Ultrafluar of N.A. 0.85 than with the Beck N.A. 0.90 reflector when the latter was provided with an annular condenser stop. These authors comment that this result is surprising: the image with the Zeiss system appeared much better than that with the Beck reflectors, even when the aperture stop was employed. Wagener and Grand (1963), who have used a series of reflecting and refracting UV objectives, comment that the best image quality in their experience was produced by the Zeiss Ultrafluars although they note that the Beck reflecting optics which they used had almost twice the transmission in the UV range. The reduced transmission of the Ultrafluars is a function of the large number of slightly absorbing optical elements which must be traversed by the radiation.

The Ultrafluar lenses are claimed to be fully corrected over the range 240–700 mμ, but it is not clear whether focus is exactly maintained over the entire range with the precision necessary for microspectrophotometry. Curves for focus *vs.* wavelength have not been presented by the firm; data for a particular lens presented by Walker (1965) indicate significant variations at wavelengths below 260 mμ. The UV-condenser of the Ultrafluar series was apparently more severely affected by wavelength changes than the objective. Such variations in focus have also been observed by Rudkin (personal communication). Since it is usually desirable to focus relatively transparent biological objects in the UV, where adequate contrast exists, the small chromatic difference between visible and UV is probably not a serious defect of these lenses in most applications.

C. Illumination

Illumination for microspectrophotometric work is usually via the Köhler method with the exit slit of the monochromator serving as the source (Fig. 3). In this way a uniformly illuminated field homogeneous in regard to wavelength in the plane of the specimen is produced. Alternatively, the slit of the monochromator may be imaged in the plane of the specimen so that illumination varying in wavelength in the plane of the specimen is obtained. For scanning instruments, in which the object measured is moved past a stationary central beam of light, this introduces no errors and simplifies the problems of alignment and adequate intensity. It is obviously not as useful when employing photographic methods or those involving scanning of the image. The size of the illuminated field must be maintained as small as possible since this is a factor of prime importance in determining the contribution of glare light to the measured absorbance at any point (Naora, 1952; King and Roe, 1953). Glare arises from radiation spread over the image plane by reflections from lens surfaces and their mechanical mountings and by diffuse scatter at mirror

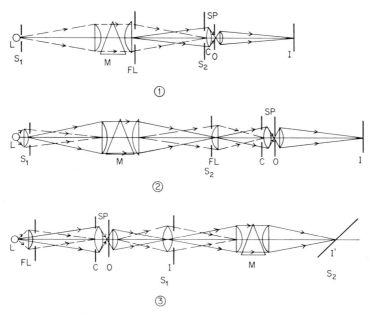

Fig. 3. Schematic diagram showing methods of illumination and arrangement of optics for microspectrophotometry. (1) The condenser is focused on the exit collimator of the monochromator, which serves as a field lens for Köhler illumination. (2) The condenser is focused on the exit slit of the monochromator to provide critical illumination. (3) The microscope is illuminated by the Köhler method with polychromatic radiation. The image is brought to a focus at the entrance slit of a spectrograph, the dispersed spectrum is detected photographically or with a television camera tube at I'. Notation: L, light source; C, condenser; SP, specimen; O, objective; S_1, monochromator or spectrograph entrance slit; S_2, corresponding exit slit plane; M, dispersing system of monochromator or spectrograph; I, location of image plane for selection of radiation to be passed to the detector. Aperture and field diaphragms normally employed are indicated at the appropriate positions. (Modified from Walker, 1956.)

surfaces. The number of optical surfaces involved in the measuring system should be as small as possible, and attention should be paid to preventing stray radiation from striking the mechanical parts of the microscope. The extent of glare can be measured by determining the apparent absorbance of an opaque object geometrically similar in relation to the photometric field to the object which it is desired to measure (Davies and Walker, 1953). The effect of glare increases with increasing absorbancy in a predictable way and measured absorbance values may be corrected for it adequately in the range 0.2–0.7 within which it is desirable to work from the point of view of overall photometric accuracy (Glick et al., 1951).

It was noted above that condenser aperture must be maintained less than about 0.3 for adequate spectrophotometric work, and adherence to this condition contributes markedly to the reduction of measured glare. Glare may also be significantly reduced if the condenser is free from chromatic and spherical aberrations. In this regard it may be noted that aberration due to slide thickness may prove to be a serious problem when objectives are used as condensers. In some cases it may be necessary to mount the specimen to be measured between two coverslips of the correct thickness, an unsatisfactory solution from a practical point of view. It should be noted that low aperture *immersion* objectives (e.g., Zeiss Ultrafluars) may be used as condensers without problems in this regard. Glare may also be reduced by providing an immersion lens of high numerical aperture with a diaphragm to reduce the aperture about one-fourth. This reduction in stray light presumably results from exclusion of light reflected from lens mounts and other mechanical parts of the objective.

Use of a narrow cone of illumination also reduces errors due to non-uniform path length through flat objects. If a large illuminating aperture is employed, oblique rays traverse a longer path through the specimen than do those parallel to the optical axis. The effect is to produce absorbance estimates that are erroneously high. Corrections have been calculated (Blout *et al.*, 1950) for illuminating cones equal to the objective aperture, and are reproduced in Fig. 4. These have rarely been applied in practice; the more usual procedure has been to keep the illuminating aperture at the minimum consistent with adequate energy in the system, but large enough to avoid excessive effects of refractive index differences in the object.

D. Sources

Various forms of discharge lamps are the most important UV sources in use at the present time. The rotating electrode resonant metallic arc originally developed by Köhler (1904) and used extensively by Caspersson continues to be employed mainly in those laboratories which have been using the equipment for many years. While it remains the most intense available source of monochromatic UV radiation, it lacks the stability necessary for photoelectric recording and is in any case such a potent source of radiofrequency disturbance as to preclude its use with most types of electronic amplifiers. With the advent of achromatic objectives the need for its high degree of monochromaticity has been reduced.

The most stable of the discharge lamps producing a continuous spectrum in the UV are the hydrogen and deuterium lamps, which also offer the advantages of a large and uniform radiant emission area (see Wyckoff,

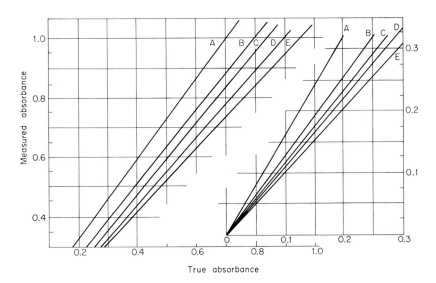

Fig. 4. Correction diagram for measurements with nonparallel light. Measured absorbance as a function of true absorbance, of material lying in a plane of finite thickness perpendicular to the optical axis. Computed for several ratios of numerical aperture (N.A.) to refractive index of medium (n). In A, N.A./n = 0.985; B = 0.841; C = 0.717; D = 0.565; E = 0.389. (After Blout *et al.*, 1950, and Walker, 1956.)

1952). Their main drawback is the relatively low intensity obtainable. However, in the photographic method, which permits the integration of intensity over time, such lamps can be of considerable aid. They have not been used extensively in recent years mainly due to the difficulties of focusing the microscope using illuminants of such low intensity and negligible output in the visible. However, with the advent of the sensitive image-converter systems discussed below, these sources may prove to be more useful.

The low-pressure mercury discharge lamp or resonance lamp produces nearly all of its radiant output as a broad band at 254 mμ. With simple monochromators or interference filters, this source can provide stable and useful illumination for photometric work at this particular wavelength (Lavin and Pollister, 1942; see also Pollister and Ornstein, 1959). It should be noted that this wavelength is quite suitable for the photometric estimation of nucleotides. Higher pressure mercury arcs—for example, the AH-6 (General Electric Co.) or the SP-500 (Phillips)—are relatively stable and have been widely used in spectrophotometry. A problem which arises with these lamps is the decreased output at wavelengths slightly greater than 254 mμ, caused by the absorption of the mercury resonance emission by the mercury vapor itself. By varying the voltage on such a lamp, it is possible to improve the energy output in this particular region, so important in the estimation of nucleic acids and proteins.

Mainly in order to overcome the difficulties in obtaining adequate energy in the mercury reversion region, a number of modern instruments employ xenon compact arcs. (Hanovia in the U.S. and Osram in Germany produce compact arc lamps in a wide range of power ratings.) These are sources of high intrinsic brightness, rich in UV continuum and providing useful output through the UV range in the region near 260 mμ. The main problem encountered in the use of these arcs is instability in the position of the arc discharge between the electrodes. The position of the discharge is stabilized within the envelope by the configuration of the electrodes; as these are eroded the arc may begin to wander in an irregular or rhythmic fashion. There appears to be considerable individual variability in the tendency of different arcs to wander and it has been recommended that when first turned on they be allowed to burn continuously for some time to establish a primary and definitive crater that will stabilize the arc during later use. Freed and Engle (1962) have employed a servocontrolled mirror to keep a xenon arc in focus on the monochromator entrance slit. Compact arc lamps with a xenon-mercury filling have also been employed (Hanovia). In these, the strong lines of the mercury spectrum are superimposed on the xenon continuum and the resulting high energy at specific wavelengths may be an advantage in some forms of UV photometry. The intrinsic brightness of compact arc lamps increases with increasing power dissipation; for this reason a 2000-watt xenon arc has been installed in the Caspersson-type microspectrophotometer at The Institute for Cancer Research. It should be noted that the very large amount of long-wave radiation extending into the infrared which comes from the xenon arc makes it imperative that a longwave cutoff filter be employed in conjunction with most commercial monochromators. Walker *et al.* (1963) employ an auxiliary monochromator for this purpose in their instrument, which uses a 1000-watt xenon arc. In some applications, the instability of the xenon arc may be overcome by using an image of the arc slightly larger than the entrance slit of the monochromator. A preferable approach is through the use of the double-beam measuring principle to compensate for variations with time in illumination of the photometric field.

E. Monochromators

The monochromator is normally used to select a particular wavelength to illuminate the microscope, although for some purposes the monochromator may be arranged to follow the microscope, accepting a portion of the microscope image at its exit slit and dispersing the heterochromatic radiation transmitted by the object in an arrangement more properly called a spectrograph. Use as an illuminator is the more commonly employed method and the optical arrangements may be of two types, as shown in Fig. 3. Either the exit slit of the monochromator may be imaged in the field of the object providing critical illumination, or the prism or grating or a field lens bearing the conjugate image of the dispersing element may be focused in the field, the latter arrangement being a form of Köhler illumination. The Köhler arrangement is more convenient for photographic work or image scanning since the radiation is chromatically homogeneous throughout the illuminated field. When the exit slit is imaged, the radiation varies in spectral distribution at right angles to the slit so that this arrangement is suitable only when the object is scanned past the axis of the microscope. The slit image method usually illuminates the object more intensely than does illumination by the Köhler method.

Efficient use of the radiation transmitted by the monochromator requires that the apertures of the monochromator and microscope condenser be matched. A properly chosen focal length for the field lens or special aperture-matching relay lenses will increase the efficiency of illumination of the microscope itself. A pair of reflecting elements may be arranged to make up a precondenser system to match the numeral aperture of condenser and monochromator. Such a system may consist of two concentrically arranged spherical elements like a reflecting objective (Pollister and Ornstein, 1959) or of a mirror pair of relatively long focal length used off axis (Wagener and Grand, 1963). These arrangements provide the complete achromacy needed for automatic recording of absorption spectra. When photometric work at a single wavelength is planned, the relay lens can consist of a simple quartz refracting element to be refocused with change of wavelength.

As has been pointed out by Walker (1958) the characteristics desirable in a monochromator for microspectrophotometric work differ from those to be found in most commercial instruments. However, since the construction of a monochromator is beyond the capabilities of most biological laboratories the more practical problem becomes one of selecting a suitable commercial instrument. Since sufficient energy in the photometric field is always a problem in microspectrophotometric work, high transmission and a minimum number of refracting and reflecting elements is of more consequence than extremely high spectral dispersion. Adequate spectral purity of the isolated light is the most important problem. A monochromator emits a main band of energy with a wavelength distribution determined by the dispersion of the refracting or diffracting element and the size of the slits. In addition, light which has not been refracted or has been diffracted in a high order also emerges and may be considered stray light. Most commercial monochromators provide sufficient dispersion for work with the broad absorption bands normally studied in biological investigations. However, most require the use of protective filters in order to remove stray light of wavelength differing greatly from the desired one. Stray light, e.g., visible radiation, lowers the apparent absorbance measured by the instrument and contributes to a systematic error. Provision of baffles and antireflective coatings within the monochromator housing frequently results in a considerable reduction in stray light. A further desirable characteristic in a monochromator for microspectro-photometry is that it should conveniently accept a variety of light sources, without extensive modification of the entrance optics. In addition to a UV source, it is frequently desirable to employ a low-pressure mercury arc for calibration purposes or a tungsten lamp for studies with visible light.

Grating-equipped monochromators have been used in a number of microspectrophotometers and offer excellent dispersion at reasonable cost. Those intended as high intensity monochromatic illuminators contain a small number of optical elements. A convenience of grating instruments is that change in wavelength is directly proportional to grating rotation, simplifying the design of automatic wavelength drives. To remove contaminating radiation of overlapping orders of diffraction, grating instruments must be used with protective filters, for example, the Corning 9863 or an interference filter, although these lower the effective transmission of the monochromator. The most efficient filter for separating a broad band of UV wavelengths from contaminating visible light remains the liquid system originally described by Bäckstrom (1940).[3]

Modern prism instruments generally employ achromatic or reflecting optical elements and pass the light twice through the prism to obtain additional dispersion. Some instruments offer a choice of crystal or fused quartz prisms, the latter providing adequate transmission for many purposes at a considerable saving in price. An advantage of these instruments is that there is no problem with the high-order radiation which is emitted by grating instruments. Change in wavelength is, however, not linear with prism rotation and various means must be employed to provide an output proportional to wavelength for the recording of absorption spectra. Use of a double monochromator, which in effect couples two similar monochromators in tandem, is an effective way of assuring high spectral

---

[3] The Bäckstrom filter used by Rudkin in this laboratory contains 240 g/liter $NiSO_4 \cdot 6H_2O$ plus 44 g/liter $CoSO_4 \cdot 7H_2O$ in glass-distilled water. A transmission curve should be determined, since not all samples of the salts have high UV transmission. A good filter of 1 cm path should transmit about 90% between 250 mμ and 310 mμ. A cell with 5 cm pathlength transmits over 65% at 257 mμ, and is used during photomicrography.

purity, although at a commensurate cost. In the instrument of Walker et al. (1963), a simple monochromator with Féry prism is used following a grating instrument to obtain adequate removal of the higher orders of the diffraction spectrum.

A monochromator should be tested for stray light in connection with the specific source with which it is to be used. It is possible to investigate the distrubution of energy in the light emitted by a monochromator by the use of a second monochromator and photoelectric detector. However, in many laboratories this procedure may not be possible. A simple test may be carried out by measuring the apparent absorbance of a filter opaque to short wavelengths as suggested by Walker (1956). (For example, 0.5 cm of carbon tetrachloride cuts off below 265 mμ.) Radiation detected with the monochromator set below this wavelength may thus be considered to be stray light of much longer wavelengths contaminating the monochromator output. This type of test is important since about one-third of 1% stray light will produce an error of 1% in determining an absorbance of unity (Opler, 1950). It has been pointed out by Krüger (1965) that stray light in a monochromator containing reflecting elements may be increased 100-fold through accumulation of dust on the mirrors and the fine scratches that may occur through cleaning. The comparison was made between recently completed monochromators and those in use for about a year.

The development in recent years of useful interference filters for the UV range offers new possibilities for their employment both as protective filters and as primary wavelength-selecting elements. Such filters are produced as first-order, second-order, or third-order systems in the range from 210 mμ through to the visible.[4] First-order filters transmit up to 20% at the peak wavelength with a half-bandwidth of between 200 and 300 Å. Transmission of unwanted wavelengths is about $\frac{1}{2}$% outside of this range. Second- and third-order filters provide narrow bandwidths with decreased transmission at the peak and may require additional blocking filters to remove secondary transmission peaks (see Fig. 5). These peaks occur at approximately 1.5 and 3 times the main wavelength in the case of third-order filters and at two times the peak wavelength for second-order filters. Thus, first-order filters can serve as useful stray light protecting elements in conjunction with single monochromators. They do not, as is true of an auxiliary monochromator, increase the spectral dispersion. Second- and third-orders filters can be used to isolate individual lines from a discontinuous spectrum for photometry at particular wavelengths.

[4] UV interference filters are available from Baird-Atomic, Inc., Cambridge, Massachusetts, or from Barr and Stroud, Ltd., Glasgow, Scotland.

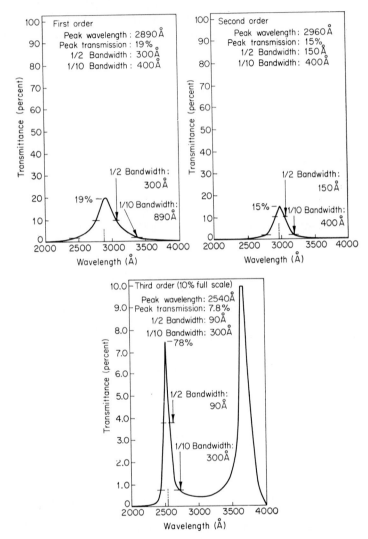

FIG. 5. Transmission curves of typical first-, second-, and third-order interference filters for UV use. (By permission of Baird-Atomic, Inc.)

Such combinations may provide energy greater than that which may be obtained through a monochromator-filter combination. Since rejection of unwanted wavelengths outside of the main passband is never complete, the characteristics of the source must be considered when using interference filters for wavelength isolation. For example, a xenon arc with its high visible and infrared emission would give rise to stray light at an objectional level. However, a mercury resonance lamp with a filter for 254 mμ could provide a useful monochromatic source for the routine photometry of nucleic acids or nucleotides.

Monochromator wavelength calibration should be checked when the instrument is put into use and periodically thereafter. Medium pressure mercury lamps with their discontinuous line output serve as a convenient source of well-defined wavelengths. The detector may be a photomultiplier tube or a fluorescent screen inspected visually. Instruments used for recording of absorption spectra may be calibrated by determining the absorption spectrum of benzene solutions or benzene vapors (for examples, see Friedel and Orchin, 1951). Exact wavelength setting can be made by adjusting the monochromator for minimum transmission at a known benzene absorption peak.

F. Focusing Devices

In any microspectrophotometer it is important to provide some means of determining the correct focus during UV operation. With the adoption of achromatic lens systems in UV microscopy, the need for special focusing devices may not be obvious. However, the necessary achromatic quality may not be present in all optical parts of the system, as for example in the illuminating optics, relay lens, or lenses used to convey radiation to a detector. Further, when the microscopic object is well matched in refractive index to the surrounding medium, no image should be detectable with visible light at the position of correct objective focus. However, there is a tendency for the observer to defocus the objective slightly in order to produce visible contrast (see comments of Trapp, 1965). It will then be found that the microscope is incorrectly focused for production of UV absorption images.

The use of phase contrast optics to determine correct focus in the visible provides one solution to this problem. Some use has been made of interchangeable objective lenses carefully parfocalized to produce phase-contrast images in the visible and a corresponding well-focused image in the UV (Taylor, 1953). These objectives were used in connection with a special quartz condenser containing a removable annular diaphragm. Walker (1958) has summarized a number of ways in which phase contrast illumination may be provided in the use of reflecting objectives. Any objective may be made to function as a phase-contrast system providing that an annular diaphragm is placed in the condenser, and a quarter-wave annular retarding plate is placed at the back focus of the objective. A removable retardation plate placed outside the objective has been used in conjunction with an illuminating annulus whose image is relayed by a lens to the appropriate position within the reflecting condenser (Walker and Davies, 1950; Norris *et al.*, 1951). The exit pupil of the objective may also be re-imaged by a mirror to a new conjugate focus where the phase plate may be conveniently placed (Payne, 1954; Walker and Deeley, 1956). As Walker (1958) has pointed out, these methods have the disadvantage that a number of optical components must be inserted and removed from the optical path, rendering it difficult to maintain correct alignment. Ruch (1960) and Schiemer (1960) have described systems in which complete auxiliary microscopes are placed in series with the reflecting UV microscope proper in order to obtain a new conjugate plane for the phase contrast effect. These latter systems require extremely critical adjustment for successful use.

A device for determining actual focus in the UV was first used by Köhler (1904) in the original form of the UV microscope and depends upon the visible fluorescence emitted by uranium glass under UV irradiation. The "Sucher" contains a uranium glass wedge on whose lower surface is formed a fluorescent image; the device incorporates a magnifier to inspect this image. The Cooke fluorescent eye piece (Vickers Inst., Ltd.) operates in a similar fashion; this firm has also produced a fluorescent telescope for examining the rear focal plane of the objective. Willemite phosphor powder deposited on glass plates may be used for low power work at short wavelength; such plates are useful devices in ascertaining the alignment of UV microspectrophotometric systems. A UV-sensitive vidicon television system has been used with the microspectrophotometer at this laboratory in order to allow focusing with reference to a bright visible image. Such a television system is necessarily more complicated and expensive than a fluorescent eyepiece and presents its own problems of adjustment and maintenance.

At the present time the most generally useful means of obtaining focus is probably the UV image-converter tube (e.g., RCA type 7404). In such a detector the UV image is formed on a photosensitive coating supported by a quartz face plate, as shown in Fig. 6. Electrons emitted are focused by a simple magnetic lens and accelerated to an aluminized phosphor screen, where they form an image having nearly the same dimensions as the UV image formed on the front face of the tube. The fluorescent screen is examined through a magnifying lens. The electrical supply for such a system is much simpler than that of a television camera, a d.c. potential of 10 kV being the only requirement. Magnetic shielding must be provided to avoid impaired tube resolution, and the operator must be adequately protected from the high voltage employed. A commercial image converter unit is supplied by Bausch and Lomb, together with a 35-mm camera for photographic recording. Similar attachments are available for the microspectrophotometric apparatus of Zeiss and of Leitz. The sensitivity and

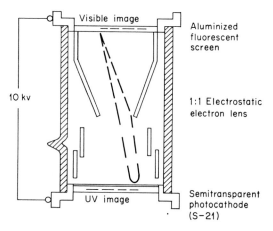

FIG. 6. Diagram to illustrate operation of an image converter like the RCA 7404. UV irradiation causes emission of electrons from the photocathode in a pattern corresponding to the UV image. An electrostatic lens brings the electrons to a focus on a fluorescent screen which emits visible light, and which is examined with a magnifier.

convenience of these image converter systems is such that they may be expected to replace other forms of focusing equipment in microspectrophotometric use.

III. Photographic Photometry

A. ADVANTAGES AND LIMITATIONS

Photographic methods are most convenient for integrating the absorbance of biological objects at a particular wavelength, while for the determination of absorption spectra the necessity of making a series of exposures for each wavelength selected makes them much more tedious than direct photoelectric recording. However, spectrographic methods (Barer *et al.*, 1950; Ruch, 1960) allow recording of spectra with a single exposure. The photographic method allows use of simple UV microscopes; since the light is integrated by the photographic emulsion over the time of exposure, the source itself need not be highly stabilized either in intensity output with time or in position. Thus, the intense but variable illumination produced by the rotating metallic arc finds its main application in photographic procedures (Caspersson, 1950; Rudkin *et al.*, 1955; Rudkin, 1961). The extent of the photometric field in the object plane which can be investigated is determined by the size of the well-corrected field obtainable from the objectives. Zeiss Ultrafluars are excellent for this purpose, as are the older monochromats, provided that the narrow wavelength requirements of the latter are fulfilled. Reflecting objectives may also be used in this way although their use in photography is limited by curvature of field and poor resolution for points in the object away from the optical axis. However, provided that these optical limitations are recognized the photographic method can yield excellent results.

In comparison with the method of photoelectric recording, use of the photographic emulsion as detector involves an error which is usually considered to be at least 5% (Thorell, 1947; Caspersson, 1950). This photographic error is in addition to the errors of the microscope, i.e., those arising through stray light, glare, distributional error, etc. which are common to both photographic and photoelectric recording. The error of delimiting the area in which the absorbancy is to be integrated may in fact be less with photography than with photoelectric recording if large photographic images and precision densitometers are used. The fact that the photographic plate or film provides a permanent record of absorbancy distribution which may be subjected to successive analyses is an added benefit of the method. For many purposes, therefore, particularly those in which fine structural analyses of complex objects are to be undertaken, the photographic method may be the one of choice (see e.g., Rudkin, 1966). The microscope equipment can remain relatively simple, although the worker must have access to a reliable densitometer.

B. Photographic Materials and Development

Photographic UV microphotometry has been successfully carried out using both plates and films. Plates offer the advantages of dimensional stability and convenience of handling in most densitometers. However, it should be recognized that it requires a great deal more energy to produce an image of adequate density covering a large photographic plate, with consequent risk of radiation damage to the specimen. The use of 2×2 inch plates should thus be considered. Thirty-five millimeter film has also been used, an entire series of exposures being processed together with calibrating exposures for development uniformity (Walker and Davies, 1950).

A variety of emulsion types has been employed successfully. Process plates (Kodak $4'' \times 5''$) are used routinely in this laboratory. The emulsion appropriate for the problem at hand should be chosen keeping in mind that graininess sets a limit to the precision of densitometric analysis, and that graininess increases with increasing film sensitivity and degree of development. Generally, high contrast photographic materials give the best results provided that image size is sufficient to compensate for the noise introduced by grain (Walker, 1956).

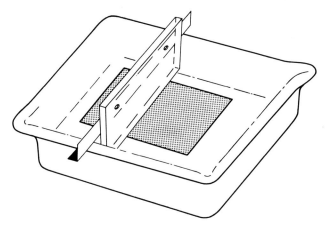

Fig. 7. Device to secure uniform development of 4 × 5 inch glass photographic plate, as used by Rudkin. The plate lies at the bottom of a 5 × 7 inch stainless steel photographic tray containing about 250 ml of developer solution. A plastic barrier is adjusted on a length of stainless steel angle stock so that it just clears the face of the emulsion. During development, the barrier is held vertically, and slowly moved the length of the plate once each second.

Processing should be carried out in such a way as to keep the development uniform over the area containing the sample image, background image and the image of the reference system used. With plates, flat tray development is quite satisfactory and a plastic barrier (Fig. 7) moved back and forth a millimeter or two above the emulsion surface provides extremely uniform development (King and Roe, 1953; Rudkin et al., 1955). "Nitrogen-burst" agitation systems, available from several commercial suppliers of darkroom equipment, should provide good uniformity of development. However, these systems are relatively complex and expensive, and would only seem justified for work on a very large scale.

The developer chosen should be one producing high contrast and acting fairly rapidly to minimize the appearance of chemical fog. Edström (1964) employs Kodak formula D-72; Davies (1950) has used Kodak formula D-19b. A similar highly active developer described by Thorell (1947) has been employed by Rudkin et al. (1955). If fresh developer is used for each plate or set of plates, the density for a given exposure time in a microscope may readily be held constant. A constant temperature developing sink is convenient, but is not necessary provided that a reference calibration image of a wedge or sector is included on each plate exposed. Individual plate calibration also compensates for errors in developing time.

C. Calibrating Emulsion Response

For photographic photometry it is necessary to know the degree of emulsion blackening produced by known exposures to light. Due to reciprocity failure, differing times of exposure to a constant light source are not a reliable means of carrying out such calibration. Instead, the emulsion should be exposed for a standard time to a series of intensities differing in known fashion. This may be accomplished by using a graded or step density wedge placed in front of the emulsion. A rhodium-coated quartz wedge with steps of known density is available from Hilger and Watts and has been used by Walker and Davies (1950) and others. Unfortunately, the rhodium coating differs in absorbance at different UV wavelengths and so must be calibrated at each required wavelength in a conventional spectrophotometer (Walker, 1956). The rotating stepped sector provides a convenient system with steps whose absorbancy is independent of wavelength (Thorell, 1947). Such sectors may be made to give zones of equal logarithmic increment so that they are linear with the logarithm of exposure (see Rudkin, 1961) or may be compensated by the method due to Edström (1964) to correct automatically for the measured glare intensity in the individual microscope system used. An example of a compensated sector is shown in Fig. 8. Sectors must be arranged to rotate sufficiently rapidly so that the interruption frequency is higher than that which results in reciprocity errors (Thorell, 1947). It has been found by a number of workers that provided more than about 40 interruptions take place during the exposure period, no reciprocity effect can be demonstrated (Thiers, 1951; Walker, 1956).

Location of a rotating step sector in the microscope system poses some problems of vibration and of finding a sufficiently large free space appro-

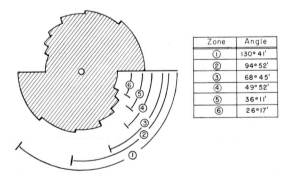

Zone	Angle
①	130° 41'
②	94° 52'
③	68° 45'
④	49° 52'
⑤	36° 11'
⑥	26° 17'

Fig. 8. Compensated logarithmic step sector (after Edström, 1964). Each step provides a decrease in plate density corresponding to an absorbance in the object of 0.15, in the presence of 7% stray light. The greatest diameter of the disk is about 7 cm.

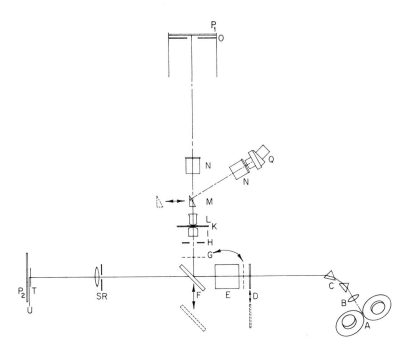

Fig. 9. Microscope for photographic cytophotometry, as used by Rudkin *et al.* (1955). The exposure through the rotating sector (*U*) is made at P_2, using light of the same wavelength as that employed in making the micrograph on the same plate at P_1. The mirror (*F*) is interchanged to direct radiation to the appropriate part of the system. *A*, spark gap; *B*, collimator; *C*, prisms; *D*, fluorescent screen to adjust prisms; *E*, Bäckstrom filter; *G*, mesh attenuator; *H*, condenser aperture diaphragm; *I*, condenser; *K*, specimen; *L*, objective; *M*, quartz deflecting prism; *N*, eyepiece; *Q*, *Sucher*. *S* is a quartz condensing lens with iris, *R*, used to adjust intensity of sector illumination.

priately located in the object plane. If the sector is mounted entirely independently of the microscope and camera, vibration can successfully be eliminated. Nevertheless, this method requires completely uniform illumination of the microscope field over a large area, which may be difficult due to the characteristics of the light source and illuminating optics used and undesirable from the point of view of increased glare (King and Roe, 1953). An alternative method, employed by Rudkin, is to place the rotating sector in an auxiliary optical path (Fig. 9) illuminated by light of the same wavelength as that used in the exposure and for the same time (Rudkin *et al.*, 1955). Even illumination in the auxiliary path, which does not require a microscope, may more easily be attained than in the microscope field itself. This solution further offers the advantage that the highest density produced by the sector may be made slightly

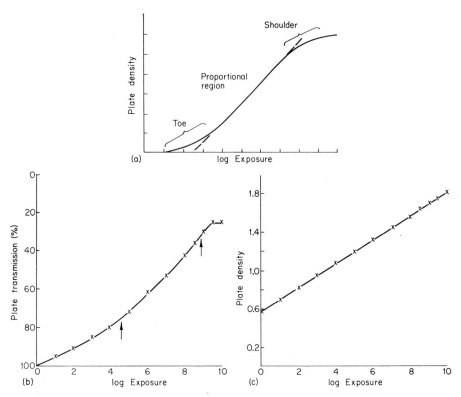

Fig. 10. Response curves of photographic emulsions. (a) Generalized H + D (Hurter and Driffield) curve relating plate density (= log $1/T$) to the log of exposure increment. The regions of the curve relating to the text discussion are indicated. (b) Working curve of a Kodak Process Plate exposed at 257 mμ and developed in Thorell's developer. Exposure varied by a rotating logarithm step sector according to Rudkin *et al.* (1955), densitometry with Jarrel-Ash microdensitometer. The approximate linear working range is indicated by arrows. (c) Working curve of a Kodak Process Plate, exposed at 265 mμ and developed in 50% Kodak Dektol (D-72), densitometry with Joyce-Loebl densitometer. (Courtesy of L. Mezger-Freed.)

greater than the background density on the photomicrograph itself, thereby facilitating the establishment of the calibration curve.

The emulsion response curve (H + D curve, Fig. 10) may be used to determine object absorbancy in two ways. At relatively low plate densities, i.e., on the "toe" of the H + D curve, it is found that the percent transmission of the plate is directly proportional to the logarithm of the incident intensity, for example, between 20 and 80% transmission of the plate (Rudkin *et al.*, 1955). Thus, differences in transmission between object and background are directly proportional to object absorbancy and the area under a transmission curve may be directly integrated to compute the total absorbancy of the object. The more usually stated emulsion characteristic is that the plate density (logarithm of $1/T$) is proportional to the logarithm of the incident intensity (Fig. 10c). Linearity of plate response using this system extends to a wider range of intensity values and therefore of permissible object absorbancies. However, this method requires a densitometer capable of recording plate density on a linear scale. It should be pointed out that a characteristic curve linear with transmission (Fig. 10b) permits use of the densitometer in the region of greatest photometric accuracy.

D. Densitometric Analysis

The convenience and indeed the accuracy with which the photographic method may be applied depends in great measure on the densitometer used for scanning the developed negatives. The necessary characteristics of the instrument are that the area measured should be readily observable and should be small enough to avoid introducing distributional error in the densitometric recording per se. Microdensitometers intended primarily for the analysis of spectroscopic plates may not be equipped to measure plates at any desired angle and a rotating plate holder may have to be provided. If the working characteristic curve is that relating plate density to the log of exposure, it is important that the densitometer should record density of the plate and not transmission, in order to provide a linear relation between the reading and the quantity of absorbing material. The areas under the curves may then be integrated by planimeter or other device. A widely employed commercial instrument is that deriving from the design of Walker (1955) and produced by Joyce-Loebl and Co.

The integrated absorbance of a structure is estimated by the procedure shown schematically in Fig. 11. If the object to be measured is, for example, the nucleus of a cell grown in monolayer culture (Fig. 11a), its cross section is as shown: i.e., absorbance in the nuclear area is due only in small part to the contribution of overlying and underlying cytoplasm (Walker and Davies, 1950). A series of densitometric traces are run along parallel and uniformly spaced paths, as shown in Fig. 11b. The plate density due to incident (background) radiation is determined and plotted as indicated by the dotted line. For objects in which "free space" cannot be included in each trace, the value to be used should be determined from a point as close as possible to the object. If the free-space intensity is not uniform across the field, appropriate inclination of the background density line may be required. The area between object and background curves $(D \cdot d_1)$ is determined over those parts of the trace corresponding to the

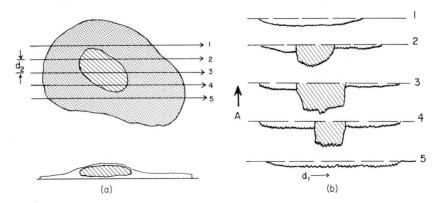

Fig. 11. Procedure for measuring integrated absorbance by densitometry, as discussed in the text.

object being measured (crosshatching in Fig. 11). These areas are summed for all traces passing over the object, e.g., *2*, *3*, and *4* in Fig. 11. The integrated absorbance (E_t) is then calculated from

$$E_t = \frac{kd_2}{M^2} \sum D \cdot d_1$$

where

$$k = \frac{\Delta D}{\Delta E} = \frac{\Delta D}{\Delta \log I}$$

the experimentally determined plate calibration factor (Fig. 10c) and M is the magnification factor between object and plate. The spacing between runs (d_2) may be chosen so that it corresponds to about 1 μ in the object; in any case it must be close to the limit of resolution of the microscope if distributional error is to be avoided. As Rudkin (1966) has pointed out, when plates are so exposed as to make transmission proportional to log I (Fig. 10b), a densitometer recording in percent transmission is not affected by this form of error.

The areas lying under the densitometric curves may be estimated with a polar planimeter or by weighing the cut-out curves after tracing on paper of uniform weight. An alternative procedure is to make use of a commercial ball and disk integrator. These mechanical devices may be attached to the output shaft of a strip-chart recorder to control the rate of rotation of a second shaft in such a fashion that the rotation rate depends upon the pen position. Cams and microswitches attached to the integrator output shaft can then be used to drive an operations pen so as to produce pips whose number corresponds to the integral between any two points along the curve. The number of pips corresponding to an equivalent length of background must be subtracted from the pip count for the curve over the specimen. Such automatic integrators, which may alternatively be made to operate as electronic systems (Lomakka, 1955), can accelerate the work involved in determining the absorbancy of a series of complex objects. Such an attachment is commercially available for the Joyce-Loebl densitometer; others can be applied to the strip-chart recorders used with other densitometers.

The analysis of densitometric traces accounts for a great deal of the time required for photographic microphotometry of complex objects. To facilitate this part of the work and increase the speed of analysis, Engle and Rudkin at this Institute have constructed a novel rapid-scanning instrument (Rudkin, 1966; Rudkin and Engle, in press). This instrument moves the plate across the optic axis, with a two-second repetition rate for complete scans: the photomultiplier signal is processed by a wide-band amplifier and displayed on an oscilloscope with long-persistence display. Electronic cursors are adjusted to select the area of interest; the length of the curve to be integrated or the integral valve may be automatically calculated and instantly displayed on a digital voltmeter. This instrument promises to accelerate considerably the analysis of giant chromosomes and similar difficult specimens.

If the plates are exposed so that transmission is proportional to log of exposure, scanning of the plate can in principle be abandoned in favor of measurements made with a large area averaging densitometer, since the photographic plate itself acts as a means of transforming from the linear to the logarithmic function. Distributional error arises in cytophotometric measurements because the summing of intensities from different parts of the microscope image by the usual type of detector takes place before transformation to the logarithmic function necessary for the calculation of absorbancy. Thus, in the normal scanning procedure, the intensity signal is logarithmically transformed at each point before being integrated in order to avoid distributional error. However, where a linear function, i.e., transmission, is directly related to the amount of absorbing material, the average intensity over the area in question is a valid measure of the amount of material present. Such area-measuring procedures have been used in microradiogram densitometry where an analogous linear relationship can be obtained (Carlson, 1957) in interference microphotometry (Svensson, 1957), and in quantitative electron microscopy (Bahr, 1966). An area densitometer was tested in this laboratory some years ago for evaluation of UV micrographs. Difficulties with this technique stemmed partly from the necessity of finding a clear space in the background of the same size as that used in measuring the object and in ensuring that the object is sufficiently well isolated from extraneous absorbing material.

But the least satisfactory aspect stems from the limited range of absorbancies in the object which can be measured (up to about 0.5, corresponding to plate transmittances between 30 and 70%). Within these limits the area densitometric technique may be used to measure isolated objects of considerable inhomogeneity when a scanning densitometer is not available (see also comments of Caspersson et al., 1957).

A nonscanning method for evaluating integrated absorbancy from photographic plates has been proposed by Mendelsohn (1958) as an extension of the two-wavelength method of microspectrophotometry used in the visible. A photomicrograph of the object is taken with monochromatic UV light and a second plate, exposed as a contact print, is developed in the presence of a dye-coupling agent. After bleaching and fixation, the positive appears as a monochromatic color transparency which is then measured by the two-wavelength procedure, using a visible microdensitometer. It demands that the object be readily demarcated by suitable diaphragms and that a spectrophotometer be used in the analysis.

E. Extraction Methods

The amount of light to which a photographic emulsion has been exposed can be determined not only by densitometry but also by extraction and by chemical analysis of the reduced silver deposited. This solution to the densitometric scanning problem for inhomogeneous objects has been employed by Niemi (1958) who analyzed silver directly. Pollister and Ornstein (1959) and Kelly (1962, 1966) have described techniques for converting the silver image to a corresponding dye image; the amount of the extracted dye is determined by conventional spectrophotometry. In the technique of Kelly, photomicrographs are made on standard 35 mm Kodachrome film using a comparison microscope system to provide a blank area of size corresponding to that of the object to be investigated. The background area cut from the film need not be the same size as the sample area if the disks are accurately weighed before extraction. Kelly's technique offers the advantage that only conventional spectrophotometers available in most laboratories are required, processing of the film being done in the usual commercial laboratories.

IV. Recording of Absorption Spectra

A. Methods of Measurement

The instrumental requirements in microscopic spectrophotometry parallel those in conventional systems; employment of microscope optics and minute biological specimens impose added problems, and it is with these special requirements that we will be concerned in this section.

The simplest method of determining an absorption spectrum is to select an extended area in the microscope image plane using a diaphragm and to allow the light from this part of the image to pass to a photomultiplier tube. The intensity transmitted at a series of wavelengths is recorded, the specimen is moved aside so that light passing through an equivalent free space in the preparation fills the photometric field and the background intensities at the same wavelengths are recorded. This procedure requires a homogeneous specimen and is more suited to measurement of micro-extracted samples than to analysis of intact cellular structures. Its advantages lie in the simplicity of the apparatus and the fact that as the area of the photometric field is increased so is the energy available for measurement and therefore the signal-to-noise ratio may be made very great. The procedure is similar to that used in visible light cytophotometry (see Chapter 4) and may make use of similar equipment if it is provided with achromatic UV-transmitting optics. With most sources and mono-chromators wide variations in available energy occur in different regions of the spectrum; it may be necessary to use some form of removable atten-uator to decrease the energy measured in some spectral regions. Stacked quartz microscope slides can serve as useful attenuators in this method. As an alternative procedure, the sample and background determinations may be made by repositioning the microscope object at each setting of the monochromator. While this method avoids errors in monochromator wavelength drive setting, it imposes severe performance requirements on the stage shifting method employed. The hydraulic stage of Caspersson (see Caspersson, 1950) was developed specifically to facilitate this form of measurement.

The effects of distributional error on the absorption spectrum may be reduced by decreasing the size of the photometric field to the minimum set by the optical properties of the system. The energy available for measure-ment is correspondingly decreased and the critical illumination arrange-ment of the monochromator may be helpful in providing sufficient signal. Measurements at a single point of minimal size introduce the possibility of errors due to inadequate sampling of the structure under study so that it is necessary to repeat the determination at a sufficient number of points within the specimen to assure a representative sample. Comprehensive sampling by a manual procedure may in practice be replaced by scanning-integration determination of integrated absorbance at each of the wave-lengths used (Davies, 1954; Freed and Engle, 1963). If errors from failure to scan the same area in the specimen at each wavelength are to be avoided, it is necessary to define the integrated area through a fixed mask and to employ an instrument which does not require resetting of the background intensity reading throughout the entire operation. When the object to be integrated is isolated in a free space of sufficient size the photometric field may be somewhat larger than the object, thus avoiding the problems of relocating the scanned area.

B. Design of Instruments

As a general rule it is desirable that UV microspectrophotometers should operate as double-beam systems. The small area used in measurement and the high degree of spectral purity required dictate the use of powerful light sources with the inherent problems of instability discussed above. Further, the gain of photomultiplier tubes cannot readily be stabilized over the time periods required for the recording of absorption spectra. In addition, the energy variations at different parts of the spectrum make it desirable that the quantity recorded be the ratio of incident and transmitted energy.

Reference beams may be derived in a number of ways as discussed in the following section. Where nonuniform or fluctuating sources such as the xenon arc are employed, it is important that reference and measuring beams be derived from the same part of the source. This is most conveniently accomplished through the use of a partially reflecting quartz plate. If the optics used for the reference beam differ in their absorption spectrum from those used in the measuring beam, the instrument baseline will contain a difference absorption spectrum which must be subtracted from the spectrum determined for the biological object (Walker *et al.*, 1963). In some instruments dual microscope systems have been employed, one containing the specimen, the other a control preparation free of absorbing material (Pollister and Ornstein, 1959; Zeiss UMSP). Even with such instruments, however, the chromatic properties of different objectives usually do not match and baseline distortions commonly occur. This problem may be eliminated if the reference beam is derived from the same optical system used for measurement, although in such instruments it is not possible to work directly on the optical axis (Wagener and Grand, 1963; Chance *et al.*, 1959).

Photomultiplier tubes as detectors provide a current proportional to the intensity of the illumination, with high gain and a linear response. The various dynode voltages required for their operation may be obtained from a battery-pack or, in most modern instruments, via a voltage divider and stabilized electronic power supply.

Photomultipliers for use in the UV must have quartz or UV transmitting glass envelopes so that the response characteristic remains high through the range of interest. The RCA photomultiplier type 1P28 has been widely applied and is typical of the side-on nine-stage type; the location of the photocathode surface is behind grid wires inside the tube.

This configuration makes for difficulty in combining two beams onto the same area of the photocathode, unless a beam mixer is employed with consequent light losses and difficulty in alignment. End-window tubes, in which the photocathode is deposited on the inside of the UV transmitting envelope, can accept two beams at slightly differing angles on the same surface. The tubes of this type frequently contain more dynode stages, thus providing a higher gain without subsequent amplification. Since the dark current is a function of the size of the photocathode, the smallest diameter end-on tube should be used which will entirely accommodate the measuring beam. Dark current may be further reduced by cooling the photocathode surface but this is usually not necessary.

Photomultiplier tubes of improved types are continually being developed by the manufacturers, whose literature should be consulted in designing new equipment. The quantum efficiency of modern tubes with tri-alkali photocathodes has been claimed to be as high as 0.3, a consideration which may be of importance in some kinds of work (EMI Electronics, Ltd.: see Herrmann, 1965).

In measuring absorption spectra, the possibility of differing responses to various wavelengths between a pair of photomultiplier tubes makes it desirable to use a single photomultiplier rather than individual detectors for reference and sample beams.[5] When a single photomultiplier is used, some means must be provided of alternating its illumination by reference and sample beam through the use of a vibrating mirror (Thorell and Åkerman, 1957) or rotating chopper disk (Wyckoff, 1952). This also allows the signals to be amplified using sharply tuned amplifiers with consequent rejection of much noise and diminished sensitivity to stray light (Wyckoff, 1952). Since the quantity which it is desired to measure is the ratio between sample and reference beam, use of a common detector and amplifier reduces the possibilities of error.

The amplified photomultiplier signal is directly proportional to the intensity passing through the object and thus to transmission. Some form of logarithmic transformation of the signal must be effected in order to convert to a measure of absorbance prior to integration by any method. This transformation may be made by holding the photomultiplier output constant, in which case the dynode voltage becomes a logarithmic function of the input light intensity and is used as the measure of absorbance (Sweet, 1946; Deeley, 1955).[6] A number of workers have made use

[5] For scanning-integration at a single wavelength, this may not be true (see Chamberlain and Walker, 1965a).

[6] A commercial photomultiplier photometer operating on this principle is available from the Gilford Instrument Co., Oberlin, Ohio, as Model 220 Absorbance Indicating Photometer.

of silicon junction diodes as logarithmic converting elements (Jansen, 1961; Engle, 1962; Walker *et al.*, 1963). Such diodes have the property that the voltage across them changes as the logarithm of the forward current. Putting these diodes in series produces a greater voltage for a given current and Engle has used a series of 30 diodes in the logarithmic converter of a flying-spot microphotometer (Freed and Engle, 1962).

C. Specific Types of Apparatus

The principles described above can best be illustrated by a discussion of representative UV microspectrophotometers that have been completed in recent years. For details of construction, the reader is referred to the original publications and manufacturers' literature.

1. *The Zeiss-Caspersson Ultramicrospectrophotometer* (*UMSP 1*)

This instrument has been developed for commercial production in consultation with Caspersson and his co-workers (Caspersson, 1965). While it is derived from the earlier instruments constructed in the Karolinska Institute (Caspersson *et al.*, 1953, 1957; Lomakka, 1957), a number of new approaches have been employed by the Zeiss group: achromatic refracting optics (Trapp, 1960), dual microscopes and single photomultiplier, precision mechanical scanning stage (Trapp, 1966).

As shown in Fig. 12, the radiation source is a 450-watt xenon compact arc provided with a spherical re-imaging mirror to focus a doubled image of the arc discharge on the entrance slit of the monochromator, a Zeiss prism instrument. The beam emerging from the monochromator is focused by an achromatic field lens alternately on the measuring and reference microscope systems, which contain identical optical elements. The beam selecting system is noteworthy in that it consists of synchronously rotating mirror sections that perform both the beam splitting and beam mixing functions without the losses of intensity incurred in fixed beam splitter arrangements. A viewing system is provided for focusing in the visible; either an image converter or UV-sensitive vidicon system can be used to establish focus. Selection of the area in the image to be measured is by means of a series of diaphragms of fixed size placed in front of the single photomultiplier tube.

The ratio between measuring and reference beams is displayed as transmission on a strip-chart recorder whose movement in the X-direction may be coupled to the wavelength drive of the monochromator. The monochromator slit adjustment is controlled by a servomechanism which keeps the reference signal constant with changing wavelengths. Other features of this instrument provide for convenient automatic scanning-integration as discussed below.

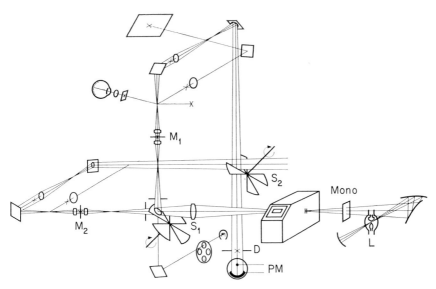

Fɪɢ. 12. Schematic diagram of the optical path of the Zeiss ultramicrospectrograph. *L*, xenon compact arc lamp; *MONO*, monochromator; *S₁* and *S₂*, ganged rotating mirror-sectors; *M₁* and *M₂*, Ultrafluar microscopes for sample and reference preparations, respectively; *D*, selecting diaphragm in image plane; *PM*, photomultiplier detector. (After Trapp, 1960.)

The UMSP has been constructed to meet extremely critical standards and is obviously capable of being used in any kind of microspectrophotometric work. However, this comprehensive design has resulted in considerable complexity and high cost and it is to be anticipated that the optics and certain other components may be equally useful in less comprehensive special instruments for many purposes (e.g., see Lomakka, 1965; Sandritter, 1966).

2. The Edinburgh Microspectrophotometer

This instrument, constructed by Walker and his colleagues (1963), uses the dual-microscope double-beam system, with single photomultiplier tube. Radiation from a 1000-watt xenon arc with reflecting mirror is passed through a commercial grating monochromator and then through a simple auxiliary prism monochromator to reduce stray light and eliminate higher-order diffraction spectra. The sample beam (Fig. 13) is reflected by a mirror smaller than the diameter of the illuminating beam so that peripheral portions continue into the reference microscope optics. The reference beam is chopped by a rotating sector disk and reflected onto the photomultiplier cathode. The sample beam is imaged onto a concave

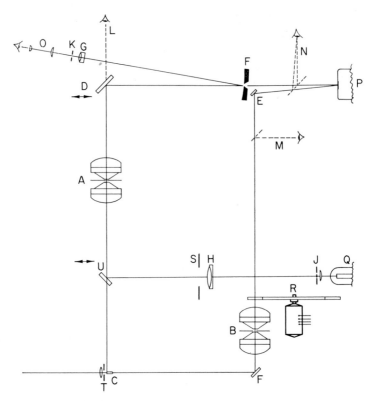

FIG. 13. Schematic diagram of the optical path of the Edinburgh microspectro-photometer. *A*, measuring microscope; *B*, reference microscope; *C*, small mirror to deflect central portion of beam from monochromator to measuring system; *U*, *S*, *H*, *J*, *Q*, annular illuminating system for phase contrast; *O*, *K*, *G*, *F*, "imaged-in" phase-contrast system. The beam corresponding to the area to be measured passes through the hole in *F* to reach the photomultiplier detector *P*. The reference beam, chopped by the rotating sector disk, *R*, is presented to the same photomultiplier as an alter-nating signal. (From Walker *et al.*, 1963, by permission.)

mirror containing a small central hole which permits light to pass to the photomultiplier. A phase-contrast viewing system makes use of this concave mirror; a phase retardation plate in a focus conjugate to the objective aperture allows the specimen to be focused with visible light. Measuring and reference signals in the photomultiplier output are sepa-rated electrically. The alternating signal from the reference beam is isolated by a four-stage tuned amplifier filter and regulates the photo-multiplier power supply so as to keep a constant reference signal with changing wavelength or fluctuations in source intensity. The direct current signal corresponding to the intensity in the measuring microscope is balanced against the sum of the dark current and the direct current portion of the reference signal, to provide a signal proportional to transmission. Logarithmic conversion is by a diode circuit; the output is displayed on a potentiometer recorder synchronized with the wavelength drive.

3. The Wagener-Grand Instrument

The instruments described above make use of dual microscope systems for the production of reference and signal beams. It is, however, possible to derive both the I and I_0 signals from the appropriate portions of the image plane in a single microscope system. In the instrument constructed in the Papanicolaou Cancer Research Institute in Miami (Wagener and Grand, 1963), full double-beam operation is obtained using a single microscope, as shown in Fig. 14. Two apertures are placed in the image plane, one to accept light from the portion of the image which it is desired to measure and the second to obtain the background intensity. Systems of this type avoid the use of accessory reference beam optics, and eliminate the problem of chromatic difference. Nevertheless, they impose limitations on the structure of the objects which can be examined, since a clear space must be obtainable at a fixed distance from the object to be measured.

In the Wagener-Grand instrument, the xenon arc illuminates a prism monochromator via a re-imaging mirror and 150-mm ellipsoid. Two spherical mirrors form a relay lens, matching monochromator exit aperture to microscope input aperture. The microscope proper may be equipped with reflecting lenses or Ultrafluar objectives and employs a quartz ocular. The aperture plate is provided with two holes whose diameter corresponds to 1 μ in the object plane with a center-to-center spacing corresponding to 35 μ. A rotating sector disk placed behind the aperture plate allows the two beams to fall alternately on the photomultiplier. A quartz lens images the eye piece exit pupil on the photomultiplier, thus ensuring a common distribution of energy on the photocathode for both beams. Both signals are amplified in the common photomultiplier and its associated amplifiers and divided by a rotary synchronous commutator into I and I_0 signals. The ratio of I and I_0 is displayed on the recorder which thus reads percent transmission. In this instrument, conversion to absorbance is used only in the scanning-integrating mode discussed below and is carried out using a logarithmically wound precision potentiometer geared to the recorder shaft. It should be noted that a similar transformation from linear to logarithmic analog

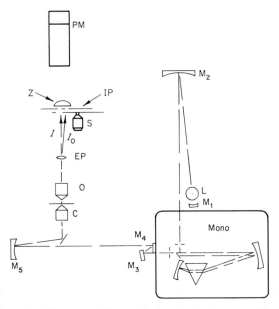

FIG. 14. Schematic diagram of the optical path in the recording microspectro-photometer of Wagener and Grand (1963). M_1, source re-imaging mirror; M_2, ellipsoidal entrance mirror, focused on entrance slit of Perkin-Elmer Model 83 monochromator; M_3, M_4, M_5, aperture-matching relay optics; C, O, reflecting microscope optics; EP, quartz eyepiece. IP, plate in image plane with holes to pass radiation corresponding to I (on axis) and I_0 (off axis). The beams are interrupted alternately by the rotating sector S. The quartz lens Z images the objective aperture on the face of the photomultiplier detector PM.

can be carried out by mounting a logarithmic cam on the recorder output shaft and using it to drive a ball and disk integrator.

A similar derivation of two measuring beams within a single microscope forms the basis of the instruments used by Thorell and Åkerman (1957) and by Chance and his associates (1959). In these instruments, a vibrating mirror pair is placed between the objective and an aperture plate in the image plane (Fig. 15). Light from sample and background areas is thrown alternately on the single measuring aperture. These instruments have been constructed for studies with visible and longwave UV and have been used primarily for detecting low concentrations of respiratory enzymes in cells whose geometry permits the necessary choice of sample and reference areas.

4. The Leitz Microspectrograph

Absorption spectra of biological objects can also be recorded by forming an image with heterochromatic UV radiation and allowing the light from a small region in the image plane to be dispersed in a spectrograph placed following the microscope. This principle is used in the Leitz microspectrograph (Thaer, 1965) which derives from the designs of Ruch (1960). Radiation from one of a variety of sources is focused upon the specimen using reflecting objectives (Fig. 16); either an image converter or an auxiliary secondary phase microscope system may be used to focus the object. The image is formed on a plane bearing the entrance slit of a prism spectrograph so that the image of the slit forms a conventional spectrographic image. A rotating step sector is provided in the plane of the entrance slit in order to calibrate photographic emulsion response. If the target surface of an orthicon television camera is substituted for the photographic plate, the absorption spectrum may be immediately observed by selecting a single television line and displaying it on an oscilloscope (Loeser and West, 1962).

The advantages of this design come from the simplicity it provides in recording absorption spectra whether by the photographic or television method. The disadvantages of the microspectrograph principle come

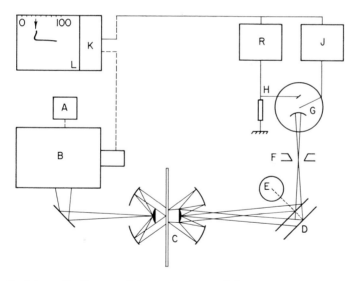

Fig. 15. Schematic diagram of the optical path in a vibrating-mirror microspectrophotometer. A, source; B, monochromator with wavelength drive coupled to strip-chart recorder K, L. The image produced by the reflecting microscope C is relayed to the image plane F by a pair of mirrors D. The mirror pair is vibrated by a magnetic drive E, so that portions of the image corresponding to I and I_0 alternately pass the aperture at F. The ratio of I and I_0 is coupled via electronic circuits R and J to the recorder, to display the absorbance spectrum. (After Thorell and Åkerman, 1957.)

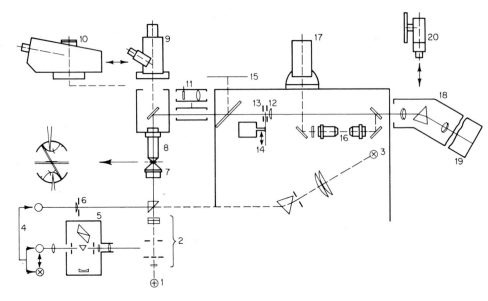

Fig. 16. Schematic diagram of the Leitz UV microspectrograph. Radiation from a variety of sources (*1, 2, 3, 4, 5, 6*) is used to illuminate the reflecting microscope (*7, 8*). A phase-contrast system (*2*) or an image converter (*10*) may be used to focus the image and select the area to be measured. The desired portion of the image is selected at the entrance slit (*13*) of the spectrograph (*18*). A photographic plate (*19*) records the image of the spectrum. A rotating step sector (*14*) at the entrance slit provides calibration for the photograph. (After Thaer, 1965.)

from the high radiation flux which is necessarily present in the object plane and the fact that the transmission losses which occur in the spectrograph are imposed on radiation which has already traversed the specimen. Thus, an instrument working on this principle incurs greater likelihood of radiation damage to the specimen as discussed below.

D. Ultraviolet Absorption Spectra of Cytological Material

A variety of compounds that are to be found in cells absorb in the region between 200 and 400 mμ (Walker, 1956) (Fig. 17). The main emphasis in published microspectrophotometric work has been on the nucleic acids and proteins present in such high concentrations that the contribution of most other absorbing molecular species is overridden (Caspersson, 1950; Davies, 1954). In the region from 200 to 230 mμ, end absorption by protein dominates. Nucleic acids exhibit their characteristic absorption peak at 260 mμ while protein-containing structures free of nucleic acids show the characteristic absorption at 280 mμ. Absorption spectra from cells in which both nucleic acids and protein are present is broadened and shifted toward 280 mμ to an extent depending on the ratio of the nucleic acid to protein.

If it is assumed that nucleic acid and a standard protein containing 5% tyrosine and 1% tryptophan are the sole absorbing components, the method of two-component analysis used in macrospectrophotometry may be employed to estimate the ratio of the two chromophores from the shape of the absorption spectra (Caspersson, 1950) (Fig. 18). This method is highly dependent on adequate correction for effects of scatter which vary with wavelength and thus cannot be employed with high precision in intact cell specimens for which exact scatter corrections are not possible (Davies, 1954). Nurnberger made a serious attempt to apply the spectrum analysis method to estimation of protein in nerve cells, comparing the results with those of microradiography

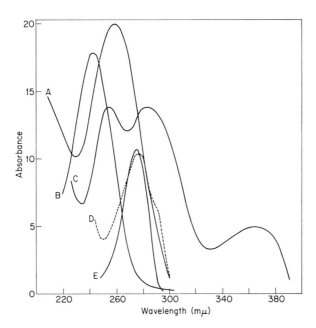

FIG. 17. Absorbance spectra of substances which occur in cells. *A*, DNA; *B*, ascorbic acid in acid solution; *C*, folic acid in alkaline solution; *D*, serum globulin; *E*, pyrocatechol. (From Walker, 1956.)

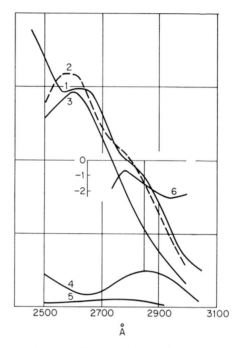

Fig. 18. An example of the application of the multicomponent analysis method to an absorbance spectrum of a cytological object. *1*, Measured absorbance spectrum of heterochromatic portion of Drosophila salivary chromosome. *2*, Curve reconstructed from sum of components. *3*, Calculated nucleic acid contribution. *4*, Calculated tyrosine contribution. *5*, Calculated tryptophan contribution. *6*, Tyrosine band. No scatter correction was applied, nonspecific light losses having been shown to be low. (Redrawn from Caspersson, 1950.)

(Nurnberger *et al.*, 1952), and presenting a detailed critique of the method (Nurnberger, 1955). It was clear from these findings that protein could not be reliably estimated in the presence of much nucleic acid; in recent years the method has essentially been abandoned.

To avoid problems of calculation from complex absorbance spectra, extraction methods may be employed. For example, the nucleic acids may be removed by hot trichloroacetic acid or nucleases and a second spectrum recorded (Rudkin and Corlette, 1957a). Thus, a difference spectrum may be plotted and used to establish the nature of the extracted material and permits a better estimate of the ratio of nucleic acid to protein.

Errors in the determination of absorption spectra in the microscope arise from several sources. Glare tends to reduce the observed absorbance in a nonlinear fashion having a greater effect on higher absorbance values. By measurement of suitable opaque objects or by estimating deviation from Beer's law with solutions of known absorbance properties, a value for glare light may be determined and used to correct the observed spectrum (Davies and Walker, 1953).

Distributional errors that arise if the sampled area is not uniform in regard to chromophore distribution in the specimen plane also tend to flatten the absorption curve. This error may be dealt with by using a sample area small enough to avoid inhomogeneities, and by methods of specimen preparation which prevent coarse precipitation of the absorbing material (Davies, 1954).

Scatter, arising from refractive index differences in the specimen, throws light out of the collecting aperture of the objective and tends to elevate the short wavelength end of the curve. The magnitude of this effect depends on the numerical aperture of the objective, so that for determination of spectra objective numerical aperture should be maintained as high as possible (Caspersson, 1936, 1950). It should be recalled that high objective apertures introduce a path length error that may necessitate corrections (Blout *et al.*, 1950). Corrections for scatter may be made by measuring apparent absorbance at a wavelength sufficiently high to avoid molecular absorption by protein, for example, in the range from 310 to 330 mμ (Caspersson, 1950; Moberger, 1954; Davies, 1954). It is assumed that absorbance at this wavelength represents nonspecific light loss due to scatter; the correction for scatter at the shorter wavelengths in the range from 260 to 280 mμ is obtained by extrapolation. The assumption is made that scatter increases exponentially with declining wavelength, the value of the exponent being chosen in the range of 2–4 by various authors. An example of such a correction method is shown in Fig. 19. In older published work, the poor image formation by monochromatic objectives has prevented full use of this method; it may have greater utility with achromatic systems. Living cells are more satisfactory objects in regard to refractive index differences than fixed ones, and the magnitude of scatter depends strongly on the method of specimen preparation.

UV absorption spectra from cytological objects generally exhibit a broad peak with its maximum near 260 mμ, broadened to a greater or lesser extent toward longer wavelengths (Caspersson, 1950). In some materials (e.g., nucleoli), a distinct plateau is found extending as far as 290 mμ (Caspersson, 1940; Caspersson *et al.*, 1940). When nucleic acids are extracted chemically, the absorption of the remaining materials shows a peak at 280 mμ (Rudkin and Corlette, 1957a). It is not clear, however, to what extent deviations from the shape of nucleic acid absorption curves for solutions are to be attributed to the contribution of proteid

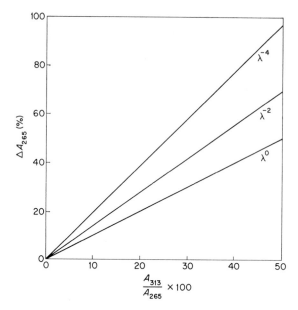

FIG. 19. Correction diagram for absorbance measured at 265 mμ, by estimation of scattered light at 313 mμ. The three lines give corrections assuming that scatter is proportional to the powers of wavelength shown. (After Walker, 1956.)

absorption, and to what extent they are effects of scatter. Changes in cellular absorption spectra which result from fixation have been studied by Davies (1954); absorbance at 280 mμ in fixed cells is higher, relative to absorbance at 260 mμ, than in living cells. Walker (1956) has reviewed at length the problems of interpretation posed by the absorption spectra published up to that time. With the improved instruments which now exist, it is anticipated that more satisfactory spectral analysis can be carried out, employing more adequate correction techniques. Nevertheless, the effects of specimen preparation may always introduce uncertainties of sufficient magnitude to hinder multicomponent analyses of native cellular material.

Changes in absorption spectrum resulting from changed physical conditions of the nucleoprotein structures may be exploited per se to study the state in which the materials exist in intact structures. For example, hyperchromic increases in the absorbancy of DNA in unfixed sperm nuclei after heating in various media have been studied by Chamberlain and Walker (1965b). A special objective mount and stage heating attachment permit nuclei to be measured during the increase of temperature in order to determine "melting" curves.

The possibilities of investigating materials other than nucleic acids and proteins by the microspectrophotometric method are limited mainly by the low concentrations at which they exist. The fundamental limitation on what can be detected in microspectrophotometry is set by the small path length involved. In favorable situations the path length available for absorption approaches 10^{-4} cm; therefore concentrations approximately 10,000 times higher than those used in conventional spectrophotometers are required. If the absorbing material under investigation is present in discrete structures, and is thus concentrated in the plane of the object, the requirements may not be so high. In such situations the probability of distributional errors is increased. Ascorbic acid, as an example, which has an intrinsic absorbance coefficient much higher than that of nucleic acid, has been investigated by Chayen (1953). The work of Chance et al. (1959) and of Thorell and Åkerman (1957) with highly sensitive microspectrophotometers working in the Soret band region of the short-wavelength visible suggests what can be accomplished with appropriate techniques. These workers have studied small but specific absorbance shifts against a background of the much larger but constant light losses from other sources. In this way they can discriminate the small changes due to respiratory effects from the larger, overall scatter from the cell. While the sensitivity of these microspectrophotometers is great enough to *detect* absorbance changes of the order of 10^{-4} absorbance units at low absorbance, corresponding accuracy at high absorbance would not be expected. This stems from the consideration that noise is inversely proportional to signal size in a highly stabilized measuring system, and increases with increasing absorbance (R. Perry, personal communication).

V. Scanning Integration Procedures

A. INTEGRATED ABSORBANCY

The spectrophotometric instruments discussed above have been considered from the point of view of the determination of absorbancy at a point. Such information is usually insufficient, in itself, to allow useful conclusions concerning the distribution of absorbing materials in biological structures. What is required in most cases is to sum the absorbancy increments of all the points in a structure: the quantity so determined, the integrated absorbancy, is proportional to the amount of absorbing chromophore in the entire structure. In ordinary spectrophotometry, sampling the absorbancy per unit path length of a uniform solution allows the calculation of amount of chromophore by the use of an average figure. With inhomogeneous geometrically irregular biological objects such a procedure leads to errors (Glick *et al.*, 1951): usually some form of sampling is employed to determine mean absorbance per unit area, and chromophore content is estimated from the product of absorbance and area. The importance of calculating amount of chromophore with reference to a biologically defined structure may be seen in the determination of DNA in nuclei and chromosomes. Computation of the amount of DNA in these structures, using the Feulgen reaction, may also be carried out using the special techniques worked out for visible light microphotometry outlined in another chapter. In UV work it is frequently necessary to determine the integrated absorbancy of structures not readily approximated by geometric formulas, in which undefined combinations of chromophore are present and which may not be isolated from other absorbing material. An example is the determination, in a flat cultured cell, of the absorbancy of a nucleus surrounded by cytoplasm.

The general procedure used in scanning has been outlined above under photographic methods. A number of instruments have been devised to provide for direct photoelectric scanning of the preparation, automatic logarithmic transformation, and the recording of absorbancy *vs.* distance automatically at fixed intervals in parallel lines. The records can then be analyzed, with reference to a photograph, to select and integrate those absorbancy increments corresponding to the desired biological structure.

Such analyses are necessarily laborious even with instruments in which scanning and transverse line movement are automated. If the structure is suitably isolated, all lines in a photometric field enclosing the object can be scanned automatically, the signal transformed to a logarithmic analog and the absorbancy above a given baseline integrated electrically. The circuit thus reads out directly a measure proportional to the amount of chromophore in the photometric field. Such rapid scanning instruments greatly increase the speed of many kinds of analyses. In the various laboratories that have been concerned with this kind of work, scanning instruments of a number of types are in use and are discussed in the following sections.

B. MOVING-STAGE SCANNERS

Scanning may be accomplished by moving the preparation itself systematically so that a narrow beam on the optical axis successively crosses the various elements of the specimen, and the transmission at a small central point in the field is recorded. This approach is straightforward and has a number of substantial advantages. The value of I_0 is uniform except for fluctuations in the light source and/or measuring circuits, or variations in the mounting medium in the vicinity of the object. Evenness of illumination over an extended field is not a problem, and glare attendant upon the illumination of large areas in the specimen plane is avoided. Further, the corrections of the optical system are at their best at the center of the object field, so fewer demands are made on the corrections of the objectives used or on the flatness of field which they present. The problems which arise are those of providing physical movement of the specimen, in synchrony with the movement of a recording instrument, with sufficient precision for the purpose.

In Caspersson's original instrument a stage mounted on vertical plates of quartz was deflected by a hydraulically actuated diaphragm connected with a mercury reservoir. By raising the mercury reservoir with the aid of a motor-driven lead screw, a constantly increasing pressure was provided. The linearity and smoothness of the movement were thus governed by the properties of the quartz plates and the hydraulically actuated diaphragm. In developing their commercial version of the Caspersson ultramicrospectrograph, the Zeiss firm has worked out a satisfactory mechanical solution to provide automatic movement in both X and Y directions (Fig. 20). The stage consists of two elements corresponding to the X and Y movements. Each is mounted on a pair of heavy flat springs which constitute an axis of rotation free of mechanical play or frictional

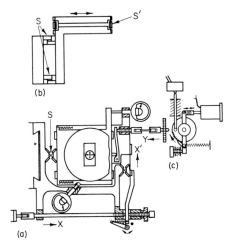

Fig. 20. Zeiss precision scanning stage. (a) plan view; (b) side view; (c) detail of ratchet mechanism for line advance in Y-direction. A micrometer screw driven by an electric motor system (not shown) provides motion in direction X synchronized to chart-paper travel. The lever (L) reduces this movement further (X'). The stage is mounted on pairs of crossed leaf springs as shown at (S), which provide a single degree of freedom. The lever (L) is similarly mounted. An analogous spring mount (S') allows motion of the upper stage for displacement in the Y-direction. (Modified from Trapp, 1966.)

forces not intrinsic in the material itself. A similar spring pivot bearing mounts a lever of great asymmetry of which the short arm is linked to the stage itself, the long arm being driven by a micrometer screw. Over a distance of about 100 μ, the movement of the specimen across the optical axis is approximately linear; the rotation of the micrometer screw is readily synchronized with the chart drive of a recording instrument.

A similar system is used to provide a stepwise movement in the Y direction, corresponding to the separation between scanning lines. Automatic switching arrangements are provided with the stage, which allow for automatic back and forth scanning. Lomakka (1965) has modified this system to provide increased scanning rates; with his system, high resolution scanning may be carried out at rates between 40 and 160 μ^2/sec.

The instrument of Walker *et al.* (1963) uses a scanning stage driven by single levers of high arm ratio, but the stage itself is carried on linear ball bearings.

C. Image Scanners

The mechanical problems associated with precision scanning over small distances in the object plane can be avoided if the scanning mechanism is instead arranged to move a measuring aperture in the plane of the microscope image. With this procedure, measurements are necessarily made off-axis, introducing the possibility of errors through failing objective corrections and curvature of field. In addition, as in the photographic method, there is a requirement for a uniformly illuminated photometric field.

A useful form of scanner to be employed in the image plane is the Nipkow disk (see Zworykin and Morton, 1954). A disk, bearing a series of holes of uniform size in a spiral arrangement, is rotated in front of a field-defining diaphragm so that its opening is traversed by a series of arcs successively scanning across the photometric field. A lens placed behind the scanning disk can image the light from all parts of this field through a common location on the photocathode (Wagener and Grand, 1963). Thus, the photomultiplier output successively displays absorbance increments from a series of lines scanning the field. Uniformity in size of the holes is required. The integrated signal corresponding to the I_0 integral must be established by scanning an area completely free of absorbing material. The object to be scanned is then located in the photometric field and a new value for integrated I is recorded. The difference between these two integrals thus corresponds to the integrated absorbancy of the object.

The scanning mechanism of Deeley (1955), which has been incorporated in the Barr and Stroud integrating microdensitometer (primarily designed for use in the visible), consists of a rotating disk with radial slots which is placed behind a second linearly deflected slot at right angles.

In the scanner constructed by Exner (1959) a movable lens is placed between the objective and the ocular of the microscope (see Fig. 21). Systematic deflection of this lens displaces the image position so that the image itself is, in effect, scanned across a fixed aperture in the image plane. The arrangement is similar to that used in the microplanimeter of Caspersson *et al.* (Caspersson, 1955).

D. TEMPLATE-CONTROLLED INTEGRATORS

In cases where the absorbing material of interest does not lie free in the field but is surrounded by or contiguous with other absorbing material, it is difficult to arrange a geometrically determined aperture in an automatic scanning system to separate the desired absorbance increments from those due to extraneous material. In such cases recourse must be had to an instrument producing a permanent record of line-by-line scans for further analysis, as in the photographic method. A number of workers have sought to circumvent this labor through devices which limit scanning to a photometric field whose shape may be determined by a boundary or template drawn with reference to the microscopic image of the structure to be measured. Using such template-controlled integrators, one can deal with objects having irregular contours, without the increased labor of trace analysis.

The system described by Exner (1959) represented an early attempt to automate the scanning process. His photometer operated as a null-point double-beam system: a servodriven attenuator (rotating polarizing prism) equalized the intensity recorded from measuring and reference microscopes. Thus, the angular position of the servo motor shaft gave an estimate of I/I_0. Figure 21 summarizes the operating principles of this instrument. Scanning was carried out by means of a movable intermediate lens, driven along the X and Y scanning axes by drive motors and appropriate gear trains. The lens was first moved by hand, using visible light illumination, to trace on a metal plate the outline of the structure to be measured. Insulating material was then used to coat the excluded area, as shown in Fig. 21. During the scanning process, then, the X-drive moved the intermediate lens so as to pass the image across the measuring aperture in the image plane. When the tracing point reached the insulated area of the plate, an electric current was interrupted, setting in motion the following sequence: stop X-drive, advance Y-drive to next scanning line, reverse X-drive. In this way, line-by-line scanning of the desired area was completed. A logarithmic cam on the output shaft of the null servo produced a linear displacement, proportional to log I/I_0, which was

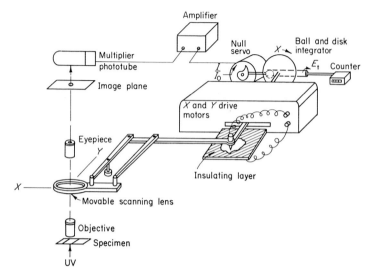

Fig. 21. Operation of a template-controlled integrator system. With the specimen stationary and uniformly illuminated, the position of the image is shifted by a movable intermediate lens. The travel of the lens in the X-direction is limited to conform to the shape of the biological specimen by a tracing point on a pantograph. When the point reaches the boundary between conducting and insulating material on the plate, the integrator is disconnected, the Y-drive is activated to advance to the next scanning line, and the X-drive is reversed. A second plate (not shown) is used to deal with reentrant contours and internal excluded areas. (After Exner, 1959.)

coupled to the ball carriage of a ball and disk integrator. The disk was driven by the same motor producing the X-axis scanning drive, so that the integrator output shaft (cylinder) registered a number of revolutions proportional to the integral (log $I/I_0\ dX$), dY being a constant. The counter reading after a complete scan was thus proportional to E_t.

This approach allowed scanning time to be confined to the area actually to be measured, a consideration with the relatively low scanning rates employed. Reentrant contours in more than one axis were dealt with by using a second tracing point and plate on the same pantograph arm. The second plate was covered with resistive material corresponding to areas included in the first outline, but from which it was not desired to record absorbance. When the tracing point was carried over these areas, scanning continued but integral was not recorded.

In the similar system of Walker *et al.* (1963), a template-controlling table is mechanically linked through lever arms to the mechanical stage drive. A narrow illuminating aperture and photomultiplier are arranged so that a black and white outline drawing (made by moving the stage with a pen connected to the levers) passes across in synchrony with the scanning of the specimen. The photomultiplier signal controls a high-speed relay, connecting the signal to the integrator as required.

Lomakka (1965) has described a method which avoids the necessity of drawing: a multileaf diaphragm is used to approximate the shape of the irregular area to be measured. His apparatus (Fig. 22) was designed for use with a high-speed scanning cytophotometer, equipped for work in either the visible or UV spectral regions. An enlarged image from the microscope is simultaneously observed with the face of a cathode-ray tube, using an optical device similar to the Abbé camera lucida. The field of the microscope eyepiece presents the microscope image, together with the movable diaphragm leaves which are adjusted to correspond to the size and shape of the area in which it is desired to perform the integration. The deflection of the beam of the cathode-ray tube is synchronized to the motion of the rapid-scanning stage and to the optical magnification of the microscope. During scanning, light from the cathode-ray tube falls on an auxiliary multiplier phototube, which controls a gate to the input of the

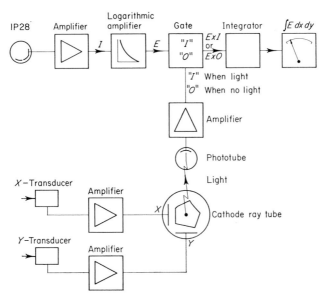

FIG. 22. Integrating system for irregular objects described by Lomakka (1965). Signals proportional to X- and Y-movement of the stage are connected to the plates of the cathode-ray tube. A portion of the tube face is masked, corresponding to the areas where integral is not to be recorded. Light from the unmasked portion of the display reaches the phototube and activates the gate, allowing integration of absorbance via the chain of measuring circuits shown horizontally at the top of the figure.

integrator as shown in Fig. 22. Thus, the integrator sums absorbance only during the period when the scan is in the desired area. This system does not appear to have been designed for geometrically complex objects, i.e., those with pronounced reentrant contours.

In the double-beam flying-spot television microphotometer of Engle and Freed (1968) an auxiliary television monitor is used in analogous fashion. With this device either geometrically regular diaphragms, or outlines drawn with reference to the image presented on the television screen may be used to control the light to a photomultiplier which similarly gates the integrator on and off.

All of the above devices thus allow selection of the area in which measurement is to be carried out to be made directly in the microscope. Scanning, integrating and delimiting operations are carried out automatically. With such systems the integrator output is registered as an accumulated voltage on a capacitor and read with a d'Arsonval meter, or may be presented to a counter as a series of pulses derived from repeated firing of the integrating capacitor. A single number is thus obtained which estimates the amount of chromophore contained within the biological structure chosen.

E. Scanning Errors

The integrated absorbance registered in a scanning microspectrophotometer is subject to error from factors arising through the scanning procedure itself. These errors have recently been considered in some detail by Chamberlain and Walker (1965a), on whose work the following discussion is based.

Distortions arise through optical as well as electrical factors, and the magnitude of these effects may be estimated in an approximate way through studies on appropriate model substances. The primary optical error arises through the use of a measuring aperture of finite size. The absorbance record of an infinitely sharp edge, for example, would not appear as a square wave in the measuring current but would be smoothed to an extent depending upon aperture size. With objects in which the rate of change of absorbance with distance is gradual, or in which the area of the object is large compared with the edges, the effects of this smoothing are likely to be small. However, in measurements of objects like metaphase chromosomes it would be expected that such errors might become important. The aperture size may be decreased to the limits set by sufficient energy for measurement or by the mechanical difficulties of constructing sufficiently small apertures.

The fact that useful apertures are likely to be circular contributes error, since absorbing material lying away from the center line of scan contributes relatively less than material lying directly on the scanning center line. The ideal aperture would be rectangular but small holes of this shape are difficult to make. Distortion of the absorbance signal will also occur through effects of diffraction and glare. Chamberlain and Walker (1965a) evaluated the effects of this error source in their instrument by moving a sharp, completely absorbing edge slowly across the field. In this way, errors due to electrical response are eliminated by the slowness of the change in voltage; the remaining distortion from the expected square wave can be attributed to the optical defects of the system.

A further optical error is inherent in the use of the template-controlled integrators described above. The error in demarcation is a function of the contrast and ease of discrimination of the desired structure from its surroundings. The magnitude of the error from this source is difficult to assess through the use of model systems; it depends strongly on the nature of the cytological object under investigation.

The measuring circuits in a scanning microspectrophotometer may operate with a wide bandwidth in order to allow accurate response to rapidly changing absorbance. If such wide-band circuits are used, the noise acceptance of the system is increased. On the other hand, if circuits of restricted bandwidth are employed, care must be exercised to ensure that rapidly changing signals are not smoothed by the time-constant of the amplifying system.

When noisy signals must be employed, as in the case of UV measurements on living cells, error may arise from the nonlinear amplification of noise and signal in logarithmic amplifiers or other logarithmic convertors. This source of error may readily be removed by employing intensities sufficient to give high signal-to-noise ratio, or by providing noise filtering at a point in the circuit before the logarithmic transformation occurs.

In general, these errors in scanning systems are most likely to be troublesome with objects approaching the size of the scanning aperture itself or having sharp absorbance edges. From their work with the scanning microspectrophotometer in Edinburgh, Chamberlain and Walker have estimated that systematic errors due to scanning in normal cytological objects may be expected to be less than 2%.

In cytological objects with local absorbance elements of a concentrated nature, e.g., heterochromatic blocks, care must be taken to observe that instantaneous absorbance signals are not so great as to have undue sensitivity to the effects of glare or to fall outside the linear range of the logarithmic transformer used. To the extent to which such points of high absorbance occur in the specimen, the observed integrated absorbance will generally be falsely low.

VI. Specimen Preparation

A. FIXATION

A great deal has been written on the desiderata for adequate fixation of cells and tissue for cytochemical studies (see reviews in Pearse, 1960; Barka and Anderson, 1963). Loss or redistribution of the molecular species under study must be avoided, as in any cytochemical method; for UV cytophotometry, the further requirements are imposed that the fixation should neither increase the light-scattering properties of the specimen nor deposit UV-absorbing compounds in the cells.

The cytochemical requirements of the fixation procedure depend upon the molecular species to be estimated. DNA, for example, appears to be adequately retained *in situ* by acid fixatives or neutral formalin (Sandritter and Hartleib, 1955), by alcohol:acetone (Zetterberg, 1966) or by the 45% acetic acid solution used in cytogenetic work (Rudkin *et al.*, 1955). Adequate retention of the several molecular forms of RNA is a more complex problem which has recently been reviewed by Swift (1966). He has concluded that soluble RNA is probably extracted by most aqueous fixatives, although most of the protein-bound RNA is preserved. Retention of other substances has been less extensively studied: Merriam (1958) pointed out that substantial losses of dry weight occur when tissues are fixed in formalin or acetic-alcohol and dehydrated and embedded by conventional means. The majority of this loss probably represents lipid and carbohydrate, although some loss of protein could be demonstrated. Obviously, it must be part of any cytochemical investigation to demonstrate that the molecular species involved is adequately retained.

Isotope techniques are useful in following the behavior of materials either in bulk tissue or by autoradiography, and should be employed as controls in microspectrophotometric work. Their use may permit study of minority species of nucleic acid as, for example, in the procedure described by Woods and Zubay (1966) for the cytochemical localization of transfer RNA. By freezing-substitution in ethanol-potassium acetate, soluble RNA is retained and may be selectively extracted in a buffered saline-magnesium solution. These authors combined chromatographic resolution of the extracted material with autoradiographic study of its localization within the cell. UV cytospectrophotometry with instruments of high precision can be employed to study problems of this kind only if such well-controlled preparative methods are employed.

The problems involved in fixing cells so as to avoid excessive scatter were studied by Davies (1954). Compared to the living state, cultured cells gave rise to increased scatter when fixed by any technique and immersed in glycerin. The observed absorbance and the shape of the absorbance spectrum were thereby altered. Most fixation and dehydration procedures cause a more or less coarse precipitation of cell material in fine strands of relatively high refractive index. Mounting media transparent to the UV cannot readily provide a good refractive index match.

Freeze-drying has been recommended as the most generally useful means of dealing with these problems (Caspersson, 1950). Freeze-substitution, since it allows more convenient processing of specimens, seems to have been more frequently applied. Where the constituent under study remains soluble after dehydration, some form of chemical postfixation is usually employed. Techniques of freeze-drying and freeze-substitution have been described in detail by many authors; Pearse (1960) and Barka and Anderson (1963) have provided valuable summaries of the procedures used. The latter authors have included an account of postfixation by including chemical fixatives in the freeze-substitution solvent. Lanthanum salts, since they form highly insoluble compounds with nucleic acids, have been added to fixatives and mounting media (Caspersson, 1936; Rudkin et al., 1955). Such chemical precipitants, however, may cause difficulty if nucleases are to be used for extraction (see Swift, 1966).

Adequate techniques of fixation need not be complex. Zetterberg, Killander and their co-workers at the Karolinska Institutet have used UV and visible microspectrophotometry to study DNA, RNA, protein and dry mass relations in cultured cells during the cell cycle. All these studies were done using ethanol freezing-substitution followed by mounting in glycerin (Killander and Zetterberg, 1965) or in later work by chemical fixation in ethanol–acetone (1:1) at 4°C for 24 hours followed by glycerin (Zetterberg, 1966).

B. Extraction

It should be possible to combine UV cytospectrophotometry with methods of selective extraction, so as to obtain a "blank" to correct for light scatter and other forms of nonspecific light loss. However, this procedure encounters difficulties if the extraction itself changes the scatter or absorbance properties of the cell. This appears to be the case when trichloroacetic acid is used, as in the Schneider method, to remove nucleic acids completely (see discussion in Swift, 1966). Nucleases can be employed successfully (Rudkin and Corlette, 1957a); precautions in their use in RNA cytochemistry have been discussed by Swift (1966).

Irradiation consequent to UV microscopy in apparatus using an intense source (e.g., rotating metallic arc) can alter the physical state of the cell material so as to interfere with enzyme action. For example, Pigon and Edström (1959) reported that exposure to the beam of the Köhler microscope to the extent necessary for focusing and photography renders DNA highly resistant to subsequent extraction by DNase. This effect has also been observed by Rudkin (1961).

C. MOUNTING MEDIA

The accuracy of microspectrophotometric measurements in the UV depends strongly on the degree to which nonspecific light losses can be minimized, since adequate techniques to correct for this factor cannot easily be designed. The requirements for a mounting medium to be used in the study of fixed cells have been investigated as long as UV microscopy has been in use, but it remains true that the matching of specimen refractive index is more difficult to achieve in this spectral region than in work in the visible. The most commonly used mounting medium is pure glycerin. This has the advantages of nearly matching the refractive index of quartz and of being highly transparent in the UV. Since pure glycerin is somewhat hygroscopic, it should be noted that the use of a defined glycerin–water mixture is advocated by the Zeiss company: a suitable mixture which equilibrates with the moisture content of normal room air is supplied with immersion Ultrafluars. Glycerin has the further advantage that it tends to permeate fixed cytological specimens, causing a slight swelling. As a result, sharp gradients of refractive index difference tend to become less steep, and the effects of scatter are thereby somewhat reduced (Caspersson, 1950). However, the refractive index of glycerin is much lower than that of nucleoprotein-containing structures (for example, chromosomes); a number of workers have attempted to increase the refractive index of the glycerin to obtain a better match. Rudkin and Corlette (1957b) investigated the refractive index matching of salivary gland chromosomes of *Drosophila*, using a low-power darkfield UV microscope. They employed an annular diaphragm in a high aperture condenser: the image of a specimen observed with a quartz objective of long focal length (6 mm) consists of light scattered from the preparation. This apparatus was used to investigate the effects on scatter of a series of mounting media made by dissolving in glycerin chloral hydrate or zinc chloride. They concluded that the refractive index of a solution of 45% zinc chloride in glycerin was considerably closer to the refractive index of the absorbing material of chromosomes than was the case with glycerin alone. From observations of the Becke line at low condenser apertures they concluded that the index of this solution was slightly lower than the index of the chromosome bands.

Paraffin oil has also been used as a mounting medium for UV work. While it is transparent to UV in the more highly purified grades, it does not swell the fibers of the specimen so that scatter remains high. It can, however, serve as a possible alternative to glycerin in studies with material that might be extracted by glycerin or glycerin–water mixtures.

D. DISTRIBUTIONAL ERRORS

The extent of the distributional errors in UV microspectrophotometry may be controlled to some extent through the choice of appropriate methods of specimen preparation. Errors of this kind must be dealt with in a primary sense in the design of the instrument used. But appropriately prepared specimens can considerably lessen dependence on the perfection of scanning and associated procedures. Improperly prepared specimens may present inhomogeneities of such magnitude as to introduce serious cumulative errors even when complete scanning equipment is used.

Absorbing material lying out of the focal plane of the objective absorbs energy that is distributed over a wide area in the image plane and thus is not correctly referred to the corresponding area in the object. It is, therefore, important with scanning microspectrophotometers to assure that the specimen has a thickness approaching the focal depth of the objective; this requirement is particularly severe due to the small depth of field of UV objectives of high aperture. For this reason air-dried smears or squashes of cells are most appropriate for quantitative work. The use of a UV crushing condenser has been proposed (Davies, 1954) and would offer advantages similar to those it gives in the evaluation of Feulgen-stained nuclei. Thin microtome sections avoid the problem of out-of-focus material but are a source of another kind of error if it is necessary to employ the section thickness in calculating the amount of absorbing material. It is difficult to measure original section thickness with sufficient accuracy for quantitative work.

Lateral inhomogeneities in the distribution of absorbing material are primarily a function of the fixative used. Such inhomogeneities may be considerably reduced by employing living cells where this is feasible or through the use of fixatives like formalin or freezing-dehydration which avoid the production of a coarse precipitation pattern. The choice of glycerin as mounting medium as noted above leads to a softening of absorption edges and consequently reduces errors in scanning microphotometry.

E. ULTRAVIOLET RADIATION EFFECTS ON THE SPECIMEN

Absorption of UV can cause partial breakdown of molecular structures and consequent decrease in the measured absorbance of a cytological specimen. Edström (1964) has noted the selective breakdown of cytidylic acid in the UV microscopy of microelectrophoretic preparations, with consequent loss of absorbancy at 257 mμ. Rudkin and his co-workers (unpublished observations) found that 10 min of continuous exposure to 257 mμ radiation in the Köhler microscope was required to decrease the absorbancy of acid-fixed chromosomes by 10%. In work of this kind it may not be easy to establish the absorbancy at the zero time of irradiation; it is therefore desirable to standardize the radiation dose used in microspectrophotometric measurements. The data referred to above were obtained with the Köhler illuminator, a particularly intense source; with weaker sources the problem can be expected to be less severe. Extended scanning procedures, however, may involve large total doses to a given specimen. Radiation-induced losses should in any case be tested for in work with a given kind of cytological preparation and a given measuring instrument.

Radiation effects in the case of work with living cells are naturally more severe and are separately discussed below.

F. Calibration Procedures: Internal Standards

In contrast to conventional chemical procedures, cytophotometric studies do not readily permit the standardization of the measuring procedure with known amounts of a test compound. However, the use of certain cytological objects of fairly well characterized absorbance properties can partially fill this need and provide a check on the proper operation of a microspectrophotometric instrument.

Isolated nuclei from the livers of adult rodents occur in polyploid classes which serve as a simple standard system (Freed and Engle, in press). A citric acid procedure is used, the washed nuclei being dried on a quartz slide and extracted with ribonuclease and cold perchloric acid to remove interfering RNA. A population of such nuclei should yield a frequency distribution demonstrating the familiar DNA classes. Published values of DNA per chromosome set for the species used allow a confirmation of the accuracy of the microspectrophotometric procedure when it is desirable to determine absolute amounts of nucleic acid. For comparative measurements the geometrical relations between ploidy classes and the dispersion of the individual ploidy groups serve as measures of the precision of the technique.

Mature sperm heads contain uniform haploid amounts of DNA, uninfluenced by premitotic synthesis, and are free of interfering RNA (Walker, 1957). The precision and linearity of scanning systems can be established by measuring photometric fields containing varying, known numbers of sperm heads. Accuracy can be estimated by comparison of observed values with biochemically determined amounts (Walker, 1957; Leuchtenberger et al., 1952; Walker and Yates, 1952). If whole sperm are used, attention must be given to the matching of refractive index by the mounting medium: scatter by sperm tails may contribute significantly to nonspecific light loss.

Nonbiological model systems may be useful in evaluating the measurement performance of a microspectrophotometer. Walker *et al.* (1963) made measurements of droplets of a UV-absorbing solution. The absorbance at the middle of a spherical droplet should be linearly related to droplet diameter, measured by a micrometer eye piece. They dissolved naphthalene in ethylene dichloride, and dispersed this solution in a glycerol-water mixture of matching density, with the addition of detergent to stablize the emulsion. They found that a satisfactory agreement with linearity could be demonstrated with their instrument, to a limit set by the difficulty of making accurate measurements of sphere diameter. Such droplet model systems should also be useful for tests of scanning-integration performance, but for this use the index of refraction and dispersion of the continuous and discontinuous phases would have to be carefully matched to avoid nonabsorptive light losses at the droplet edges.

VII. Study of Living Cells by Rapid Scanning

Since the absorbance of nucleic acid bases and of the aromatic amino acids can be observed without subjecting the cell to cytochemical reactions, it should, in theory, be possible to make sequential quantitative analyses of individual living cells.

The low scatter and relatively homogeneous distribution of absorbing material of unfixed cells (Davies, 1954; King and Roe, 1958) offer further advantages for microspectrophotometry. However, the extreme sensitivity of live cells to UV radiation at absorbed wavelengths sets severe limits to this approach (King and Roe, 1954; Walker and Davies, 1950). The motility of cultured cells during measurement is a further obstacle.

The photographic method has been employed for a number of UV studies of living cells. If precautions are taken to use a miniature film format, the radiation dose delivered in formation of the image is reduced. (Dose is inversely related to the square of the final magnification.) Davies, Walker, and their co-workers carried out a number of investigations of cultured cells, using the R. and J. Beck UV microscope with 35-mm camera; the primary objective image was recorded photographically (Walker and Davies, 1950; Davies, 1950; Walker and Yates, 1952). They reached the conclusion that the irradiation required to produce even a single picture with useful signal-to-noise ratio caused eventual damage artifacts. However, up to twelve images could be recorded in rapid succession, so that absorbance spectra could be constructed or integrated absorbance could be calculated. Similarly, the Polaroid color-translating UV microscope has been employed as a sensitive photographic microscope to study the distribution of Nissl substance in living cultured neurons (Deitch and Moses, 1957). Sequential studies of apparently uninjured cells were reported by Wyckoff (Wyckoff et al., 1932; Wyckoff, 1934), who also used a miniature film format.

Since the quantum efficiency of a photoelectric detector may be made much greater than that of a photographic emulsion, it was appreciated early that photoelectric recording should be more useful for work with living cells (Davies, 1950). However, the dose delivered in focusing, and the general inconvenience of early direct-recording cytospectrophotometers remained severe obstacles; the introduction of UV television methods, which provide automatic line-by-line scanning, have renewed interest in this approach (Flory, 1951). In recent years, television UV microscopes of several varieties have been described and applied to qualitative and quantitative studies of living cells. While the individual instruments used in television work are inherently complex, at least a brief discussion is required in a chapter on UV cytospectrophotometry, to outline their possibilities and limitations.

A. TELEVISION EQUIPMENT

A conventional UV microscope may be employed to produce an image that is recorded by a television camera tube sensitive to UV radiation. Vidicon tubes require the simplest associated equipment. However, the photoconductive detector employed in the vidicon is inherently nonlinear in its response to radiation and thus introduces complexity in the camera-associated electronics if quantitative measurements are to be made. Systems that have been developed to overcome these problems have been described (Williams, 1957); images of quality approaching those obtained with photographic microscopes have been demonstrated (Williams and Neuhauser, 1962).

The more complex camera tubes of the orthicon type employ inherently linear photoemissive detector surfaces and may be operated under conditions that should provide a video signal directly proportional to intensity in the specimen (Ramberg, 1958; Zworykin and Morton, 1954; Zworykin and Hatke, 1957). The intensifier-orthicon, which employs an image converter stage as input to the camera tube, has been employed in fluorescent studies where extremely low light levels must be dealt with (Loeser and West, 1962).

An alternate approach to the formation of the television image is through the flying-spot scanner technique (see Zworykin and Morton, 1954). The flying-spot microscope, originally proposed by Young and Roberts (1951), was applied to the UV by Montgomery and his co-workers (Montgomery et al., 1956a; Montgomery and Bonner, 1959;

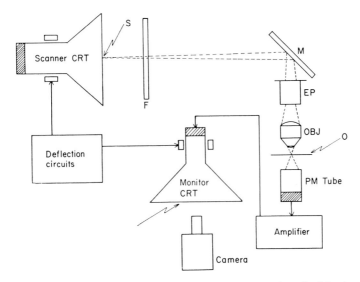

FIG. 23. Operating principle of a flying-spot microscope, as described in the text.

Montgomery, 1962). In the flying-spot system (outlined in Fig. 23) a cathode-ray tube (*CRT*), emitting UV radiation from a special phosphor through a quartz face plate, is imaged onto the specimen by a UV microscope operated in reverse. Thus, a reduced image of the raster appearing on the face of the cathode-ray tube is superimposed on the specimen (*O*). A photomultiplier tube serves as the detector and records the time-varying changes in transmission as successive lines across the specimen are scanned. By using this video signal to modulate the beam in a television picture tube deflected in synchrony with the scanner tube, a translated image of the cell is produced (*I*).

The relative merits of the camera tube and flying-spot approaches to low dose UV microscopy have been considered by several authors (Ramberg, 1958; Freed and Engle, 1962, 1963). If the losses of radiation imposed by the microscope are considered, flying-spot systems enjoy a considerable advantage for work with living specimens. Losses incurred in the microscope are imposed on radiation before it traverses the specimen. Radiation actually transmitted by the cell may be transferred to the detector with high efficiency.

Considering the large number of parameters that enter into a comparison of the differing types of television microscopes in regard to quantitative work, few direct comparisons have been made. The precision with which absorbance information can be determined and the consequent radiation damage to the cell are both dependent on the dose delivered.

Use of some standard biological test objects and a standard signal-to-noise ratio could permit adequate comparison of the sensitivity of the differing television methods. However, such comparisons have not been made.

Spectral selectivity adequate for spectrophotometric work may readily be achieved with camera tube systems but is severely limited, in the cathode-ray tube flying-spot microscope, by the properties of the phosphor used. In the cathode-ray tube system, the introduction of a device to limit spectral bandwidth (monochromator or interference filter) results in ratios of signal-to-noise too low for quantitative work. Integration methods to improve signal-to-noise ratio by summing a number of scans have been employed (Montgomery et al., 1956b), but are difficult to incorporate in quantitative scanning systems. As noted above, logarithmic transformation of a signal containing a large noise component may lead to systematic error.

The author and his colleagues have sought to avoid the difficulties inherent in the UV flying-spot scanner tube by use of a microscope operating with a mechanically generated television raster. In the vibrating-mirror flying-spot microscope (Freed and Engle, 1962, 1963), a conventional source of monochromatic UV radiation is employed together with a microscope used in the reverse direction, as shown in Fig. 24. A movable mirror, placed between source and eyepiece, displaces the reduced image of the source in the specimen plane so that a raster of parallel lines is produced. The photomultiplier, placed immediately after the specimen, generates a signal proportional to the line-by-line transmission changes in the cell. This signal is fed to appropriate analog circuits which calculate absorbancy in the photometric field, or the signal may be fed to a synchronously deflected television picture tube to produce an image for focusing and adjustments of the field. A similar instrument, described by Berndt et al. (1963), has been constructed in Sandritter's laboratory at Giessen.

The vibrating-mirror flying-spot microscope in this laboratory has recently been provided with a template-controlled integrator, operating with reference to a masked image on an auxiliary television monitor to allow calculation of absorbancy of irregularly shaped or contiguous areas. An automatic precision stage movement similar in principle to that described by Caspersson has been constructed to allow initial setting-up of the measuring circuits on a clear space in the specimen (Engle and Freed, 1968).

No extensive quantitative studies of UV absorbance changes in individual living cells have been reported as yet with any of the television techniques. However, studies of the increase in absorbancy in whole cultured cells have been carried out with the vibrating-mirror flying-spot

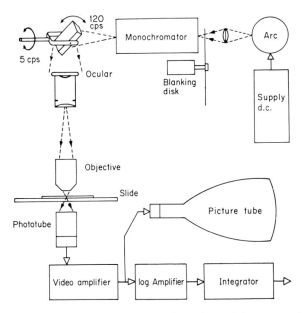

FIG. 24. Operating principle of the vibrating-mirror flying-spot microscope, as described in the text.

microscope (Freed and Benner, 1964). The data suggest that measured cells double in absorbancy in essentially linear fashion, in a time consistent with the mean cell generation time determined by cell counting in parallel cultures. The radiation doses employed have thus presumably been held to a level below that which delays the synthesis of nucleoprotein materials.

The precision with which measurements at 260 mμ may be carried out is limited to the 10–20% range by the sensitivity of the cells (Freed and Benner, 1964; Freed and Engle, in press). Direct lethal effects on the cells are produced more readily by wavelengths absorbed strongly by protein than by nucleic acid, implicating damage to a cytoplasmic system responsible for the integrity of the cell via maintenance of the intact cell membrane (Freed et al., 1959; King and Roe, 1954).

B. Cell Culture Methods for Ultraviolet Microscopy of Living Cells

Extended examination of live cells in the UV requires a means of maintaining the cells in normal condition under the optical conditions for high-resolution microscopy. The growth media normally employed contain substantial concentrations of protein and amino acids. As a result, the medium may absorb a substantial fraction of the incident energy, resulting in low signal-to-noise ratios.

If cells are grown in perfusion chambers provided with quartz coverslip windows, periodic replacement of complete medium by a simple UV-transparent salt solution may be employed during the period of photometric measurements (Freed and Benner, 1964). However, growing cells normally condition the medium, and it has been found in this laboratory that the growth of repeatedly perfused cells is eventually inhibited, even if the original medium is used to replace the salt solution.

Petriconi (1964) has employed extremely thin perfusion chambers (100 μ separation of coverslips) with continuous perfusion of medium. A rocking pair of reservoirs provide a periodically reversing flow of medium, so that the cells are brought into contact with a volume of medium larger than that contained by the chamber itself. In this way he avoids the exhaustion of the small quantity of medium that would otherwise be available. Since a fixed volume of medium is utilized repeatedly, the normal conditioning by the cells can take place.

In the work of this laboratory a perfusion chamber with 3–4 mm path length is used (Sykes and Moore, 1960; Freed, 1963), together with a special culture medium nearly transparent to UV (Freed and Engle, in press). Eagle's (1959) growth medium is modified by reducing the concentrations of all amino acids except glutamine by one-half and omitting serum; vitamin concentrations are normal. Cells of established lines may be propagated in this medium provided that serum is present at 5–10% when the cells are inoculated. After attachment, the cells may be washed to remove the serum and cultured in the UV-transparent medium during microscopy.

The absorbancy at 260 mμ of the serum-free medium is almost doubled in the first 24 hours in the presence of cells. The absorption spectrum of the added material resembles that of the original medium, suggesting that the increase occurs as the result of cellular synthesis and leakage of amino acids or proteins. The conditioned medium remains sufficiently transparent to permit useful signal-to-noise ratios. Continuous growth of the cells is maintained at a rate lower than that obtained in normal medium supplemented with serum, but adequate for kinetic studies.

C. Radiation Damage Artifacts

The effects of UV radiation produced by the small doses involved in television microscopy are recognized by changes in characteristic cell shape and motility (Freed et al., 1959; Freed and Engle, 1963). Pinocytosis is inhibited by small doses and ability of the cell to maintain an extended configuration on the growth surface is impaired as the dose is increased.

With sufficiently large doses, the cells become round and exhibit instability of the cell membrane (zeosis or blebbing) similar to that seen just after mitotic division. The latter effect may be followed by lysis of the cell with clumping of cytoplasmic material about the altered nucleus.

The rate of increase of UV absorbancy is depressed in cells exposed to excessive doses of UV radiation (Freed and Benner, 1964). Decreases in UV absorbancy are associated with morphologically obvious changes in cell behavior. Exposure to wavelengths below 250 mμ has been found to be particularly damaging (Freed et al., 1959; King and Roe, 1954).

D. FUTURE DEVELOPMENTS

In time-lapse cytophotometry of living cells with television systems, the signal-to-noise ratio which may be attained is limited by the sensitivity of the cell to radiation. As a result, the precision of measurement is inherently limited, and future applications may be confined to studies of rapid changes in individual cells or to comparisons between the fixed and living condition. However, if fixed cells are used as objects, higher radiation intensities are usable and the resolving power of the system may be increased to a limit set only by the fundamental limits on scanning of the optics themselves. Television systems used in this way are capable of rapid processing of large amounts of absorbance information from complex cytological objects.

Increased ease and precision in handling extensive absorbance data can be attained by conversion of the analog absorbance signal to digital form for subsequent computer processing. Medelsohn and his co-workers, using CYDAC (Bostrom and Holcomb, 1963), have explored this area in connection with an attempt at automated analysis of human karyotypes (see Mendelsohn et al., 1966). Using stained metaphase preparations, and a visible light flying-spot microscope, data are recorded from a series of 0.5 μ spots in a 200×200 array, absorbance being recorded at one of 256 levels with a precision of about 1%. Resolution of human chromosome groups in terms of integrated absorbance by the dye was found to agree with UV data obtained by photographic scanning cytophotometry reported by Rudkin et al. (1964). Analysis of cell images by computer techniques is likely to increase in importance as computers become more readily available. The facility that they offer in handling complex data may allow work with materials, such as individual mammalian chromosomes, which it is now too laborious to carry out with conventional cytospectrophotometry on the scale required (Carlson et al., 1963).

As an alternative to scanning procedures for studying large numbers of cells, Kamentsky et al. (1965) have proposed the use of a rapid cell spectrophotometer to evaluate the optical properties of large numbers of suspended cells as they pass through a flow chamber. The field of view of a Zeiss Ultrafluar objective is uniformly illuminated with UV from a low-pressure mercury arc, and dichroic mirrors and filters are used to divide the transmitted radiation at 254 mμ and 410 mμ to two separate photomultipliers. As a cell passes through the field, the intensity at 254 mμ is reduced, giving rise to a pulse whose magnitude is a measure of nucleic acid content. A simultaneous pulse at 410 mμ depends on the scatter properties of the cell, and is used as an estimate of cell size. The two pulses are fed to the horizontal and vertical amplifiers of an oscilloscope, to display a point whose coordinates are determined by the nucleic acid content per unit volume of the cell. Small numbers of aberrant cells can be recognized in the presence of very large numbers of normal cells. A fluid-flow system has been developed to allow separation and collection of optically aberrant cells for further examination (Kamentsky and Melamed, 1967). The instrument is also intended for studies of cells stained with fluorescent and ordinary dyes, and for multiple wavelength studies in which distributional error may be measured as an index of dye distribution and thus of morphological character of the cell (Kamentsky and Melamed, in press). While this approach sacrifices resolution at the intracellular level, it offers an attractive means of dealing with large cell populations.

VIII. Ultramicrochemical Spectrophotometry

As a way of avoiding the problems of photometry of cellular constituents *in situ*, it is possible, as Edström has shown, to perform chemical manipulations on a cytological scale using a micromanipulator. A given substance can thus be quantitatively extracted from the cytological specimen, and determined by spectrophotometry of the small volume of extract. This procedure requires the use of a microscope as the spectrophotometric instrument, and is here considered from that point of view. The micromanipulative extraction procedures for nucleic acids have been given in detail by Edström (1964).

A. Existing Techniques

Samples of tissue are prepared as sections or as squashes, so that the material is deposited on a coverslip in microscopically accessible form. The micromanipulator is used to isolate the desired structure; similar entities may be pooled to provide samples of sufficient size. For example, Edström and Beermann (1962) pooled from 30 to 80 defined segments of chromosomes from *Chironomus* salivary glands to determine the differences in RNA base composition in separated chromosome regions.

The quantity of extracted RNA may be determined in amounts as low as 25 $\mu\mu$g. Successive extractions of the sample with ribonuclease are carried out, and the extract is deposited as a microdrop on a quartz slide. After drying, the material is redissolved in buffer which contains glycerol. Round, lens-shaped drops of regular outline are formed, and UV microphotometry is used to determine the amount of RNA recovered. The DNA content of a sample is determined similarly, after extraction with deoxyribonuclease. A rapid method for calculating the total amount of absorbing substance in such microdrops has recently been described by Slagel and Edström (1967).

Samples of nucleic acid may be hydrolyzed to yield the mixture of constituent bases for electrophoretic separation. Edström (1964) gives details for carrying out separations of bases from RNA; a similar procedure has been used to determine the ratio of adenine to guanine in isolated segments of dipteran giant chromosomes (Edström and Beermann, 1962). The extract is applied to a fiber of treated cellulose having a diameter of 25–30 μ. After application of an electric current through the fiber, the bases are resolved as separated UV-absorbing bands. A UV photomicrograph of the preparation is analyzed by scanning densitometry to determine the relative amounts of material in each band.

Related methods have been designed for the estimation of soluble nucleotides from preparations on the cytological scale (Brattgard et al., 1966).

B. MICROPHOTOMETRIC APPARATUS

Photographic microspectrophotometry has been employed in published studies with Edström's techniques, using either the Köhler microscope with metallic arc illuminator (Edström, 1964) or a xenon arc and monochromator (Koenig, 1965). Since the preparations are examined with low power objectives, and are mounted without a coverslip, the microscope system need not be as complex as that used in direct cytospectrophotometric work (see, for example, Fig. 25). The Ultrafluar objective 10×, N.A. 0.20, which has recently been added to the Zeiss lens series, should prove particularly convenient to use, since it can be brought close to focus in visible light. Reflecting objectives of existing designs may not be readily used. For example, the author has found the adequately corrected field of the Polaroid-Grey 53× objective too small for photographing an entire microelectrophoretic separation. Further, lack of a coverslip introduces an unacceptable degradation of image quality.

At the low power used in this work, the traditional fluorescent eyepiece, or Köhler *Sucher*, serves as an adequate focusing device. Final adjustment of focus may be checked by providing the photomicrographic camera with a focusing screen of Willemite, deposited on a clear focusing glass of

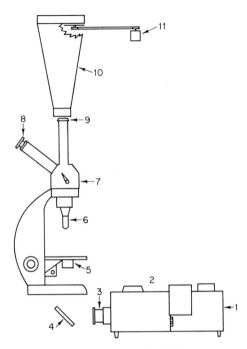

Fɪɢ. 25. Simplified UV microscope for use in the Edström technique. The following components are employed: 1, Bausch and Lomb Xenon Arc Source; 2, Bausch and Lomb high intensity monochromator with UV grating; 3, Bausch and Lomb achromatic condensing lens; 4, First surface mirror; 5, Vickers (Cooke) quartz condensing lens; 6, Vickers (Cooke) 2537 Å 16 mm monochromat *or* Zeiss 10× Ultrafluar; 7, Vickers M-15 stand with trip-reflector and single objective holder; 8, Vickers (Cooke) fluorescent eyepiece with focus-adjusting collar; 9, Vickers (Cooke) 10× quartz eyepiece; 10, 4 × 5 inch view camera on copying stand (Burke and James Orbitar); 11, compensated sector, belt-driven from tape recorder capstan motor. In addition to the usual ground glass, the camera is provided with a clear focusing glass, on the lower surface of which a phosphor screen (Willemite) is deposited. Final adjustment of focus is made using this screen. Magnification of system: 100×.

the type normally supplied with plate cameras. In an instrument illuminated by a xenon arc and monochromator (Fig. 25), the author has found that such a screen may be used at 265 mμ and 100× total magnification after a few minutes of dark adaptation.

When microelectrophoretic separations are to be photographed, any necessity for dark adaptation on the part of the analyst is a nuisance. Diffusion of the separated bands is rapid, and the UV micrographs should be completed without delay. The additional intensity available from an image converter tube may make it desirable to incorporate such a device.

If the Edström techniques, or similar methods, are to be employed in a laboratory not equipped with a good recording densitometer, consideration should be given to a direct scanning method. A precision densitometer, reading directly in plate density, may be considerably more costly than the UV microscope itself. The Zeiss UMSP in its standard form can cover a distance only 100 μ, which may be rather too small for the samples encountered in extraction work. Further, the predictable geometry of microchemical samples allows good estimates from single scans (Slagel and Edström, 1967). Thus it should be possible to couple a simple scanning stage to the chart-drive of an absorbance-recording photometer (e.g., that manufactured by the Gilford Instrument Co.) to provide a useful analytical instrument.

C. FUTURE DEVELOPMENTS

A number of the analytical techniques used in current histochemical work appear to be capable of adaptation to ultramicrochemistry. Electrophoresis in acrylamide gels separates RNA's of differing molecular size (e.g., Loening, 1967); scaling down of this technique may allow study of the various molecular species of RNA from cytological samples. Density gradient centrifugation on the requisite small scale might be possible, although maintaining the gradient over the short distances required is likely to prove a serious obstacle. Edström and Daneholt (1967) have circumvented this by applying isotopically labeled extracts from small-scale samples to conventional density gradient tubes in the presence of unlabeled carrier RNA.

Other analytical methods can be based on the formation of absorbing products of specific reactions. Enzyme determinations using chromogenic substrates could in this way be carried out on single cells. Ornstein and Lehrer (1960) have proposed a "shrinking droplet" procedure to increase the sensitivity of such methods by reducing the volume of the reaction mixture to the extent necessary to produce measureable absorbance.

GENERAL REFERENCES

Reviews and Symposia on UV Cytospectrophotometry

1950 "Cell Growth and Cell Function," by T. O. Caspersson. Norton, New York.
1950 Optical Methods of Investigating Cell Structure. *Discussions Faraday Soc.* **9.**
1952 Conference on Microspectrophotometry of Cells. *Lab. Invest.* **1.**
1953 Ultraviolet microscopy and ultraviolet microspectroscopy, by E. R. Blout. *Advan. Biol. Med. Phys.* **3.**
1953 Microspectrometry of Living and Fixed Cells, by H. G. Davies and P. M. B. Walker. *In* Progress in Biophysics, Vol. 3, Academic Press, New York.
1956 Ultraviolet absorption techniques, by P. M. B. Walker. *Phys. Tech. Biol. Res.* **3.**

1957   Cytochemical Methods with Quantitative Aims. *Exptl. Cell Res. Suppl.* **4.**
1958   Ultraviolet microspectrophotometry, by P. M. B. Walker. *Gen. Cytochem. Methods* **1.**
1960   Physikalisch-optische Methoden in der Histochemie. *Acta Histochem.* **9.**
1962   Scanning Techniques in Biology and Medicine. *Ann. N.Y. Acad. Sci.* **97,** Art. 2.
1965   Methoden und Ergebnisse der Zytophotometrie und Interferenzmikroskopie. *Acta Histochem. Suppl.* **6.**
1966   "Introduction to Quantitative Cytochemistry." Academic Press, New York.

REFERENCES

Bäckstrom, H. L. J. (1940). *Acta Radiol.* **21,** 327.
Bahr, G. F. (1966). *In* "Introduction to Quantitative Cytochemistry" (G. L. Wied, ed.), pp. 137–152. Academic Press, New York.
Barer, R., Holiday, E. R., and Jope, E. M. (1950). *Biochim. Biophys. Acta* **6,** 123.
Barka, T., and Anderson, P. J. (1963). "Histochemistry." Harper & Row, New York.
Berndt, R., Sandritter, W., Rappay, G., and Kiefer, G. (1963). *Acta Histochem. Suppl.* **6,** 85.
Blaisse, B. S., Bouwers, A., and Bulthuis, H. W. (1952). *Appl. Sci. Res.* **B2,** 453.
Blout, E. R. (1953). *Advan. Biol. Med. Phys.* **3,** 285.
Blout, E. R., Bird, G. R., and Grey, D. S. (1950). *J. Opt. Soc. Am.* **40,** 304.
Bostrom, R. C., and Holcomb, W. G. (1963). *IEEE (Inst. Elec. Electron. Engrs.), Intern. Convention Record* **9,** 110.
Brachet, J. (1940). *Compt. Rend. Soc. Biol.* **133,** 88.
Brachet, J. (1944). "Embryologie Chimique." Masson, Paris.
Brattgard, S. O., Lovtrup-Rein, H., and Moss, M. L. (1966). *J. Neurochem.* **13,** 1257.
Burch, C. R. (1947). *Proc. Phys. Soc. (London)* **59,** 41, 47.
Carlson, L. (1957). *Exptl. Cell Res. Suppl.* **4,** 193.
Carlson, L., Caspersson, T., Foley, G. E., Kudynowski, J., Lomakka, G., Simonsson, E., and Soren, L. (1963). *Exptl. Cell Res.* **31,** 589.
Caspersson, T. (1936). *Skand. Arch. Physiol. Suppl.* **8,** 73.
Caspersson, T. (1940). *Chromosoma* **1,** 562, 605.
Caspersson, T. (1950). "Cell Growth and Cell Function," Norton, New York.
Caspersson, T. (1955). *Experientia* **11,** 45.
Caspersson, T. (1965). *Acta Histochem. Suppl.* **6,** 21.
Caspersson, T., Schultz, J., and Aquilonius, L. (1940). *Proc. Natl. Acad. Sci. U.S.* **26,** 515.
Caspersson, T., Jacobsson, F., and Lomakka, G. (1951). *Exptl. Cell Res.* **2,** 310.
Caspersson, T., Jacobsson, F., Lomakka, G., Svenson, G., and Säfström, R. (1953). *Exptl. Cell Res.* **5,** 560.
Caspersson, T., Lomakka, G., and Svensson, G. (1957). *Exptl. Cell Res. Suppl.* **4,** 9.
Chamberlain, P. J., and Walker, P. M. B. (1965a). *Acta Histochem. Suppl.* **6,** 55.
Chamberlain, P. J., and Walker, P. M. B. (1965b). *J. Mol. Biol.* **11,** 1.
Chance, B., Perry, R., Åkerman, L., and Thorell, B. (1959). *Rev. Sci. Instr.* **30,** 735.
Chayen, J. (1953). *Intern. Rev. Cytol.* **2,** 77.
Davies, H. G. (1950). *Discussions Faraday Soc.* **9,** 442.
Davies, H. G. (1954). *Quart. J. Microscop. Sci.* **95,** 433.
Davies, H. G., and Walker, P. M. B. (1953). *Progr. Biophys. Biophys. Chem.* **3,** 195.
Deeley, E. M. (1955). *J. Sci. Instr.* **32,** 263.
Deitch, A. D., and Moses, M. J. (1957). *J. Biophys. Biochem. Cytol.* **3,** 449.

Eagle, H. (1959). *Science* **130**, 432.
Edström, J.-E. (1964). *In* "Methods in Cell Physiology" (D. M. Prescott, ed.), pp. 417–447. Academic Press, New York.
Edström, J.-E., and Beermann, W. (1962). *J. Cell Biol.* **14**, 371.
Edström, J.-E., and Daneholt, B. (1967). *J. Mol. Biol.* **28**, 331.
Engle, J. L. (1962). *Rev. Sci. Instr.* **33**, 123.
Engle, J. L., and Freed, J. J. (1968). *Rev. Sci. Instr.* **39**, 307.
Exner, G. (1959). Ph.D. Thesis, Friedrich-Schiller University, Jena.
Flory, L. E. (1951). *Cold Spring Harbor Symp. Quant. Biol.* **16**, 505.
Freed, J. J. (1963). *Science* **140**, 1334.
Freed, J. J., and Benner, J. A., Jr. (1964). *J. Roy. Microscop. Soc.* **83**, 79.
Freed, J. J., and Engle, J. L. (1962). *Ann. N.Y. Acad. Sci.* **97**, 412.
Freed, J. J., and Engle, J. L. (1963). *In* "Cinemicrography in Cell Biology" (G. G. Rose, ed.), pp. 93–121. Academic Press, New York.
Freed, J. J., and Engle, J. L. (in press). *Ann. N.Y. Acad. Sci.*
Freed, J. J., Engle, J. L., Rudkin, G. T., and Schultz, J. (1959). *J. Biophys. Biochem. Cytol.* **5**, 205.
Friedel, R. A., and Orchin, M. (1951). "Ultraviolet Spectra of Aromatic Compounds," p. 10 and Spectrum 7. Wiley, New York.
Glick, D., Engström, A., and Malmström, B. G. (1951). *Science* **114**, 253.
Grey, D. S. (1950). *J. Opt. Soc. Am.* **40**, 283.
Grey, D. S. (1952). *Lab. Invest.* **1**, 85.
Herrmann, R. (1965). *Acta Histochem. Suppl.* **6**, 189.
Jansen, M. T. (1961). *Histochemie* **2**, 342.
Kamentsky, L. A., and Melamed, M. R. (1967). *Science* **156**, 1364.
Kamentsky, L. A., and Melamed, M. R. (in press). *Ann. N.Y. Acad. Sci.*
Kamentsky, L. A., Melamed, M. R., and Derman, H. (1965). *Science* **150**, 630.
Kelly, J. W. (1962). *Science* **138**, 1272.
Kelly, J. W. (1966). *In* "Introduction to Quantitative Cytochemistry" (G. L. Wied, ed.), pp. 247–280. Academic Press, New York.
Killander, D., and Zetterberg, A. (1965). *Exptl. Cell Res.* **38**, 272.
King, R. J., and Roe, E. M. F. (1953). *J. Royal Microscop. Soc.* **73**, 82.
King, R. J., and Roe, E. M. F. (1954). *Proc. 1st Intern. Photobiol. Congr., Amsterdam* pp. 149–151.
King, R. J., and Roe, E. M. F. (1958). *J. Roy. Microscop. Soc.* **76**, 168.
Köhler, A. (1904). *Z. Wiss. Mikroskopie* **21**, 129, 275.
Koenig, E. (1965). *J. Neurochem.* **12**, 357.
Krüger, H. G. (1965). *Acta Histochem. Suppl.* **6**, 171.
Lavin, G. I., and Pollister, A. W. (1942). *Biol. Bull.* **83**, 299.
Ledley, R. S. (1964). *Science* **146**, 216.
Leuchtenberger, C., Leuchtenberger, R., Vendrely, C., and Vendrely, R. (1952). *Exptl. Cell Res.* **3**, 240.
Loening, U. E. (1967). *Biochem. J.* **102**, 251.
Loeser, C. N., and West, S. S. (1962). *Ann. N.Y. Acad. Sci.* **97**, 346.
Lomakka, G. (1955). *Exptl. Cell Res.* **9**, 434.
Lomakka, G. (1957). *Exptl. Cell Res. Suppl.* **4**, 54.
Lomakka, G. (1965). *Acta Histochem. Suppl.* **6**, 47.
Lucas, F. F. (1930). *Proc. Natl. Acad. Sci. U.S.* **16**, 599.
Lucas, F. F., and Stark, M. (1931). *J. Morphol.* **52**, 91.
Mendelsohn, M. L. (1958). *J. Biophys. Biochem. Cytol.* **4**, 425.

Mendelsohn, M. L., Kolman, W. A., and Bostrom, R. C. (1964). *Ann. N.Y. Acad. Sci.* **115**, 998.

Mendelsohn, M. L., Conway, T. J., Hungerford, D. A., Kolman, W. A., Perry, B. H., and Prewitt, J. M. S. (1966). *Cytogenetics* **5**, 223.

Merriam, R. W. (1958). *J. Histochem. Cytochem.* **6**, 43.

Moberger, B. (1954). *Acta Radiol. Scand. Suppl.* **114.**

Montgomery, P. O'B. (1962). *Ann. N.Y. Acad. Sci.* **97**, 490.

Montgomery, P. O'B., and Bonner, W. A. (1959). *IRE (Inst. Radio Engrs.), Trans. Med. Electron.* **ME6**, 186.

Montgomery, P. O'B., Roberts, F., and Bonner, W. (1956a). *Nature* **177**, 1172.

Montgomery, P. O'B., Bonner, W. A., and Roberts, F. F. (1956b). *Proc. Soc. Exptl. Biol. Med.* **93**, 409.

Naora, A. (1952). *Science* **115**, 248.

Niemi, M. (1958). *Acta Anat. Suppl.* **34.**

Norris, K. P., Seeds, W. E., and Wilkins, M. H. F. (1951). *J. Opt. Soc. Am.* **41**, 111.

Nurnberger, J. (1955). *In* "Analytical Cytology" (R. C. Mellors, ed.), 1st Ed., pp. 4/1–4/44. McGraw-Hill, New York.

Nurnberger, J., Engström, A., and Lindström, B. (1952). *J. Cellular Comp. Physiol.* **39**, 215.

Opler, A. (1950). *J. Opt. Soc. Am.* **40**, 401.

Ornstein, L., and Lehrer, G. M. (1960). *J. Histochem. Cytochem.* **8**, 311.

Payne, B. O. (1954). *J. Roy. Microscop. Soc.* **74**, 108.

Pearse, A. G. E. (1960). "Histochemistry, Theoretical and Applied," 2nd Ed. Little, Brown, Boston, Massachusetts.

Petriconi, V. (1964). *Z. Wiss. Mikroskopie* **66**, 213.

Pigon, A., and Edström, J.-E. (1959). *Exptl. Cell Res.,* **16**, 648.

Pollister, A. W., and Ornstein, L. (1959). *In* "Analytical Cytology" (R. C. Mellors, ed.), 2nd Ed., pp. 431–518. McGraw-Hill, New York.

Ramberg, E. G. (1958). *IRE (Inst. Radio Engrs.), Trans. Med. Electron.* **12**, 58.

Ruch, F. (1960). *Z. Wiss. Mikroskopie* **64**, 453.

Rudkin, G. T. (1961). *Microchem. J. Symp. Ser.* **1**, 261.

Rudkin, G. T. (1966). *In* "Introduction to Quantitative Cytochemistry" (G. L. Wied, ed.), pp. 387–407. Academic Press, New York.

Rudkin, G. T., and Corlette, S. L. (1957a). *Proc. Natl. Acad. Sci. U.S.* **43**, 964.

Rudkin, G. T., and Corlette, S. L. (1957b). *J. Biophys. Biochem. Cytol.* **3**, 821.

Rudkin, G. T., and Engle, J. L. (in press). *Ann. N.Y. Acad. Sci.*

Rudkin, G. T., Aronson, J. F., Hungerford, D. A., and Schultz, J. (1955). *Exptl. Cell Res.* **9**, 193.

Rudkin, G. T., Hungerford, D. A., and Nowell, P. C. (1964). *Science* **144**, 1229.

Sandritter, W. (1966). *In* "Introduction to Quantitative Cytochemistry" (G. L. Wied, ed.), pp. 159–182. Academic Press, New York.

Sandritter, W., and Hartleib, J. (1955). *Experientia* **11**, 313.

Schiemer, H. G. (1960). *Acta Histochem.* **9**, 131.

Slagel, D. E., and Edström, J.-E. (1967). *J. Cell Biol.* **34**, 395.

Svensson, G. (1957). *Exptl. Cell Res. Suppl.* **4**, 165.

Sweet, M. H. (1946). *Electronics* **19**, 105.

Swift, H. (1966). *In* "Introduction to Quantitative Cytochemistry" (G. L. Wied, ed.), pp. 1–39. Academic Press, New York.

Sykes, J. A., and Moore, E. B. (1960). *Texas Rept. Biol. Med.* **18**, 288.

Taylor, W. (1953). *J. Opt. Soc. Am.* **43**, 299.

Thaer, A. (1965). *Acta Histochem. Suppl.* **6,** 103.

Thiers, R. E. (1951). *J. Opt. Soc. Am.* **41,** 273.

Thorell, B. (1947). "Studies on the Formation of Cellular Substances During Blood Cell Production." Kimpton, London.

Thorell, B., and Åkerman, L. (1957). *Exptl. Cell Res. Suppl.* **4,** 83.

Trapp, L. (1960). *Acta Histochem.* **9,** 126, 158.

Trapp, L. (1965). *Acta Histochem. Suppl.* **6,** 186. (Discussion following Exner.)

Trapp, L. (1966). *In* "Introduction to Quantitative Cytochemistry" (G. L. Wied, ed.), pp. 427–435. Academic Press, New York.

Wagener, G. N., and Grand, C. G. (1963). *Rev. Sci. Instr.* **34,** 540.

Walker, P. M. B. (1955). *Exptl. Cell Res.* **8,** 567.

Walker, P. M. B. (1956). *In* "Physical Techniques in Biological Research" (G. Oster and A. W. Pollister, eds.), 1st Ed., Vol. III, pp. 401–487. Academic Press, New York.

Walker, P. M. B. (1957). *Exptl. Cell Res. Suppl.* **4,** 86.

Walker, P. M. B. (1958). *In* "General Cytochemical Methods" (J. F. Danielli, ed.), Vol. 1, pp. 164–219. Academic Press, New York.

Walker, P. M. B. (1965). *Acta Histochem. Suppl.* **6,** 346. (Discussion Figure 1.)

Walker, P. M. B., and Davies, H. G. (1950). *Discussions Faraday Soc.* **9,** 461.

Walker, P. M. B., and Deeley, E. M. (1956). *Exptl. Cell Res.* **10,** 155.

Walker, P. M. B., and Yates, H. B. (1952). *Proc. Roy. Soc. (London)* **B140,** 274.

Walker, P. M. B., Leonard, J., Gibb, D., and Chamberlain, P. J. (1963). *J. Sci. Instr.* **40,** 166.

Wilkins, M. H. F. (1950). *Discussions Faraday Soc.* **9,** 363.

Wilkins, M. H. F. (1953). *J. Roy. Microscop. Soc.* **73,** 77.

Williams, G. Z. (1957). *J. Histochem. Cytochem.* **5,** 246.

Williams, G. Z., and Neuhauser, R. G. (1962). *Ann. N.Y. Acad. Sci.* **97,** 358.

Woods, P. S., and Zubay, G. (1966). *Proc. Natl. Acad. Sci. U.S.* **54,** 1705.

Wyckoff, H. (1952). *Lab. Invest.* **1,** 115.

Wyckoff, R. W. G. (1934). *Cold Spring Harbor Symp. Quant. Biol.* **2,** 39.

Wyckoff, R. W. G., and Ebeling, A. H. (1933). *J. Morphol.* **55,** 131.

Wyckoff, R. W. G., and Ter Louw, A. L. (1931). *J. Exptl. Med.* **54,** 449.

Wyckoff, R. W. G., Ebeling, A., and Ter Louw, A. (1932). *J. Morphol.* **53,** 189.

Young, J. E. Z., and Roberts, F. (1951). *Nature* **167,** 231.

Zetterberg, A. (1966). *Exptl. Cell Res.* **42,** 500.

Zworykin, V. K., and Hatke, F. L. (1957). *Science* **126,** 805.

Zworykin, V. K., and Morton, G. A. (1954). "Television," 2nd Ed., p. 236, Wiley, New York.

CHAPTER 3

Electron Microscopy of Cells and Tissues

FRITIOF S. SJÖSTRAND

I. Introduction

One basic principle of structural organization of living systems is found in the occurrence of building elements consisting of a large number of a few species of more or less complex organic molecules arranged spatially in a regular way. Geometrically rather simple components are formed this way, such as particles, filaments, and membranes. The latter can constitute the wall of a tubule or of a small or large vesicle or form the boundary delimiting larger territories like cells or subcellular organelles. This organization at a supramolecular level leads to the establishment of some of the most basic functional properties of living systems like contractility in muscle tissue, selective permeability of the plasma membrane, coordinated catalysis through multienzyme systems, and electron transfer and energy transduction in mitochondria and chloroplasts. To reveal the particular properties of such systems as due to molecular interaction and intramolecular configurational changes represents some of the most basic biological problems today.

Subcellular differentiation and morphogenesis involves the mechanisms by which these supramolecular building blocks of the cells are formed by association of the newly synthesized constituent molecules. To analyze the factors that determine the precise arrangement and selection of the molecules and of the locus at which the supramolecular-building elements develop represent basic problems to be solved in order to develop an understanding of the evolution of life.

Modern electron microscopy allows the tackling of such problems with respect to a precise identification structurally of the supramolecular building elements, and also makes it possible to reveal certain features regarding their inner structural geometry. The identification and distinguishing between different components is based on measurements of dimensions and on the observation of structural patterns. The precision and reliability by which the identification can be made depends on the precision by which the measurements and observations of patterns have been made. Since the dimensions are in the range of dimensions of macromolecules and the differences in dimensions might range between 10 and 20 Å, it is important that the electron microscopy be pursued at a high resolution. The limit of resolution of a first-class electron microscope today is about 3 Å, and the best resolution that has been achieved on biological material is 5–10 Å (Sjöstrand, 1963, 1966). Structural analysis pursued at such a high resolution imposes completely new problems as to the preservation of the biological material in order to make full use of this resolving power. These problems have not yet been solved. They deal primarily with preservation of the conformation of protein molecules in connection with preparing biological material for electron microscopy and the retaining of the arrangement of lipid molecules.

In addition to the application of electron microscopy to the study of basic structural components of cells and tissues, which involves high resolution electron microscopy, the electron microscope is widely used as a refined light microscope on problems inherited from light microscopy. When these problems were stated, the severe technical limitations of the light microscope as an imaging tool frequently interfered. The elimination of such limitations should lead to a reconsideration of what type of problems should be attacked by means of structural analysis. The enormous mass of descriptive information which is being collected at a low resolution, with many researchers hunting for *the* species of animal that might contain some kind of structural component that has not yet been described by electron microscopists, reflects a certain incapability to define suitable biological problems. This picture collecting can be pursued at low resolution electron microscopy, which technically is by far simpler than the high resolution electron microscopy to be dealt with here. Many of the rules and instructions given in this chapter are important for high resolution microscopy but can be more or less neglected for the more common medium and low resolution work done today.

II. Physical Conditions for High Resolution Electron Microscopy of Cells and Tissues

Assuming a perfect electron microscope, the image quality of an electron micrograph depends on (1) specimen thickness, (2) contrast conditions in the specimen, and (3) contrast enhancement in the microscope owing to phase contrast.

The thickness of the specimen affects the resolution in two ways. The great depth of focus of the electron microscope has the effect that all object points at different depths in the specimen are imaged with identical sharpness. The images of all these object points are, therefore, superimposed in the image plane. This superposition effect is more critical the smaller the object details are in relation to the thickness of the specimen and the more densely they are arranged. Opaque, spherical particles with a diameter of 50 Å in a closely packed hexagonal array would not be imaged without superposition if the thickness of the section exceeds 50 Å. If a thicker specimen is analyzed, superposition can produce spurious patterns and can contribute to an apparent particle size that is different from the real particle size. Under certain conditions section staining can result in the staining of a thin layer at the surface of the section. If the contrast enhancement due to section staining exceeds greatly the contrast of the unstained parts of the section, this surface layer can dominate the contrast of the image, which then will mainly represent a thin surface layer of the section. This effect can make it possible to achieve a higher resolution than would be expected from a uniformly stained section of the same thickness.

The thickness of the specimen affects the resolution also by reducing the contrast enhancement owing to phase contrast because this effect is reduced when the proportion of scattered electrons increases at the expense of nonscattered electrons (Haine, 1961).

In practice the specimen thickness to be aimed at should not be more than 100–200 Å. That sections can be cut that are 100 Å thick, or less, was demonstrated by Sjöstrand (1953a; see discussion in Sjöstrand, 1966).

A fairly high resolution can be achieved in thicker specimens when the structural pattern extends uniformly through the entire thickness of the specimen, as in the case of membranes that are oriented parallel to the electron beam in a section. In this case the contrast is enhanced because the contrast due to electron scattering of the membrane layers at various depths of the section is added up in the image plane.

An extremely thin section appears to lack contrast as compared to a less thin section in which the cell nucleus and mitochondria stand out clearly owing to their higher opacities as compared to the surrounding cytoplasm. In very thin sections this difference is not apparent. On the other hand, the contrast of minute structural details is considerably greater in the thin section than in the thick section.

In practice, electron microscopy at a resolution considerably below 30 Å depends on contrast enhancement by means of section staining according to the technique originally described by Gibbons and Bradfield (1957). Section staining mainly results in a further enhancement of the contrast of structural components that already are stained with osmium in connection with osmium tetroxide fixation. To a lesser extent components that are unstained or weakly stained with osmium become intensely stained with the stains used for section staining. Certain differences exist in the staining of structural components by the different stains used in section staining.

When section staining with several different stains it is also obvious that the contrast enhancement mainly involves the same structural components although one particular stain can have a greater effect on one component than another.

When examining section-stained material it becomes obvious that the stain appears in small clusters consisting of the accumulated anhydrous stain (Sjöstrand, 1963). The density of these clusters, therefore, approaches that of the anhydrous stain, which in the case of uranyl nitrate is 3.7 g cm^{-3} and is close to 1 for organic material. The size of clusters of stain molecules will determine the resolution like the size of the developed photographic grain determines the resolution of a photographic emulsion. With a size of the clusters of stain molecules of about 10 Å, a resolution of 10 Å could be demonstrated (Sjöstrand, 1963). The most powerful contrast-enhancing stains contain lead, and the staining is characterized by large clusters of the stain which frequently measure 50 Å in diameter. This reduces the resolution to about 50 Å.

Phase contrast is considered necessary in order to obtain sufficient contrast to observe object details at the limit of resolution of the electron microscope. Phase contrast appears in out-of-focus pictures. The in-focus picture, ideally, is a pure representation of electron scattering by the specimen without contributions to the contrast owing to diffraction or phase contrast. The in-focus picture is therefore a low contrast picture and the limit of resolution for an in-focus picture is less than that for a slightly defocused picture owing to the unfavorable contrast conditions in the former case. Defocusing results in a drastic increase in contrast and the phase contrast and diffraction effects dominate as contrast modulating factors. With increasing defocusing the image patterns produced by these effects gradually become coarser and the limit of resolution is determined by the coarseness of phase contrast patterns. These appear as a randomly distributed granularity extending uniformly over the whole field of view whether there is a biologic specimen or only a supporting film in the field of view (Sjöstrand, 1955). For maximum resolution it is therefore necessary to examine the specimen at a minimum of defocusing to allow phase contrast to contribute to the image contrast while the granularity introduced by phase contrast does not exceed the desired resolution in dimensions.

The performance of the electron microscope should be checked regularly. An ideal test specimen that is easy to prepare is important in this connection. A very simple such specimen consists of carbon black particles that have been deposited on a freshly etched copper grid by passing the grid rapidly through the smoke from a small cluster of burning camphor crystals. Such a specimen allows excluding that the image defects are due to a contaminated or improperly prepared specimen.

Assuming that the electric stabilizing circuits of the microscope are in perfect condition, the most common image defects observed are due to astigmatism, mechanical or thermal movement and electric charging and discharging of contamination in the microscope column. The most likely sources of astigmatism are the objective aperture and contamination of the objective lens pole piece. Test pictures without objective aperture are first taken and the contribution to the image defect of the aperture determined by comparing the test pictures taken with and without aperture.

Cleaning of the objective aperture for high resolution work is a fairly tricky business. According to the author's experience, the use of molybdenum apertures that are cleaned by prolonged heating in a shadowcasting unit is most reliable. The apertures should be heated, placed on a molybdenum ribbon for up to 4 hours to white glow and close to the melting point of molybdenum.

The use of silicon grease and silicon oil should be avoided as far as possible since silica is the contaminant that is most difficult to remove.

The objective lens pole piece can be cleaned by the electron microscopist if the design of the pole piece is simple as in the RCA microscopes. The cleaning of the objective lens pole piece of the Siemens microscope should be left to the Siemens servicemen since the correct position of the parts of that type of pole piece is critical and difficult to reproduce without time-consuming trial and error. On the other hand, this type of pole piece contaminates very slowly since the critical surfaces are well protected from contamination.

All parts of the microscope column should be kept meticulously clean. A contamination of the column at any place between the specimen and the image plane can result in rhythmic movement of the image due to charging and discharging of the contamination in case the contaminating material has a low electric conductivity. The charging is due to the contamination being hit by scattered electrons. This source of image movement—image "drift"—can easily be identified by changing the conditions for charging the contamination. This is done by varying the condenser current or by moving the beam by the beam deflecting system. Such changes enhance the movement.

Mechanical drift is frequently caused by an improperly adjusted or designed specimen stage. The movement of the stage should come to a stop quickly after the stage has been moved. This source of drift can easily be identified because it has the same direction as that in which the stage is moved when the stage is moved in one or predominantly one of the two coordinates along which stage movements are made. When the direction of the movement cannot be established visually, stage movement can be tested for by making three to five exposures at 1-minute intervals of the same specimen area on the same photographic plate, without moving the plate. The first exposure can be made immediately or 30 sec after the stage has been moved by means of one of the stage movement controls. If the stage is good, all the pictures (with the possible exception of the first) should be more or less perfectly superimposed. The distance the stage moves per unit time can be estimated by measuring the distance the two pictures of consecutive exposures are separated and the tolerable drift established from the exposure times used and the resolution aimed for.

Mechanical movements due to vibrations transferred to the microscope column through the floor of the laboratory building can be tested for by placing a petri dish with mercury on the microscope table and on the floor. No vibrations should be noticeable when the mercury is placed on the microscope table. Efficient shock mounting is available to eliminate such vibrations, but it should be considered important that the microscope laboratory is not located close to any heavy machinery that can be a source of vibrations. Such machinery should be shock-mounted in any decent laboratory building or placed in a separate building.

Thermal drift can be caused by the heating of the specimen holder after it has been introduced into the column when changing specimens. The specimen holder should always be left in the microscope when the microscope is turned on and the specimen should be changed as rapidly as possible to allow the specimen holder to reach thermal equilibrium with the surroundings in the column as quickly as possible. For work close to the resolution limit, the specimen holder with the specimen should be left in the microscope column for some time before the microscope examination is started.

Thermal drift can also be caused by the heating effect of the electron beam. This applies particularly to the specimen grid and the supporting film. To correct this error, the range within which the beam can transfer heat should be kept small by the use of a double condenser. Exposure of the metal of the grid to the beam should be avoided. Single large-hole specimen grids (Sjöstrand, 1958) eliminate thermal drift greatly, due to the fact that the area exposed to the beam can be selected, located sufficiently far from the metal to secure practically symmetrical conditions for heat dissipation. Such grids are important for use in electron microscopy close to the limit of resolution of the electron microscope.

Improper contact between the supporting film and the grid bars is a common source of thermal drift. Dipping the grids in a Formvar solution before the Formvar film is put on the grid secures improved contact between grid and film.

A not uncommon cause of thermal drift is asymmetrical and too restricted contact between the specimen grid and the specimen holder. The latter should be equipped with a cap that is screwed onto the holder. The surface around the base of the specimen holder against which the grid is pressed should be flat. If films break easily, the reason is very likely improper contact between the grid and the specimen holder.

These types of drift are identified by observing the movement of the image. Improper contact between film and grid appears as a movement of the film in relation to the grid bars. Improper contact between grid and specimen holder appears as a movement of the grid bars.

The evaporation of a thin layer of carbon onto the specimens after they have been stained stabilizes the supporting film considerably.

III. The Material for High Resolution Electron Microscopy of Cells and Tissues

The preservation of the elementary structural components of cells represents a major problem in ultrastructure research. The material examined in the electron microscope must be dried and fragmented into thin specimens either by random fragmentation, homogenization, or ultrathin sectioning. The extent to which the structure should be preserved varies with the type of problem that is being studied. For a detailed analysis of the molecular structure of the elementary structural components, it would be necessary to retain the conformation of protein molecules and to prevent any phase transition to occur in places where a continuous lipid phase might be present. The problem of preservation has not yet been attacked with such structural problems in mind.[1] The

[1] Since this manuscript was delivered, this problem has been attacked and a study published by Sjöstrand and Barajas (1968). According to this study the proteins of cellular structures like membranes are denatured in connection with conventional

preservation that is achieved at the present time does not prevent structural modifications at a molecular and supramolecular level. On the other hand, the presence and arrangement in the cytoplasm of cellular membranes, of filamentous structures and of particulate components appears to be rather truthfully represented after preservation with the best fixation techniques available today, even if the internal structure of these components might have been modified. This conclusion is based on the similarity in appearance of such structural components after chemical as well as after physical fixation by means of freeze-drying. Simple dehydration without exposure of the tissues to fixatives also preserves cellular membranes with the same general arrangement as the other methods of preservation (Pease, 1966).

The preservation aims at transferring the labile living tissue cells into a stable enough state to allow dehydration, embedding, and sectioning without further structural modifications. The fixation interrupts enzymatic activities in the cells and aims at strengthening the forces that maintain the supramolecular structural organization. The fixative should act as rapidly as possible after the conditions of cell metabolism have been changed by interruption of the blood supply to the tissue. This is achieved by rapid handling of the material in cases where it must be excised from the animal, by dripping the solution of the preserving agent onto the exposed intact surface of the organ while the blood circulation to the organ is maintained normal, or by perfusion of the tissue through the blood vascular system under such conditions that the fixative is distributed in the tissue with the shortest possible interval between stoppage of normal blood circulation and perfusion.

At the present time the best results with respect to preservation are obtained with dripping the fixative onto the surface of an organ while the blood circulation is intact, and with perfusion. In the latter case, perfusion with glutaraldehyde or, in certain cases, formaldehyde is to be preferred to osmium tetroxide perfusion because the former fixatives do not produce constrictions of the blood vessels to the same extent as osmium tetroxide. The perfusion, therefore, becomes more uniform in the former cases.

The medium in which the fixative is dissolved is of importance. Particularly the osmolar concentration of the medium is critical while the overall osmolar concentration of the fixative can be varied over a fairly

---

techniques for preparing tissues for electron microscopy. The denaturation of the proteins leads to extensive modifications of the molecular structures of membranes. Exploration of the possibilities to preserve the cellular structural components without producing great changes in the native conformation of protein molecules is continued in the author's laboratory.

large range (Maunsbach, 1966b). The pH was found to be of minor importance, and the use of buffers as medium for the fixative is not necessary. Techniques for perfusion fixation of the central nervous system have been described by Pease (1962), who used formaldehyde as fixative, and by Palay et al. (1962), who used osmium tetroxide. Maunsbach (1966a,b), Karlsson and Schultz (1965, 1966), and Schultz and Karlsson (1965), analyzed systematically different factors in connection with perfusion fixation like osmolar concentration of the vehicle, total osmolarity of the fixative, ionic strength, pH, the composition of the buffer system, the lack of buffering, various fixatives with glutaraldehyde, formaldehyde and osmium tetroxide, and different concentrations of the fixatives.

When the tissue is fixed in glutaraldehyde or formaldehyde, postfixation in osmium tetroxide improves the quality of preservation and particularly the contrast.

The following solutions for tissue fixation are recommended:

The osmium tetroxide solution introduced by Sjöstrand (formula published by Zetterqvist, 1956) contains potassium chloride and calcium chloride in addition to sodium chloride with an osmolar concentration close to that of blood plasma.

1. Stock Solution A:	Sodium acetate	9.714 g
	Veronal acetate	14.714 g
	Distilled water to make	500 ml
2. Stock Solution B:	Sodium chloride	40.25 g
	Potassium chloride	2.1 g
	Calcium chloride	0.9 g
	Distilled water to make	500 ml
3. Hydrochloric acid 0.1 N		

The solutions are mixed according to the following scheme:

		Mammalian tissue	Frog tissue
Solution A		10 ml	7.4 ml
Solution B		3.4 ml	2.6 ml
0.1 N HCl	about	11 ml	8.1 ml

Distilled water is added to make 50 ml, and pH is adjusted to 7.2–7.4 by adding 0.1 N HCl.

To this mixture 0.5 g osmium tetroxide is added. The solution is stored in a brown, glass-stoppered bottle in a refrigerator.

The osmium tetroxide solution has been modified in different ways by a number of investigators. Sodium phosphate buffer instead of Veronal acetate buffer was recommended by Millonig (1962). Still another modification was proposed by Caulfield (1957). All these modifications satisfy the condition that the osmolarity of the solutions should approach that of blood serum.

Veronal acetate is not suitable as a buffer in connection with formaldehyde (Holt and Hicks, 1961), and an ordinary phosphate buffer or that described by Millonig (1962) is recommended as vehicle for formaldehyde and glutaraldehyde. For postfixation in osmium tetroxide it is recommended to use the same vehicle for this fixative as for the formaldehyde and the glutaraldehyde used as first fixative.

The Millonig fixative is prepared according to the following schedule:

Solution A	2.26% $NaH_2PO_4 \cdot H_2O$ (dibasic)
Solution B	2.52% NaOH
Solution C	5.4% glucose
Solution D	41.5 ml Solution A plus 8.5 ml Solution B.
45 ml solution D, 5 ml solution C and 0.5 g osmium tetroxide are mixed. The pH is corrected to 7.3–7.6.	

In case *formaldehyde* is selected as fixative (Pease, 1962), a solution C_{form} is prepared which consists of 40% formaldehyde and 5.4% glucose. This solution replaces solution C above and 5 ml C_{form} is mixed with 45 ml solution D. The pH is corrected to 7.3–7.6.

Glutaraldehyde introduced as a fixative by Sabatini *et al.* (1963) is a most useful fixative both in connection with cytochemical studies and as an all-around fixative, in the latter case combined with postfixation in osmium tetroxide. The concentration of glutaraldehyde can be varied over a rather wide range, 0.80–3%, although higher concentrations might introduce shrinkage. Concentrations between 1 and 2.5% are recommended, and the following solutions are given as examples. The osmolarity of the medium is of great importance; it should be isotonic to or close to isotonic to blood plasma (Karlsson and Schultz, 1965; Maunsbach, 1966b).

Glutaraldehyde solution (2.5%) for perfusion of the brain, according to Karlsson and Schultz (1965):

$NaH_2PO_4 \cdot H_2O$	3.31 g
$Na_2HPO_4 \cdot 7 H_2O$	22.77 g
H_2O	925 ml
25% commercial glutaraldehyde	100 ml
Final volume 1025 ml, pH 7.3–7.4, 782 milliosmolar.	
The osmolarity of the phosphate buffer approaches that of the cerebrospinal fluid, 320–327 mOsM.	

Glutaraldehyde solution (1%) according to Maunsbach (1966b):

$NaH_2PO_4 \cdot H_2O$	2.98 g
$Na_2HPO_4 \cdot 7\ H_2O$	30.40 g
25% commercial glutaraldehyde	40 ml
H_2O, to make	1000 ml
The tonicity of this phosphate buffer approaches that of blood serum (300 mOsM).	

Glutaraldehyde solution (1%) for perfusion fixation of kidney according to Maunsbach (1964, 1966b):

NaCl	0.6 g
KCl	0.02 g
$CaCl_2$	0.02 g
$MgCl_2$	0.01 g
$NaH_2PO_4 \cdot H_2O$	0.005 g
$NaHCO_3$	0.1 g
Glucose	0.1 g
25% commercial glutaraldehyde	40 ml
H_2O, to make	1000 ml
The medium for the glutaraldehyde is in this case a Tyrode's solution with reduced amount of NaCl.	

The commercial glutaraldehyde solutions vary considerably with respect to the presence of contaminants. Distillation of the solution might be tried to remove contaminants, although no process of purification appears to have been worked out with rigorous chemical analysis of the product.

The time of fixation should be as short as possible to prevent extraction of material from the tissue. Perfusion with glutaraldehyde and formaldehyde solutions should extend over at least 5 min and the tissue should be transferred to osmium tetroxide as soon as it has been removed from the animal and cut up into small pieces or thin slices by means of a sharp razor blade. Perfusion with osmium tetroxide solutions requires longer time of perfusion, up to 40 min (Palay *et al.*, 1962) in the case of brain tissue.

For fixation in osmium tetroxide solution the time of fixation can range between 10 min and 4 hours. At very short fixation times, only a very thin surface layer of the tissue will be fixed. These short times are recommended when the fixative is dripped onto the surface of the exposed organ in the living animal with intact blood circulation through this organ.

After fixation, a brief washing for 10–15 minutes in an isotonic salt solution such as Ringer's solution or Tyrode's solution is recommended before dehydration is started.

Freeze-drying preservation allows the analysis of structural features after a treatment of the tissue which is drastically different from fixation with chemicals. Freeze-drying involves a physical preservation by means of removal of water while the tissue is kept frozen. It was introduced in electron microscopy by Sjöstrand (1943a,b,c) and has been used to check the reliability of observations made in chemically fixed material (Sjöstrand, 1953b) with the idea that if the same structural patterns are observed after chemical as well as after freeze-drying preservation, it appears likely that the observed structures are preformed and are not artifacts produced by the fixation method. The reason for this assumption is that two so different methods of treatment would most likely affect the tissues differently as far as modification of the structure is concerned.

Freeze-drying cannot be considered a routine procedure for tissue preservation. It has still not been possible to overcome the artifacts introduced by ice crystals in connection with freezing the tissue. In order to obtain a specimen with few ice crystals within a minute region of the tissue, it is necessary to prepare a large number of specimens and find the acceptable piece of tissue by chance.

The freezing should be as rapid as possible. Small pieces of tissue, 0.1–0.2 mm thick slices, are immersed in a medium like isopentane or propane chilled to close to its melting point by means of liquid nitrogen. The dehydration is done by means of molecular distillation of the water from the frozen tissue kept at $-40°$ to $-50°C$. Any system to keep the tissue at that temperature, such as a freezer, can be used. The molecular distillation of the water is achieved by keeping the tissue under vacuum with a cold trap in the form of a cold finger reaching close to the tissue. The cold trap is chilled with liquid nitrogen. There are no advantages in using any very elaborate apparatus for the freeze-drying.

After several days of drying at a low temperature, the temperature of the specimens is gradually raised to room temperature and maintained under vacuum for several hours before the cold finger is allowed to warm up and the ice on its surface allowed to sublime under vacuum.

The embedding medium can be added while the specimens are in the vacuum chamber or the tissue can be removed from this chamber for embedding if precautions are taken to prevent the tissue from absorbing moisture from the air. The infiltration of the embedding medium must take place under vacuum.

The water can be removed from the frozen tissue by means of freeze substitution in which the frozen tissue is immersed in a medium such as acetone or methyl alcohol. The water is slowly substituted by this medium. However, the time for complete substitution must be determined, since otherwise the substituting media will act as a fixative in connection with thawing of the tissue. As Baker (1962) has shown, fixation in connection with thawing results in a complete reconstitution of the cellular structure by redistribution of the water that in the frozen state was separated as ice crystals. Most pictures published of material preserved by freeze-substitution obviously have been preserved by freeze-thawing in connection with dehydration which has mainly taken place after thawing.

Dehydration and embedding. The embedding of the tissue in a plastic is indispensable to allow the preparing of sufficiently thin sections. The embedding is a most critical step in the preparatory procedure. Considerable artifacts can be introduced during the setting of the plastic and particularly the polymerization of methacrylate mixtures was found to produce damage to the tissue structure. The introduction of epoxy resins, starting with the work of Maaløe and Birch-Andersen (1956), meant an important improvement of the embedding technique. The epoxy resin Araldite introduced by Glauert et al. (1956) was for some time the most satisfactory embedding medium. At present several other epoxy resins are used. The most satisfactory embedding medium for high resolution electron microscopy, however, is Vestopal W, which was introduced by Ryter and Kellenberger (1958).

The value of an embedding medium is determined by (1) the artifacts introduced by the medium, (2) the ease by which ultrathin sections (100–200 Å) can be cut, and (3) the degree to which the medium is evaporated in connection with exposure of the sections to the electron beam in the microscope.

The last factor is of importance for high resolution electron microscopy since extensive sublimation of the embedding medium leads to distortions due to the surface tension deforming the part of the structural components which is located in the layer of the section from which the embedding medium was removed. Up to 50% of most embedding media, with the exception of Vestopal W, is removed due to such sublimation.

Araldite embedding according to Glauert et al. (1956) and Glauert and Glauert (1958). The Araldite casting resin M, or Araldite No. 6005, is mixed with a hardener, 964B, or dodecenyl succinic anhydride (DDSA) in equal parts by volume. The setting of this mixture is speeded up by the use of an amine accelerator, 964C, or trimethamine methylphenol. A plasticizer, dibutyl phthalate or *n*-butyl phthalate, is added to control the hardness of the fixed block. The following mixture has been recommended by Glauert and Glauert (1958):

Araldite casting resin M, or Araldite No. 6005	10.0 ml
Hardener 964B or dodecenyl succinic anhydride	10.0 ml
Dibutyl phthalate or n-butyl phthalate	1.0 ml
Accelerator 964C or trimethamine methyl phenol	0.5 ml

Slight variations of this formula are recommended to adjust the conditions for different types of tissue.

The Araldite mixture is prepared at 60°C by warming the components in an incubator. The first three components are mixed in a conical flask 15 min before use and stirred for about 0.5 min with a glass rod. The accelelerator is added later.

The embedding of the specimens which have been dehydrated in alcohol starts by removal of half the absolute alcohol from the specimens and the addition of an equal quantity of the Araldite mixture without accelerator. The specimens should be kept in glass-stoppered bottles. The bottles are shaken until the two liquids have mixed, and incubated for 0.5 to 1 hour at 48°C. The alcohol–Araldite mixture without accelerator is then removed with a pipette and replaced with pure Araldite mixture 5–6 times at intervals of 1–2 hours. The last change can be kept overnight at 48°C. Time of embedding varies with the specimen between 24 and 48 hours, or even longer.

The accelerator is added to the Araldite mixture used 2–3 hours before the final embedding. During these hours the complete mixture should be changed at least three times before transfer of the specimens to gelatin capsules.

Dry gelatin capsules or glass tubes are used for setting of the resin. The specimens are transferred to the capsules by means of a pipette, and the capsule is filled with the complete Araldite mixture. Introduction of air bubbles should be avoided. The capsules are closed and incubated at 48°C. The maximum time for setting of the Araldite mixture is about 6 hours. The capsules should be hard after 30 hours' incubation at 48°C.

For American Araldite, Luft (1961) has recommended the following resin mixture:

Araldite 502	27 ml
DDSA	23 ml
Accelerator DMP-30	1.5–2.0% v/v added just before use

Mixtures without DMP-30 may be stored several weeks, but precautions against moisture accumulation should be taken.

The following procedures are followed:

1. Dehydration in alcohol with one change of absolute alcohol.

2. The specimens are immersed in two changes of propylene oxide for 10–15 min each. Precautions should be taken to avoid evaporation of the liquid to such an extent that the tissue dries, and the vapors should not be inhaled.

3. The second change is poured off and 1–2 ml of fresh propylene oxide is added. An equal quantity resin mixture is added. After 1 hour another equivalent volume of resin mixture is added. Three to six hours are allowed for infiltration; a longer period of time is preferred.

4. Specimens are transferred to gelatin capsules with as little propylene oxide–resin mixture as possible. The capsules are filled with pure resin mixture.

5. Polymerization is done overnight at 35°C, the next day at 45°C, and the next night at 60°C. The capsules can also be placed directly into a 60°C oven for 12 hours.

Tissues being embedded in Araldite must be very small, with at least one dimension not exceeding 0.1–0.2 mm.

Liquid Araldite is soluble in absolute alcohol, but after setting it is insoluble in organic solvents. The use of inexpensive disposable glassware is recommended.

Epon embedding according to Luft (1961). This embedding medium is another epoxy resin with great similarities to Araldite. The original procedure described by Luft called for the use of two different mixtures, both containing Epon 812, which can be mixed in different proportions to vary the hardness of the blocks.

Mixture A:	Epon 812	62 ml
	DDSA	100 ml
Mixture B:	Epon 812	100 ml
	Methyl nadic anhydride (MNA)	89 ml

These mixtures can be stored in the refrigerator but should not be mixed until the day they are used. They may be used mixed in any proportions. Before use, 1.5% v/v of accelerator trimethylamine methylphenol (DMP-30) is added. The mixing of A, B, and accelerator should be done very thoroughly.

Mixture A alone gives soft blocks, and mixture B hard blocks. A mixture of two-thirds A and one-third B is recommended for general use.

The tissue can be dehydrated in alcohol, but before transfer to the Epon mixture ethanol should be replaced by propylene oxide. Some small contamination of Epon with propylene oxide does not seriously affect the setting of the resin.

The following schedule is recommended:

1. Dehydration in ethanol.
2. One hour in propylene oxide, two changes.
3. One hour in 50:50 mixture resin–accelerator mixture and propylene oxide.
4. Twenty to thirty minutes in 100% resin–accelerator mixture.
5. Transfer to gelatin capsules filled with resin–accelerator mixture.
6. Setting of resin either at 60°C for 3 days or by raising the temperature in steps according to the following scheme: 35°C overnight, 45°C the next day, and 60°C the night and following days.

Sources of supply: Epon 812–Shell Chemical Corporation, Shell Building, San Francisco 6, California. Dodecenyl succinic anhydride (DDSA) and methyl nadic anhydride (nadic methyl) (MNA)—National Aniline Division of Allied Chemical and Dye Corporation, 40 Rector Street, New York 6, New York. Trimethyl amino methylphenol (DMP-30 accelerator)—Rohm and Haas, Washington Square, Philadelphia 5, Pennsylvania.

Vestopal W embedding according to Ryter and Kellenberger (1958). The Vestopal W is mixed with a 1% initiator (tertiary butyl perbenzoate) and 0.5% activator (cobalt naphthenate). It shares with Araldite and Epon the property of high viscosity. In order to secure a uniform penetration without shrinkage, the tissue is passed through a series of acetone–Vestopal W mixtures. Acetone should be used for dehydration instead of alcohol because Vestopal W is insoluble in alcohol. The polymerization takes place at 60°C and is finished in 12–24 hours.

The Vestopal W, initiator, and activator must be protected from exposure to light and should be stored in a refrigerator. Vestopal W can be stored for several months; the initiator and activators should not be stored for more than about 2 months, although often storage up to 4 months is possible. Softness of the blocks results from inactivation of the initiator and activator.

Porosity of the tissue is caused by incomplete removal of the acetone, and shrinkage of the tissue is caused by too rapid passage through the graded series of acetone–Vestopal W mixtures.

The following scheme for dehydration and subsequent embedding in Vestopal W is recommended:

1. Dehydration in: 30% acetone   15–30 min
                    50% acetone   15–30 min
                    75% acetone   15–30 min
                    90% acetone   30–60 min
                    100% acetone (dried over $CuSO_4$) 30–60 min
2. Transfer to a mixture of:
   3 parts dry acetone, 1 part Vestopal W   30–60 min
   1 part dry acetone, 1 part Vestopal W   30–60 min
   1 part dry acetone, 3 parts Vestopal W   30–60 min
   Vestopal W 1% initiator 0.5% activator, repeated
   changes to prevent polymerization   12–24 hours
3. Transfer to gelatin capsules filled with the last mentioned mixture and
   polymerization at 60°C for 12–24 hours.

When the complete mixture is prepared for embedding, the initiator is first mixed carefully with Vestopal W before the activator is added. The three components must be carefully mixed. This mixture does not keep for more than a few hours at room temperature.

IV. Techniques

A. FRAGMENTATION TECHNIQUES

Before the development of modern techniques for preparing ultrathin sections, fragmentation techniques represented the most efficient methods of specimen preparation for electron microscopy. The results of these techniques are, however, easily misinterpreted and they must therefore be applied in a very cautious way.

The fragmentation techniques have gained new actuality in connection with the introduction of the negative staining method. This method to enhance contrast is of considerable value in the study of the structure of viruses and large protein molecules in which it is applied to simple and well defined systems. When using negative staining to enhance the contrast of fragmented tissues, we face the same problem of interpretation as in the past when fragmented material was analyzed after metal shadowing. Homogenization of tissues can produce extensive modifications in the structure of elementary cellular components like membranes (Sjöstrand *et al.*, 1964), where the lipids and proteins represent a labile system. The lipid–protein structures can be modified through phase transitions in the lipid components provoked by changes in the environment, and in addition the protein molecules can form aggregates. If the chemical composition of a particular structural element is constant and the components are present in certain more or less fixed proportions, which is likely to be the case in, for instance, the mitochondrial membranes, the fragmentation technique can very well produce reproducible artifacts. These artifactual structures can exhibit rather constant shapes and dimensions that reflect highly probable modifications. The reproducibility reflects the probability for such modifications and can therefore not be used as an argument in favor of such structures being preformed. Such argumentation would lead to accepting classical myelin figures as preformed.

A prerequisite for applying a fragmentation technique is the presence in the tissue of a characteristic elementary structural component which constitutes a dominating part of the tissue from a quantitative point of view. (Collagen fibrils in dense connective tissue is an example of such component.) If this is not the case, the tissue should be fractionated after homogenization and the part of the cells isolated in which the elementary structural component constitutes a dominating part. The outer segments of retinal receptor cells is an example of such a cell part which almost entirely consists of one type of elementary structural component, the outer segment disks. The structural component that is isolated should be mechanically and chemically rather stable in order to tolerate the forces applied for fragmentation and the changes in the environment. Collagen is favorable to work with from this point of view.

The fragmentation can be performed in steps. When preparing collagen filaments, connective tissue can be subjected to fragmentation in a Waring blendor and then treated by means of a sonic oscillator. For this latter treatment, sonic or ultrasonic frequencies can be chosen. A sonic oscillator generating a frequency of 9 kc has been proved valuable, and this frequency is to be preferred to ultrasonic frequencies owing to the risks for secondary aggregation at high frequencies (Pohlman and Wolpers, 1944). During the fragmentation procedures the sample should be carefully cooled. It is recommended that the work be done in a cold room. At one step of the treatment, most material must be fixed to prevent an autolytic decomposition. In connection with negative staining, the drying of the material at an increasing concentration of the stain represents a means of preservation which might in principle remind one of a fixation procedure. The negative stains are known in light microscopy as rather poor tissue fixatives. Figures 1 and 2 show an example of a study in which fragmentation techniques were used (Sjöstrand, 1949). The outer segments of retinal receptor cells were removed from the retina by gently shaking the retina in a Ringer's solution for 60 sec. After a short time the retinal fragments had sedimented and the supernatant consisted of a rather pure dispersion of whole outer segments. After osmium fixation the dispersion of outer segments was fragmented by means of a sonic oscillator (9 kc) and drop preparations were made on a filmed microscope grid. Metal

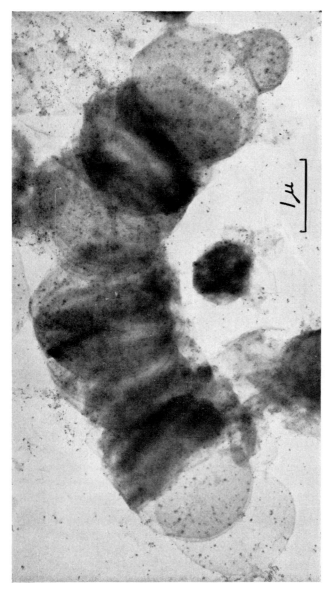

FIG. 1. Isolated retinal rod outer segment from guinea pig eye partially fragmented. × 21,000. (From Sjöstrand, 1949.)

Fig. 2. Disks isolated from retinal rod outer segments through fragmentation. Chromium shadowed. In this case the outer segments were separated from the rest of the retina by gentle shaking of the retina in Ringer's solution. Rather pure dispersions of outer segments were then obtained after a few minutes' sedimentation and after decantation of the supernatant fluid, which contained the isolated outer segments. After fixation in 1% osmium tetroxide solution, the outer segments were subjected to sonic treatment (9 kc). Dispersions of outer segment material representing different degrees of fragmentation were then obtained through fractionated centrifugation at low speeds. Figure 1 shows an outer segment where the disks have been partially separated, and Fig. 2 an elementary disk in the lower left corner and a pile of a few disks in the upper right corner. In this case the stepwise fragmentation could be followed and the origin of the disks securely analyzed. × 22,000. (From Sjöstrand, 1949.)

shadowing was used to enhance the contrast and to allow measuring the thickness of the isolated unit disks of the outer segments. Without fixation these disks disintegrated to more or less queer platelike structures which could be observed after negative staining.

When the results obtained by applying fragmentation techniques are considered critically, several factors should be taken into account.

1. The origin of the isolated component should be identified; frequently this is possible by combining the fragmentation technique with ultrathin sectioning of a pellet consisting of the isolated material.

2. When drop preparations are being made, the surface tension which acts during drying can cause severe distortion of the material, cause aggregation of various components into granulelike bodies and into drying patterns.

3. The pictures taken of such material should represent parts of the specimen *chosen at random* to make sure that an unconscious selection will not distort the conclusions. Large particles or particles aggregated into large clumps cannot always be analyzed and should not occur if one is to avoid that an appreciable amount of the material will be excluded from analysis.

4. Only such components should be considered as structural elements which are well defined as to form, outlines, and size and appear consistently in all preparations.

5. Fragmentation is likely to produce artifacts if the material is unfixed. Such artifacts can appear as well defined structural components with a high degree of reproducibility. This fulfillment of the requirement mentioned under (4) therefore does not exclude that the component has been formed as a result of the preparatory treatment. (See also discussion above.)

B. Ultrathin Sectioning

The development of microtomy for electron microscopy has proceeded in several steps. Some early trials did not result in reproducible or in sufficiently efficient techniques (Sjöstrand, 1943a,b,c, 1951; Fullam and Gessler, 1946). The first decisive step toward a reliable technique was taken by Pease and Baker (1948) when they demonstrated that about 0.5 μ-thick sections could be cut with a modified standard microtome. The additional modifications of the Spencer microtome, introduced by Hillier and Gettner (1950a,b), made it possible to improve the sectioning technique to allow a reproducible cutting of about 0.2 μ-thick sections. The resolution that could be obtained on these sections was about 200 Å. Another important step was taken when methacrylate embedding was introduced by Newman *et al.* (1949). Applying this embedding technique and using glass knives as cutting edge, according to Latta and Hartmann (1950), Palade (1952) succeeded in cutting sections about 1000 Å thick with a microtome designed by Claude and Blum (see Claude, 1948). These sections did not allow high resolution electron microscopy and, therefore, were not suitable for a detailed analysis of the ultrastructural cell components.

A decisive step toward high resolution electron microscopy of tissues was taken in 1952 (Sjöstrand, 1953c,d) when a resolution of 25 Å was demonstrated in pictures of tissue sections cut on a Spencer microtome, still further modified than the microtome used by Hillier and Gettner, and using as cutting edge razor blades that had been sharpened according to a new procedure. Routine cutting of about 200 Å-thick sections for high resolution work became possible through the construction of a new type of microtome in 1952 (Sjöstrand, 1953a). Since then a large number of microtomes have been designed which perform excellently and at the same time are simple to install and to use.

1. The choice of embedding medium is important for cutting the thinnest possible sections. Vestopal W is recommended as the best embedding medium for high resolution work, but Araldite and Epon are very useful when slightly thicker sections can be used.

2. Very minute areas—0.1 mm² or less—should be sectioned when the thinnest possible sections are desired. This means that the tissue block should be trimmed to a very fine tip, a procedure that requires considerable skill. The tip of the block should be formed to a tapered four-sided pyramid. A too thin and too long tip vibrates easily at a supersonic frequency when hitting the knife edge. Such vibrations introduce periodic variations of the thickness of the section—"chatter" (Fig. 3).

For larger sections the block should be trimmed to the shape of a rooftop and oriented in such a way that the long sides are parallel to the knife edge.

For cutting the thinnest possible sections, the consistency of the blocks should be hard and the cutting speed rather high. Large sections are cut more easily from soft blocks, and the cutting speed should be slow. In fact, the cutting speed sets a limit with respect to the maximum size of the block face that can be cut. Increasing the size of the block face, on the other hand, reduces the chances of obtaining very thin sections.

The quality of the cutting edge and the rake angle (Fig. 4) is of great importance in ultrathin sectioning. As knife edge, glass knives are recommended, prepared according to some modification of the original method described by Latta and Hartmann (1950). Steel knives are of importance for sectioning in connection with the freeze-etching technique where the greater heat conductivity of a metal knife, as compared to glass knives, is important to reduce the melting of the ice in connection with sectioning. Diamond knives are useful but cannot be used with advantage for sectioning all embedding materials. It is not possible to stretch the sections cut from a Vestopal block with a diamond knife if the block face is not very minute. The ease by which glass knives can be prepared with available tools or with the glass knife breaking apparatus manufactured by LKB Products makes glass knives the knives of choice.

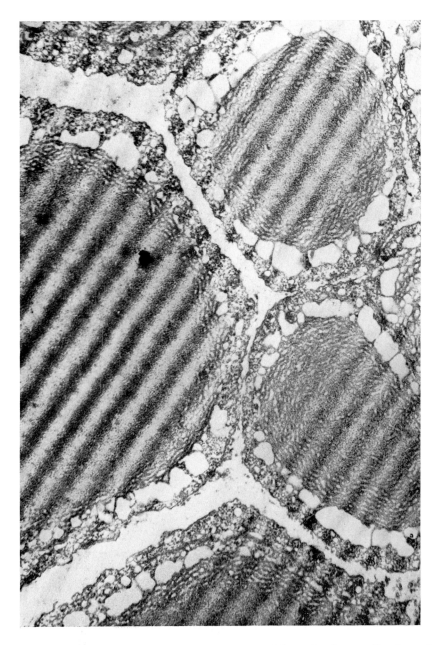

FIG. 3. Periodic variations in section thickness—"chatter"—due to vibrations of the tissue block tip at a supersonic frequency. (From Sjöstrand, 1966.)

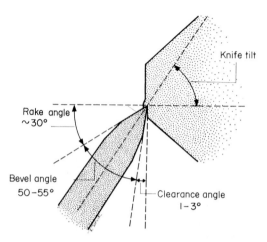

Fɪɢ. 4. Definition of rake angle, bevel angle, and clearance angle and their approximate magnitudes in ultrathin sectioning. (From Sjöstrand, 1966.)

1. Breaking Glass Knives

A glass plate approximately 150–200 mm wide, 200–300 mm long, and 5.7 mm thick is first broken into a number of rectangular pieces about 25 mm wide. A glass cutter is drawn along a wooden ruler placed parallel to the long side of the plate and at about 25 mm distant from the side (Fig. 5). The score made by the cutter edge should be very shallow and narrow. After a glass plate with a deep scratch is broken, the cleavage surface will show extensive irregularities (Fig. 6).

With the scored surface facing upward, a straight steel wire or a match is placed immediately below and parallel to the scored line. Both hands are applied to the upper surface of the plate, one on each side of the pivot formed by the steel wire or the match, and pressure is applied downward until the plate breaks apart. Care must be taken not to contaminate the two new surfaces thus obtained.

The final breaking of the glass can be made either from the long rectangular strips or after the strip has been broken up into square pieces. In the first case, the first break is initiated by scoring a line at a 45° angle in the surface opposite that scored when the rectangular strips were broken (Figs. 7 and 8). The scored line should reach within 0.5 mm from a freshly broken edge surface of the glass and the line should aim at a point about 0.5 mm from the corner of the rectangular strip.

The strip is now placed on the table with the scored line parallel to the edge of the table. A steady pressure is applied to the main part of the strip while the part extending free over the edge of the table is grasped with pliers (Fig. 9). A very steady force directed perfectly horizontally and perpendicular to the scored line is applied. The pliers should be closed only tightly enough to prevent them from sliding off the glass. Attention should be directed to the pulling force exerted on the glass, and when the glass breaks the arm should swing out freely in a direction perpendicular to the scored line.

The piece that has been broken off is discarded, the edge formed at the corner of the glass strip being a possibly useful cutting edge. The glass knife is now obtained by breaking off a triangular piece from the glass strip (Fig. 10).

With this method, which we have used in our laboratory since 1956, the breaking of the glass to produce the cutting edge is always done by a line bisecting the 90° angle at one of the corners of the rectangular strip. This modification of the original method described by Latta and Hartmann (1950) reduces the degree at which the cleavage of the glass bends toward the long side of the glass strip and therefore makes it easier to obtain bevel angles that are about 50°. A too large bevel angle will make it impossible to cut with a sufficiently large rake angle to prevent chatter.

If square pieces are prepared from the rectangular glass strip, these can be broken after scoring one surface as described above and by cracking the glass by means of a pair of pliers. A pivot in the form of a piece of a match or a short piece of a copper wire is mounted to one of the surfaces of the pliers by means of tape. The opposite surface of the pliers is

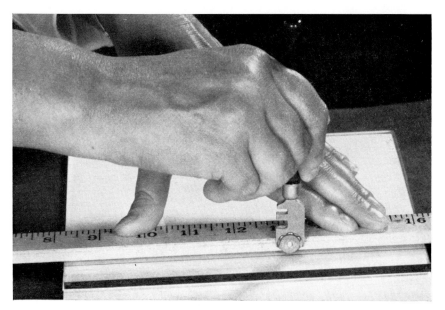

FIG. 5. Scoring a glass plate to make a rectangular glass strip. (From Sjöstrand, 1966.)

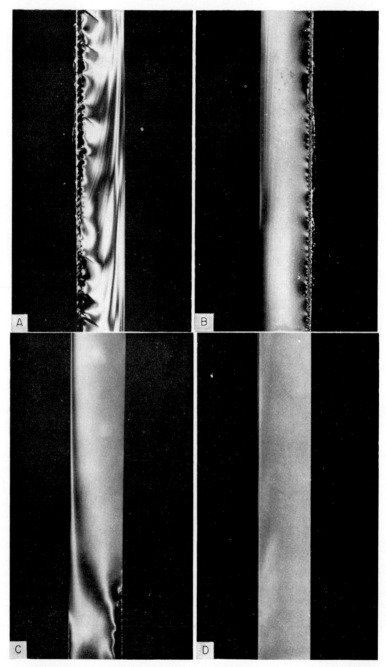

FIG. 6. Strain patterns in the cleavage surface and their dependence on the depth of the scoring. (A) Very deep scoring results in not useful cleavage surface. (B) Slight scoring with a useful cleavage surface. (C) Free break that has proceeded from a short scoring shown in the lower part of the picture. (D) The cleavage surface of a free break. (From Sjöstrand, 1966.)

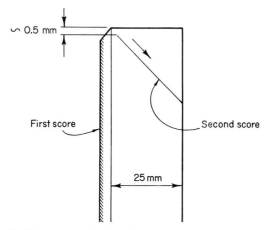

Fig. 7. Schematic illustration of orientation of second score in relation to first score. (From Sjöstrand, 1966.)

covered with tape. The square pieces of glass are now broken by the pressure applied through the pliers with the scored line opposite the pivot. A pair of pliers with one surface machined to form a pivot has been introduced by Ivan Sorvall, Inc., and this simple tool is very useful indeed.

2. Evaluation of Glass Knives

When inspecting the knife edge by naked eye (Fig. 11), it is possible to use certain characteristics for a preliminary selection of those knives that

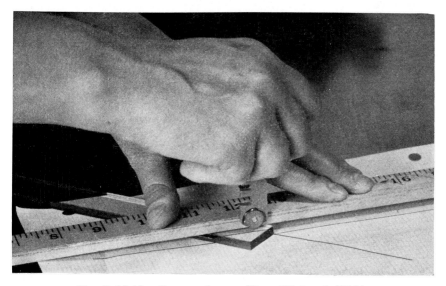

Fig. 8. Making the second score. (From Sjöstrand, 1966.)

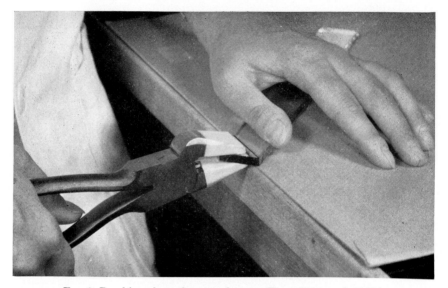

FIG. 9. Breaking along the second score. (From Sjöstrand, 1966.)

might be useful. The knife edge should be as straight as possible, although convex edges are frequently good. Concave edges show a "horn" at the side where the first scoring of the rectangular glass strip was made (Fig. 11). From this horn the cleavage surface frequently shows a series of steps sometimes extending as far as 2–3 mm from the horn. The edge in this region is not suitable for sectioning. The opposite end of the edge

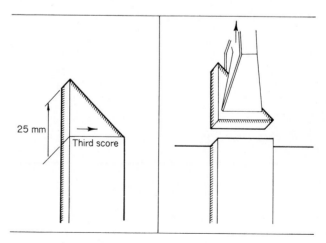

FIG. 10. Breaking off a triangular piece of glass with the possibly useful cutting edge at the top of the picture. (From Sjöstrand, 1966.)

is usually smoother, possibly with the exception of the outermost 0.5 mm.

The smaller the horn and the less steps and lines indicating an irregularly shaped glass surface, the greater the chances that the knife is useful. Straight edges without horn should be the objective.

A further evaluation of the knife involves an approximate determination of the bevel angle and a microscope examination of the edge.

The bevel angle can, in the most successful breaking of the knife, be estimated to be at least 5° larger than the angle at between the scorings.

The microscopic examination should be done at at least 80× magnification and with strong illumination of the edge. A good edge appears as a very thin unbroken line. The quality of the edge is determined by the width of the line of reflected light, which should be thin; by breaks in the line which indicate knicks at the edge; and by the straightness of the line.

3. The Procedure of Sectioning

The tissue block should be trimmed to the shape of a four-sided pyramid, or of a rooftop when larger sections are desired. It should be

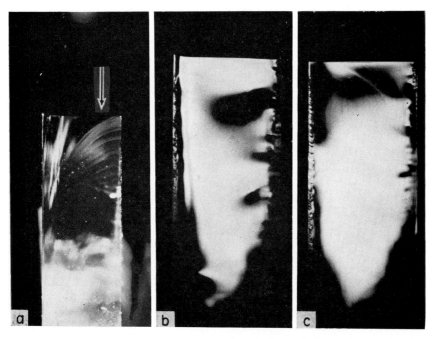

FIG. 11. Examples of glass knives of varying quality. (a) A knife edge of rather inferior quality. The "horn" is shown at the left end of the edge, and the arrow points to the position of the best part of the edge. (b) A rather perfect edge as judged from the inspection with the naked eye. (c) A glass knife of fair quality with convex edge and no horn. The curved lines shown in the glass indicate that most likely only a limited stretch of the edge is good. (From Sjöstrand, 1966.)

adjusted in such a way that one side of the pyramid or the long sides of the rooftop-shaped tip are parallel to the knife edge.

The knife tilt should be adjusted to give a 1–3° clearance angle, and the rake angle should be about 30°. It is important, in order to prevent chatter, that the rake angle be of this order of magnitude, particularly when cutting hard blocks. Chatter depends either on too small a rake angle or too thin a block tip. The proper rake angle is obtained by adjusting the knife tilt to the minimum clearance angle if the bevel angle is not too large. Cutting soft blocks requires a larger clearance angle than hard blocks.

To check whether the microtome cuts properly, a block of pure plastic should be cut. If a section is cut at every cutting cycle, the microtome is functioning properly and lack of success in obtaining good sections from the tissue block depends on the properties of the block. The most common cause is improper embedding of the tissue resulting in macro- or microscopical porosity of the block. The checking of the quality of the knife edge described above should exclude the knife as the cause of the trouble.

The minimum thickness of the layer that can be cut off the block face is 100 Å, or possibly less. Due to "compression," that is, not reversible plastic deformation of the section, the thickness of the section exceeds that of the layer that was cut off the block face. The compression can amount to 50% when cutting very thin sections of a plastic such as methacrylate. It is much less when cutting Vestopal W, which is another advantage of this embedding medium.

The thickness of the sections is evaluated by observing the color of the sections when on the liquid surface in the trough. The light is adjusted to allow total reflection at the liquid surface. The thin sections suitable for high resolution electron microscopy should then appear dark gray. The relationship between interference colors and section thickness determined by Peachy (1958) refers to section thicknesses that are unsuitable for high resolution work. The method used by him to determine the thickness of the sections by means of interference microscopy unfortunately does not allow measurements within the useful range of section thicknesses.

When lower resolution is acceptable, a section thickness of about 700 Å is acceptable. Such sections show a silvery shine in reflected light. A golden interference color corresponds to a section thickness of 900–1500 Å.

The results of Peachy were confirmed by Zelander and Ekholm (1960), who, however, could extend the measurements of section thicknesses to the 100–200 Å range by using a special interference microscope designed by Johansson (1957). The claim of Sjöstrand (1953a) that sections with a thickness of about 100 Å could be cut was confirmed through the study of Zelander and Ekholm as well as by the analysis of structural patterns observed when sectioning through objects with periodic structures, such as skeletal muscle fibers or crystals of poliomyelitis virus (Sjöstrand and Polson, 1958).

4. Serial Sectioning

The method of serial sectioning is extremely important in the study of, for instance, the circuitry of the nervous system or of morphogenetic problems. It has been developed in our laboratory to allow the three-dimensional representation of large volumes of tissue. In the future such analysis will not be seriously restricted by limitations as to the volume of tissue that can be analyzed. Series consisting of 500–600 consecutive sections have been prepared repeatedly in our laboratory, and whole cell bodies of neurons have been reconstructed in three dimensions (Karlsson, 1966a,b).

By means of repeated serial sectioning (144 times), a depth of 0.7 mm has been covered for three-dimensional reconstruction (Karlsson and Andersson-Cedergren, 1966a,b).

When a suitable microtome is used, the main problem in serial sectioning is the collection of the sections. This problem has been solved by the introduction of large one-hole "grids" by Sjöstrand (1958). The hole can be made in the shape of a slit with a width of 1 mm and a length of 2 mm. In presently available standard electron microscopes, the maximum length of the slit is determined by the range of the movement of the specimen stage of the electron microscope. In an especially designed stage for the Akashi Tronscope, the use of specimen grids with a slit length of 7 mm was tried in our laboratory and found useful for mounting serial sections. In order to develop this technique further, certain modifications in the electron microscope and in the microtome design are necessary.

The sections are collected either according to the method described by Sjöstrand (1958), which is a modification of that published by Gay and Anderson (1954), or directly on the large one-hole grids. The method worked out in our laboratory by Galey and Nilsson (1966) is recommended.

REFERENCES

Baker, R. F. (1962). *J. Ultrastruct. Res.* **7**, 173.
Caulfield, J. B. (1957). *J. Biophys. Biochem. Cytol.* **3**, 827.
Claude, A. (1948). *Harvey Lectures Ser.* **43**, 121.
Fullam, E. F., and Gessler, A. E. (1946). *Rev. Sci. Instr.* **17**, 23.
Galey, F., and Nilsson, S. E. G. (1966). *J. Ultrastruct. Res.* **14**, 405.
Gay, H., and Anderson, T. F. (1954). *Science* **120**, 1071.
Gibbons, I. R., and Bradfield, J. R. G. (1957). *Electron Microscopy, Proc. Stockholm Conf.*, 1956, p. 121.
Glauert, A. M., and Glauert, R. H. (1958). *J. Biophys. Biochem. Cytol.* **4**, 191.

Glauert, A. M., Rogers, G. E., and Glauert, R. H. (1956). *Nature* **178**, 803.

Haine, M. E. (1961). "The Electron Microscope." Wiley (Interscience), New York.

Hillier, J., and Gettner, M. E. (1950a). *J. Appl. Phys.* **22**, 135.

Hillier, J., and Gettner, M. E. (1950b). *Science* **112**, 520.

Holt, S. J., and Hicks, R. M. (1961). *Nature* **191**, 832.

Johansson, L. P. (1957). *Exptl. Cell Res., Suppl.* **4**, 158.

Karlsson, U. (1966a). *J. Ultrastruct. Res.* **16**, 429.

Karlsson, U. (1966b). *J. Ultrastruct. Res.* **16**, 482.

Karlsson, U., and Andersson-Cedergren, E. (1966a). *J. Ultrastruct. Res.* **14**, 191.

Karlsson, U., and Andersson-Cedergren, E. (1966b). *J. Ultrastruct. Res.* **14**, 212.

Karlsson, U., and Schultz, R. L. (1965). *J. Ultrastruct. Res.* **12**, 160.

Karlsson, U., and Schultz, R. L. (1966). *J. Ultrastruct. Res.* **14**, 47.

Latta, H., and Hartmann, J. R. (1950). *Proc. Soc. Exptl. Biol. Med.* **74**, 436.

Luft, J. H. (1961). *J. Biophys. Biochem. Cytol.* **9**, 409.

Maaløe, O., and Birch-Andersen, A. (1956). *Symp. Soc. Gen. Microbiol.* **6**, 261.

Maunsbach, A. B. (1964). *J. Cell Biol.* **23**, 108A.

Maunsbach, A. B. (1966a). *J. Ultrastruct. Res.* **15**, 242.

Maunsbach, A. B. (1966b). *J. Ultrastruct. Res.* **15**, 283.

Millonig, G. (1962). *Intern. Congr. Electron Microscopy, 5th, Philadelphia* **2**, 8.

Newman, S. B., Borysko, E., and Swerdlow, M. (1949). *J. Res. Natl. Bur. Std.* **43**, 183.

Palade, G. E. (1952). *Anat. Record* **114**, 427.

Palay, S. L., McGee-Russell, S. M., Gordon, S., and Grillo, M. A. (1962). *J. Cell Biol.* **12**, 385.

Peachy, L. D. (1958). *J. Biophys. Biochem. Cytol.* **4**, 233.

Pease, D. C. (1962). *Anat. Record* **142**, 342.

Pease, D. C. (1966). *J. Ultrastruct. Res.* **14**, 356.

Pease, D. C., and Baker, R. F. (1948). *Proc. Soc. Exptl. Biol. Med.* **67**, 470.

Pohlman, R., and Wolpers, C. (1944). *Kolloid-Z.* **109**, 106.

Ryter, A., and Kellenberger, E. (1958). *J. Ultrastruct. Res.* **2**, 200.

Sabatini, D. D., Bensch, K., and Barrnett, R. J. (1963). *J. Cell Biol.* **17**, 19.

Schultz, R. L., and Karlsson, U. (1965). *J. Ultrastruct. Res.* **12**, 187.

Sjöstrand, F. S. (1943a). *Nord. Med.* **19**, 1207.

Sjöstrand, F. S. (1943b). *Arkiv Zool.* **35A**, 1.

Sjöstrand, F. S. (1943c). *Nature* **151**, 725.

Sjöstrand, F. S. (1949). *J. Cellular Comp. Physiol.* **33**, 383.

Sjöstrand, F. S. (1951). *Nature* **168**, 646.

Sjöstrand, F. S. (1953a). *Experientia* **9**, 114.

Sjöstrand, F. S. (1953b). *Nature* **171**, 31.

Sjöstrand, F. S. (1953c). *J. Appl. Phys.* **24**, 117.

Sjöstrand, F. S. (1953d). *Experientia* **9**, 68.

Sjöstrand, F. S. (1955). *Sci. Tools* **2**, 25.

Sjöstrand, F. S. (1958). *J. Ultrastruct. Res.* **2**, 122.

Sjöstrand, F. S. (1963). *J. Ultrastruct. Res.* **9**, 340.

Sjöstrand, F. S. (1967). "Electron Miscoscopy of Cells and Tissues," Vol. 1. Academic Press, New York.

Sjöstrand, F. S., and Barajas, L. (1968). *J. Ultrastruct. Res.* **25**, 121.

Sjöstrand, F. S., and Polson, A. (1958). *J. Ultrastruct. Res.* **1**, 365.

Sjöstrand, F. S., Andersson-Cedergren, E., and Karlsson, U. (1964). *Nature* **202**, 1075.

Zelander, T., and Ekholm, R. (1960). *J. Ultrastruct. Res.* **4**, 413.

Zetterqvist, H. (1956). The Ultrastructural Organization of the Columnar Absorbing Cells of the Mouse Jejunum. Thesis, Karolinska Institutet, Stockholm.

CHAPTER 4

Microphotometry with Visible Light[1]

A. W. POLLISTER, H. SWIFT, and E. RASCH

I. Introduction

Microphotometry can be applied with advantage to a wide variety of biological problems. In almost any histological preparation where pigments occur, either naturally or induced by staining, microphotometry can be a useful tool. It can provide adsorption curves on intact cells that aid in chemical identification of colored compounds. It can also determine the amounts of pigment present in areas varying in size from large tissue

[1] Aided by grants from the U.S. Public Health Service and the Abbott Memorial Fund. The help of Dr. John Woodard in drawing the figures is gratefully acknowledged.

regions down to minute portions of a single cell. Microphotometry can thus be of importance to the histochemist who wishes to know in quantitative terms the intensity of a particular reaction, the rate of color production, whether the reaction involves one or several colored compounds, or whether the reaction products are the same or different with different tissues or substrates. It can be important to the cell physiologist who wishes to know, for example, the amounts and type of carotenoid, chlorophyll, or other natural pigments in individual cells, and whether the absorption characteristics of such compounds are altered on extraction. Photometry can also be important to the cytologist or cytogeneticist anxious to know, through nucleic acid analysis, whether a particular cell or tissue contains a haploid, diploid, or multiple chromosome complement. It can also be of importance to the cytochemist interested in localization and quantitative behavior of the various major components of the cell.

Visible light microphotometers are easy to operate and may be readily constructed. The basic units—microscope, monochromator, photometer—are at hand in many laboratories or are readily obtained commercially. This chapter discusses such simple visible-light microphotometers. It does not consider more complex apparatus, such as that for twin-beam recording (Pollister and Ornstein, 1959; F. Kasten, 1960) or scanning and integrating systems (Deeley, 1955; Jansen, 1961). Elaborate instruments have been constructed in general by workers already thoroughly familiar with problems of microphotometry, and often for rather specific purposes (e.g., see Chance, 1954).

The subject of cell photometric analysis and instrumentation has frequently been reviewed (Moses, 1952; Pollister, 1952; Swift, 1953a, 1966; Vialli and Perugini, 1954; Pollister and Ornstein, 1959; Walker and Richards, 1959). Several excellent authoritative articles are in Wied's (1966) "Introduction to Quantitative Cytochemistry." It is the special aim of the present chapter to guide the beginner in the field toward selection or assembly of an apparatus, toward operation and testing of instruments, and toward critical evaluation of sources of error.

II. Instruments

Much useful work in visible microspectrophotometry can be done with uncomplicated apparatus. The simplest consists of (1) a microscope with a side tube; (2) a photometer with housing, power supply, and galvanometer; (3) a photometer mount of the rotating plate type; and (4) a lamp assembly with filters for isolation of a narrow spectral region. Some of the earliest instruments were of this type, with the rotating plate photometer mount on a photomicrographic camera in place of the plateholder (Pollister, 1952; Pollister and Ornstein, 1959). Such equipment is hardly beyond the resources of a biological laboratory with average shop facilities, and it is adequate for estimating concentration in homogeneous cell areas or relative amounts in homogeneous spherical nuclei (e.g., as in Swift, 1950a). By the two-area method (Garcia, 1965) heterogeneous sections or flattened cell nuclei can be measured.

The addition of a monochromator to the above makes it feasible to run absorption curves and, by the two-wavelength method, to extend the range to heterogeneous distributions and irregularly shaped cell regions. This type of laboratory-fabricated apparatus is illustrated in Fig. 1A. Figure 1B shows an excellent, commercially available, complete assembly. A wide variety of components are available if one wishes to assemble his own equipment; below are a few suggestions as to the choice and arrangement of these basic components: microscope, photometer and mount, monochromator, and light sources; others are given in Pollister and Ornstein (1959).

A. LIGHT SOURCES

In visible light photometry, because of the extreme sensitivity of photomultiplier tubes, the light source need not be of unusually high intensity unless areas approaching 1 μ in diameter are to be measured, or the red end of the spectrum is used. The spectral emission of several visible light sources is shown in Fig. 2. Sources with continuous emission spectra, such as tungsten filaments or zirconium arcs, are most satisfactory for use with monochromators. Line sources, such as mercury arcs, are useful when a monochromator is not available, where individual lines, such as the mercury green line may be isolated with appropriate filters. Standard tungsten 100-W projection lamps with coil filaments are generally satisfactory. Irregularities in the filament image, however, are inconvenient, particularly where large uniformly illuminated areas are needed, as in the two-wavelength method. In such cases the filament image must be slightly off focus in relation to the object plane, so that local intensity variations are reduced. Six volt, 18 ampere ribbon filaments provide more uniform illumination, but are generally less stable, although some individual bulbs show more stability than others. Instability may be partly due to poor electrical contacts, particularly in the low voltage lamps, so that bases and sockets should be thoroughly cleaned. All lamps should be run from constant voltage transformers, e.g., Sola units, to reduce instability due to fluctuations in line current.

The light source should contain a condensing lens that focuses the filament image on the monochromator entrance slit, and also a diaphragm so that the monochromator is not illuminated with too wide a cone of light. For an output of maximum intensity and light purity, the distance

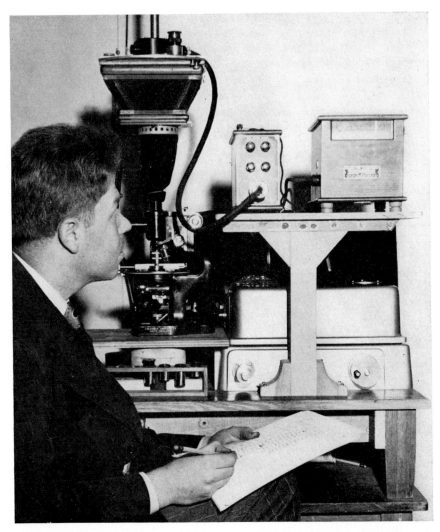

Fig. 1A. Microspectrophotometric apparatus constructed in the Columbia University laboratory. The Model DDE Bausch and Lomb microscope is equipped for side observation by a retractable prism in a side tube (partly hidden behind the worker's face). At lower right is a Perkin-Elmer Model 83 monochromator, behind which is the black shielding for the lamp assembly on a short optical bench (Pollister and Ornstein, 1959). Mounted on the camera is a rotating-plate type of photometer mount (Pollister and Moses, 1949; Swift, 1950a; Pollister, 1952) which carries two interchangeable elements: left, the photomultiplier tube housing (Farrand) and right, the focusing magnifier (of the type used in photomicrography) which images the iris diaphragm that delimits the photometric field. On the shelf above the monochromator are the battery power supply for the phototube and the microammeter (Rubicon) of range 0.2 μA.

Fig. 1B. Complete Leitz microspectrophotometric apparatus. (Photograph courtesy of E. Leitz, Inc.)

between light source and monochromator should be dictated by the monochromator numerical aperture. The cone of light from the lamp should be large enough to fill the prism or grating (Fig. 3). It should not be greater, or bad flare and consequent light impurity may result. Where maximum intensity of light output is not needed, it may be desirable to use the monochromator at less than full aperture to decrease flare within the instrument (Stockbarger and Burns, 1933).

Some commercial microscope lamps are satisfactory, although the light source components, lamp, condensing lens, diaphragm, may be more conveniently assembled on a simple optical bench (Pollister and Ornstein, 1959). Lamps preferably should not contain reflectors behind the bulb. Ground glass filters greatly reduce light output and are quite unnecessary if Köhler illumination is used. Lamp components should be carefully aligned and rigidly mounted. Adequate tungsten sources are obtainable as an integral part of Bausch and Lomb monochromators. If a Beckman DU spectrophotometer is used as a monochromator, the built-in 6-V lamp may be used, or it may be removed and a lamp of higher wattage and more uniform field may be directed into the entrance aperture.

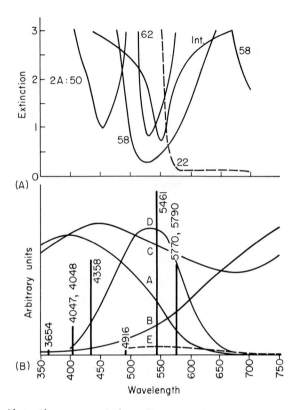

FIG. 2. (A) Absorption curves of filters (Eastman Kodak Co., 1945). Wratten 2A and 50 are recommended for isolation of the mercury 4358 Å line. Wratten 62 isolates the mercury 5461 Å line, and Wratten 22 the lines at 5770 and 5790 Å. The absorption curve of Wratten 58 is too broad for accurate measuring, unless corrections are made at higher extinctions (see Fig. 5). Absorption of an interference filter with peak transmission at 550 mμ is also shown. (B) Curve A: The spectral response curve of a 931 A or 1 P 21 electron multiplier phototube. Curve B: The approximate energy output of a 100-W tungsten lamp. Curve C: The approximate energy output of a xenon arc lamp (from Anderson, 1951). Curve D: Instrument sensitivity for constant mono-chromator dispersion with a 100-W tungsten lamp and 1 P 21 phototube. Curve E: Same, except with a 1 P 22 phototube. This phototube is much less sensitive except for a very small region above 675 mμ. The emission lines from an AH 4 mercury arc lamp are drawn, the height corresponding to instrument sensitivity with a 1 P 21 phototube.

B. MONOCHROMATORS

A number of commercially available monochromators have been used for microphotometry, including the Beckman DU (Commoner, 1948; Swift, 1950b) or B (Alfert, 1952), with phototube housings removed, the

Perkin Elmer Model 83 (Pollister, 1952), the Bausch and Lomb grating monochromator 33-86-40 or 33-86-45, and the Leitz high-power instrument. It is necessary to use an instrument of good optical quality and moderately high dispersion. The Perkin Elmer and Bausch and Lomb instruments have f ratings of 1:4.5, equal to a numerical aperture of 0.11. Many dyes have broad absorption maxima, and can be accurately measured with wide bandwidths, and thus monochromators of relatively low dispersion can be used. The effect of spectral purity on Feulgen absorption curves is shown in Fig. 4. No measurable error is obtained for nominal bandwidths up to 14 mμ at the absorption maximum. For sharper absorption maxima, such as those in the chlorophyll curves shown in Fig. 16, much narrower bandwidths and better monochromator dispersion are required. With any new material the effect of slit width on the absorption curve is readily tested. Since the absorption spectrum of didymium is intricate, with abrupt absorption maxima and minima, didymium glass or salt solutions make excellent test objects for monochromator performance. If absorption curves are to be run, it is important that monochromator slits be of good quality and accurately adjustable as, for example, in the Beckman and Perkin-Elmer instruments.

There are several ways in which light from the monochromator can be directed into the microscope. In some instruments the microscope has been placed only a few centimeters away, and light from the exit slit has been directed into it, or a simple collimating lens placed at the exit slit (Fig. 3A). The condenser is then focused so that the slit image falls on the object plane of the microscope. This method is simple, but has several disadvantages. Except with long focal length condensers the slit image is often too narrow for easy measuring; it varies in wavelength distribution

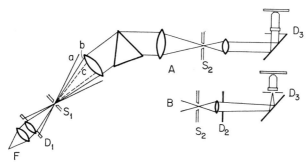

Fig. 3. Methods of illumination of the microscope condenser. (A) Monochromator exit lens is a simple collimator, producing an image of the slit on the object plane. (B) Monochromator exit lens focuses the slit image on the rear focal plane of the condenser, producing an image of diaphragms D_1 and D_2 on the object plane. The lamp diaphragm should never be opened beyond position b.

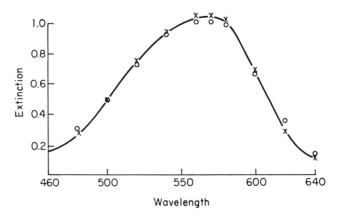

FIG. 4. Absorption curve of a Feulgen-stained *Tradescantia* nucleus, measured at a nominal bandwidth at 560 of 2.8 mμ (solid line), 14.0 mμ (crosses), and 28.0 mμ (circles). No significant differences are shown between 2.8 and 14.0 mμ bands. The 28.0 band causes a 3% depression at the peak.

from one edge to the other; and in curve running it is inconvenient to balance out variations in phototube sensitivity by changing slit width. In addition, very slight changes in alignment can cause significant variation in the wavelength reaching the specimen. It is much more convenient to place a lens at the exit slit which approximately focuses the slit image on the condenser back focal plane (Fig. 3B). The condenser is then focused on a field diaphragm, and wavelength variation in the image is reduced. The characteristics of this lens are dictated by several factors, particularly the distance between monochromator and microscope, and the condenser numerical aperture (N.A.). It is often desirable that the projected slit image be wide enough to fill the condenser aperture used. If monochromator and microscope are placed close together, a lens of correspondingly shorter focal length is required. Low-power objectives make good lenses for this purpose. For example, if an 0.3-mm slit is to be projected on a 10-mm 0.3-N.A. condenser, it needs to be enlarged 20 times to fill an aperture approximately 6 mm in diameter. This would be accomplished by a lens of 16-mm focal length, with the microscope placed 32 cm away.

It is often inadvisable, however, to enlarge the slit image too greatly. With higher magnification the size of the field illuminated becomes progressively smaller and may be made too small for convenience (although the added brightness may sometimes be desirable). Field stops are much harder to place when a short focal length lens is used. For these reasons it is often more practical to project a slit image narrower than the full condenser aperture. In such case the microscope is used at one aperture along the plane of the slit (for example 0.3), and at a lower aperture at right angles to it (for example 0.05). This results in a slight loss of microscope resolution, but except for objects below 1 μ in diameter this is usually unimportant. Where the condenser aperture is not filled, longer focal length lenses can be used at the exit slit. A convenient lens, for example, is the lower element of a 10× Huygenian ocular.

The monochromator exit lens should contain a field diaphragm, placed in the image plane of the lamp diaphragm (Fig. 3B). This diaphragm may easily be made from sheet metal or aluminum foil. It is convenient to make it of a size sufficient to limit an area from 10 to 50 μ in diameter of the microscope field.

It is important that internal reflections in the monochromator be reduced to a minimum. In some instruments it is possible, and often necessary, to insert dull black baffles of metal or cardboard in suitable places. Monochromator flare can be tested with line sources, such as AH-4 mercury arc lamps, by determining the intensity of light emitted on either side of an emission band when this theoretically should be zero. With light from the 546 mμ line set equal to 100, light from the monochromator should be less than 0.2 when the wavelength knob is set two nominal bandwidths on either side. Line sources are also convenient for calibration or periodic checking of the wavelength scale. With grating instruments it is necessary to use filters at wavelengths above 600 mμ to filter out the second-order (near ultraviolet) spectrum.

Filters may be used to replace monochromators for singlewave length determinations, but only under certain conditions. In most cases filters emit too broad a spectral band for photometry. Individual mercury lines may be isolated by appropriate filters, producing light of adequate purity, but only at a few wavelengths (Fig. 2A). The mercury green line (546 mμ) is completely isolated by Wratten filter No. 77A, or, with only a small amount of yellow contamination, by Nos. 62 or 77. The mercury yellow lines (577 and 579 mμ) are isolated by Wratten No. 22, which allows some red light to pass, but this may usually be disregarded because of the insensitivity of photomultiplier tubes to red. The mercury blue-violet line (436 mμ) may be isolated by Wratten filters 2A and 50 combined. Interference filters (Farrand or Swiss-made G.A.B.) have narrower spectral transmissions than most gelatin filters and can be obtained for a variety of wavelengths. If they are used with continuous sources an error is introduced (impure light error) that becomes larger at higher optical densities. Correction may be made for this error provided the pigment to be measured can be obtained in solution for comparison. Cuvettes containing the dye at various concentrations can be measured with a commercial spectrophotometer such as a Beckman, and then with the microphotometer, with

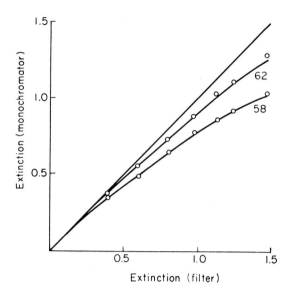

FIG. 5. The effect of filters on extinction measurements of Feulgen-stained mouse liver nuclei. Nuclei were measured both with a monochromator (nominal bandwidth 3 mμ) and with a filter. The impure light error increases with higher extinctions, and is much greater with the relatively less pure light from Wratten 58. Curves of this type may readily be used to correct extinctions where a monochromator is not available.

the filter in place, and the values compared. A correction curve for the Feulgen dye and a 500 mμ Farrand interference filter is shown in Fig. 5. Unfortunately the absorption characteristics of most dyes are different when in solution than when bound to tissue sections. Thus the proper correction curve can only be approximated in this way. If a microphotometer with a monochromator is available, accurate correction curves for filters can be made by measuring regions of different optical densities with pure light, and then remeasuring exactly the same regions with the filter.

The monochromatic light for measuring should illuminate only a small central portion of the microscope field. The full field should be brightly illuminated, however, when choosing the areas to be measured. It is thus convenient to place a scanning light between monochromator and microscope. A mirror can be used that swings into the optical path, interrupting light from the monochromator, and directing light from the side scanning lamp into the microscope.

Light from the monochromator may be directed into the microscope with the standard substage mirror. Since the usual rear-surfaced mirror gives multiple reflections, however, it is advisable to substitute a right-angle prism or first-surfaced mirror. The position of this mirror is critical for alignment, so that the usual mirror mount is best replaced by a firmer mounting fastened to the table top, with set screws to provide fine tilt adjustments. In some instruments the mirror has been avoided by mounting the microscope horizontally or by placing the monochromator vertically below the microscope. These arrangements have certain awkward features. For oil immersion work a horizontal microscope is inconvenient, and alignment of light source and microscope is usually much easier when these parts are placed on a table top.

C. MICROSCOPES

Any good standard microscope is satisfactory, if provided with the following parts. A good *mechanical stage* is essential, preferably one that can be moved very slight distances for centering of the object. Stage knobs may be enlarged, for example, with cork or metal flanges, or with levers for easier fine manipulation. A convenient lever may be made that, with a twist, locks onto the spindle of a mechanical stage knob, and readily disengages to allow for coarse turning. Micrometer screws may be built into the stage; one micrometer stage for accurate positioning of slides is made commercially (Cooke Nuclear Research Stage). *Centerable condenser* or *objective mounts*, preferably both, are necessary. Rotating nosepieces may contain so much play that objectives continuously get out of alignment. Centerable objective clutches are preferable.

Since accurate microphotometry frequently depends upon careful examination and centering of the specimen before measuring, a *side viewing tube* that allows a clear view of the preparation is necessary. Most modern research microscopes are available with a sliding prism above the objective to direct the beam into a side-view tube; this prism slides out of the optical path, allowing direct projection to the phototube (for example, as in the microscope of Fig. 1B).

Standard microscope *lenses* are satisfactory, if in good condition. Apochromatic objectives with their better color correction retain adequate focus throughout the visible range and are preferable where absorption curves are run. Achromats, however, are satisfactory for single-wavelength measurements. Either standard Huygenian or Ramsden oculars are adequate. Fully or partially compensated oculars should, of course, be used with apochromatic objectives. A diaphragm, with aperture 1 to 3 mm in diameter, placed in the ocular helps to eliminate stray light, particularly when preparations produce much scattering or when a wide field of illumination must be used. An adjustable objective diaphragm (e.g., Leitz "irtis") may be easily turned down to fit a Ramsden ocular.

It is essential, if possible, to use condensers at low numerical apertures (0.2–0.4). For measuring curves, the best condensers are 16- or 8-mm objectives, mounted in the adapters which most manufacturers provide. Standard Abbé-type condensers (e.g., Leitz "ilpen") provide fairly good color correction and may be used if stopped down to low numerical aperture. Most workers have preferred to use a 16-mm apochromatic objective.

Where extremely small areas are to be measured, a condenser aperture above 0.4 may be required for increased resolving power. For such purposes an oil immersion objective has been used as a condenser, with the specimen mounted between two cover glasses (Naora, 1955). Use of a high condenser numerical aperture presents several serious complications (see page 237) and is not recommended. The optical path through an absorbing layer is significantly increased; the danger of loss of light from scatter is greatly increased; and lens flare may become serious.

D. Photometer Head

This head should meet the following requirements: (1) provision for viewing and determining size of the region to be measured; (2) a diaphragm to limit size of the measured area; (3) phototube housing, preferably light tight, with a lens to focus the area to be measured on a small area of the phototube cathode. Other functions may be added to the photometer head, such as provision for photographing measured areas (Pollister, 1952), or means for projecting an image on to a screen for outline drawing (Lison, 1950). The following conditions are also desirable. The phototube should be firmly supported and should be exactly centerable in relation to the diaphragm. The head should be attached to the microscope with a light-tight sleeve or bellows, of sufficient diameter to eliminate internal reflections. The viewing system should be conveniently placed; a horizontal tube, containing a telescope or magnifier, is convenient, although ground glass screens have been used (Moses, 1952). A simple magnifying lens of approximately 20-mm diameter and 40- to 60-mm focal length is adequate; an achromatic magnifier provides a somewhat clearer image The lens should be permanently mounted so that the diaphragm is sharply focused. It is convenient to place a light shield and aperture at the eyepoint, as shown in Fig. 6. If a telescope is used, its objective lens must be of large enough numerical aperture to include an area considerably wider than the measured field, so that the size of large areas can be determined and centered, and a suitable smaller included region chosen for measurement. Size is best determined with an ocular micrometer, either in the viewing tube if it is a telescope, or cemented to the viewing prism, if a magnifier is used. A micrometer scale may be

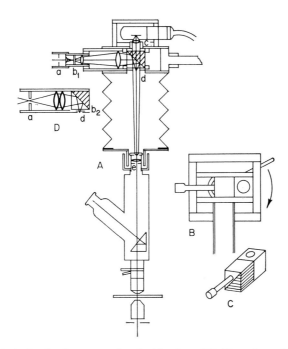

FIG. 6. (A) A simple photometer head, side view. (B) Top view with top plate removed. (C) Sketch of moving prism. (D) Alternate suggestion for viewer, employing a simple magnifier instead of a telescope. a = light shield; b_1 and b_2 = position of measuring reticle; c = lens for focusing image of diaphragm on phototube cathode; d = adjustable field diaphragm to control size of measured area; e = diaphragm in Ramsden ocular.

drawn, photographed, printed on film, and placed in the viewer. There should be provision for centering the micrometer in relation to the diaphragm. In the two-wavelength method (page 225) the exact size of the measured area may be very important; consequently means for inserting diaphragms of fixed dimensions may be included. A simple photometer head is diagrammed in Fig. 6. For measurement of areas 1–5 μ in diameter, a size range convenient for most stained preparations, it is convenient to have the photometer head placed above the microscope so that the image at the diaphragm level is magnified 1000 times. The instrument shown in Fig. 6 is operated most comfortably from a chair when the lower and upper viewing tubes are close together, with 15 or 20× oculars in the microscope. If a 4× magnifier is used in the upper viewing tube, then the image is viewed at 4000 times magnification, and measured with a micrometer scale which is magnified 4 times. These conditions are satisfactory for accurate measuring of the specimen. Magnification of the instrument is, of course, readily adjusted by changing oculars and objectives, or by adjusting the distance of the photometer head above the microscope.

E. Light-Measuring Equipment

Electron multiplier tubes, with their high sensitivity and low noise level are excellent for visible light measurements. Several photometer units, including photomultiplier, power supply, and microammeter, are commercially available. The Photovolt 520 M is line operated and contains a variable sensitivity control, as well as fixed resistances in steps of 10. The range of the variable sensitivity is too small for convenient use, and the instrument is too unstable and insensitive for use at high magnifications in orange to red light. The Farrand electron multiplier photometer is battery operated, and, if used with the recommended Rubicon galvanometer, is several times more sensitive. It contains adequate fine and coarse sensitivity controls, and can be used with a decad resistance shunt if desired. A convenient and compact, line-operated photomultiplier is manufactured by American Instrument Company (Oster, 1953).

The 931 A phototube is useful only where light intensity is no problem, e.g., at low magnification and at wavelengths below 600 mμ. For high magnification or with orange or red light, the more sensitive 1 P 21 must be used. The 1 P 22 phototube is much less sensitive than the 1 P 21, except for a small region at the red end of the spectrum (650–750 mμ) (Fig. 2). These multiplier tubes contain cathodes with only a small central region (about 5 $\times$ 12 mm) of maximum sensitivity. Within this area some variations in sensitivity usually exist, and outside it the sensitivity falls off sharply (Marshall et al., 1948). In most cases the light measured may be so focused that it falls entirely in the region of highest sensitivity. Where it is necessary to project areas larger than 5-mm diameter on the cathode the end-window phototubes (5819 type) must be used.

III. Alignment of the Instrument

The elements of the light source, lamp filament, lens, and diaphragm, should be carefully aligned. The procedure is briefly outlined below; other alignment steps are described in the literature (Shillaber, 1944; Pollister and Ornstein, 1959). Place a white cardboard about a foot in front of the lamp; focus the filament image upon it, adjusting lens or lamp bulb so that all color fringes are symmetrical. Adjust the diaphragm so that the symmetry is maintained as it is stopped down to its smallest aperture. The filament image, from a properly aligned lamp, should be focused on the monochromator entrance slit, and the lamp diaphragm stopped down so that all light entering the monochromator is focused on the prism or grating.

The path of light through the monochromator is readily traced by placing a white card at various places in the beam. A mercury arc lamp (e.g., AH-4 type) is useful for checking alignment of the monochromator elements and the wavelength scale. If illumination method B (Fig. 3) is used, the exit slit lens should form an image of the slit that is finally centered on the closed condenser iris, after preliminary centration on a white card held beneath the condenser. Finally, with a telescope the condenser aperture should be centered vertically and horizontally about the slit image.

With the low-power objective on the microscope, it is focused on a microscope slide. The lamp diaphragm and monochromator slits are opened and the mirror is adjusted so that light from the monochromator enters the condenser. At this point it is convenient, but not essential, to use a focusing telescope of the type used for aligning phase microscopes. This can be inserted in place of the ocular in the side viewing tube, and the various optical units adjusted so that all diaphragms are concentric, the slit images when narrowed transect the optical axis (i.e., the slit margins are equally sharp at all points), and all secondary images reflecting from various lens surfaces also appear concentric when the focus is shifted on lamp, monochromator, condenser, and objective lenses. Finally the low-power objective is replaced with an oil immersion lens and the alignment is rechecked. In a properly adjusted instrument, illuminated with method B, light from the monochromator should appear as a central spot 10–50 μ in diameter. The rest of the field should be dark, so that a spot measured about 5 μ away from the illuminated area contains less than 2% the intensity. If this reading is higher, the condenser numerical aperture should be checked, and also the lenses and specimen for dirt. The central spot should show no lateral shift with wavelength. If it does, light is probably entering the condenser off axis.

If a phase telescope is not available, the condenser may be approximately aligned by looking down the microscope tube with the ocular removed or by using a pinhole eyepiece. Then, with the ocular in place, the condenser diaphragm stopped down, the condenser and mirror should be further adjusted so that all fringes are symmetrical and stay concentric when the condenser is moved up and down, and the diaphragm is opened.

Alignment of microphotometers is simple in principle, but in practice it takes patience and empirical manipulation. It is usually necessary first to align the lamp and monochromator; and then to test for condenser alignment. If, for example, the condenser is found to be badly out of line, moving it into place may disalign the monochromator, so that it may be necessary to start once again from the beginning. Lamp and monochromator alignment are often awkward, and it may be necessary to use sheet metal strips or wooden blocks to adjust the optical axis along a vertical plane.

IV. Measuring Technique

A. ABSORPTION LAWS

Absorption theory is discussed by Hiskey (1955) in Volume I of this series. Any determination of light absorption involves two measurements: the intensity of incident or background light (I_0), and the light intensity of the incident beam reduced by passing through the specimen (I_s). The light transmitted by the specimen (I_s/I_0) is the *transmission* (T). This obviously varies from 0 for opaque objects to 1.0 for objects that are completely transparent. Light absorption is a molecular phenomenon; thus in ideal cases it varies with the number of absorbing molecules in the light path. As the number of absorbing molecules is increased, either by increasing thickness (d) or concentration (c), the transmission decreases logarithmically. For example, light passing through a filter of 0.1 transmission is reduced from 1.0 to 0.1; if it traverses two such filters the total T is 0.01; and three filters, 0.001. Thus it is obvious that the transmission is a reciprocal logarithmic function of the number of absorbing molecules in the light path. The extinction (E), or optical density,[2] is defined as

$$E = \log_{10} \frac{1}{T} = \log_{10} \frac{I_0}{I_s}$$

and thus, where the molecular absorption laws hold, the extinction bears a linear relationship to the number of absorbing molecules. Thus $E = Kc$ (Beer's law) or $E = Kd$ (Lambert's law), and also $E = Kcd$. In these equations $K = e$, where e is the extinction coefficient, usually taken as the extinction, at one particular wavelength of light, given by a 1-cm path of a molar (or sometimes a 1%) solution of the absorbing substance.

In most microspectrophotometric studies of cells, the main problem is solved by obtaining relative concentrations or amounts, and absolute values are not necessary. Therefore, the constant k can be ignored and E computed as cd. If needed, k for a substance in its cellular state can be approximately computed if absolute values are available from biochemical analyses of cells or cell fractions (Pollister, 1955; Pollister and Ornstein, 1959). For example, there are extensive data on the amount of deoxyribonucleic acid (DNA) in tissue nuclei of the rat (Vendrely, 1955), the mean

---

[2] Although extinction (E) is generally being displaced by absorbance (A) it seems less confusing to continue to use E in microspectrophotometry and to retain A as an unambiguous symbol for area of the cell measured. By contrast, where absorbance was used Mendelsohn (1966) found it necessary to introduce symbol B for area.

value being approximately 6.0×10^{-12} per nucleus. Dividing this by the nuclear volume in cubic microns gives the concentration of DNA per cubic micron. From the extinction (E) of a known optical path through the nucleus (see Fig. 8 and Section IV, C), one can readily compute an absolute k value for cellular DNA-Feulgen. For cellular data a convenient k is the extinction of 10^{-10} mg per cubic micron. Commonly this value for DNA-Feulgen at wavelength 546 mμ comes out to be about 0.200; this curiously enough, is close to the k of undenatured DNA *in vitro*.

Since, in practice, this k-value is by no means reproducible even from one block of a given tissue to another, it cannot be reliably used for conversion of random microspectrophotometric data to absolute values. Differences in dye intensity seem largely due to uncontrollable and inestimable variables in the development of the reaction on the slide. At least for the common less condensed tissue nuclei (but cf. Garcia, 1968) it is perhaps a safe assumption, supported by finding similar values for diverse nuclear types in one organ on one slide, that in any single test the variables will be similar for each nucleus. In an early study, Swift (1950b) found that he could correct for the Feulgen variability from test to test by carrying a control, or standard, slide of rodent liver along with each new organ measured. DNA-Feulgen amounts per nucleus, thus corrected, were closely similar for all diploid nuclei of the mouse, a cytological demonstration of DNA constancy which is now widely accepted as an approximate rule that is supported by both biochemical and cytochemical data. Obviously this experiment also showed that the correction yielded approximately the same k value for DNA-Feulgen for each nuclear type and each test. Hence, it should be possible to estimate absolute amounts in a wide variety of nuclei by use of such a standard slide as a control. This has not been done often because, as stated, most cytochemical questions are quite adequately answered by relative, or arbitrary, values.

B. EXCEPTIONS TO ABSORPTION LAWS

Beer's law does not hold in cases of molecular interaction. Many dyes form aggregates at high concentration. These aggregates have different absorption characteristics from solutions of single dye molecules, and form in greater amount with increasing concentration (Fig. 17). The linear relation between extinction and concentration is thus upset. Dye aggregation is responsible for metachromatic staining (Michaelis, 1947). Beer's law can be assumed to hold for a particular stain, where absorption curves from lightly and darkly stained regions of the same specimen are found to be of the same shape. Beer's law does not concern the stoichiometry between a dye and the substrate to which it is bound. Apparent deviations

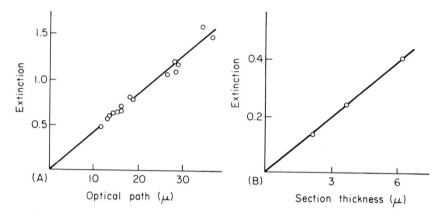

Fig. 7. Lambert's law. (A) Photometric determination of droplets of Fast Green dissolved in glycerin, suspended in mineral oil. (B) The extinctions of rat liver nuclei cut at different thicknesses and stained with the Feulgen reaction. Each point is the mean of 10 readings.

from Beer's law may be caused by photometric variables, for example scatter in the specimen or distributional error (see pages 225, 232).

Lambert's law may be readily tested by determining the extinction for specimens of differing known thicknesses (Fig. 7). It would fail to hold where dyes are unevenly distributed through the specimen, for example, where a stain is stronger on the outer surface of a tissue section. Apparent deviations again may be caused by errors in the instrument, light scatter, or distributional error. For these reasons a test of the Beer-Lambert laws offers a check both on the biological material and on the instrument (see page 243).

C. GEOMETRY OF THE SPECIMEN

In practice a specimen is centered in the microscope field. The photometer diaphragm is stopped down to contain only the area to be measured, and a reading (I_s) is taken. The specimen is moved away and the background reading (I_0) is made. Provided none of the errors listed below are operating, the extinction computed from the two readings bears a direct relation to the number of absorbing molecules in the light path. Where only qualitative determinations are wanted, or ratios between the concentrations (amounts per constant area) of two pigments, the actual amount of absorbing material per cell may not be important. In many cases, however, it is necessary to compute the amount of dye bound per nucleus, nucleolus, or cell. The following geometric considerations then become important.

1. Sections

In sections where the specimen has flat parallel sides normal to the optical axis (Fig. 8A) the amount of absorbing material (M) is given by $M = EA/e$, where A is the area measured. The extinction coefficient (e) at the wavelength used can be disregarded for relative measurements. It is omitted, for convenience, from the following equations. Dye concentration (c) = E/d, where (d) is the section thickness. Total amount (M) is obviously $M = cV$, where V is the volume. The total amount of dye bound, for example, per nucleus and cytoplasm in a thin tissue section can be determined by taking representative measurements through cells, determining section thickness carefully on folds immediately adjacent to the measured areas, measuring nuclear volume with an ocular micrometer, and calculating cell volume by the method of Chalkley (1943).

2. Spheres

The total amount of absorbing substance in a sphere (for example, a Feulgen-stained nucleus) has been estimated in several ways.

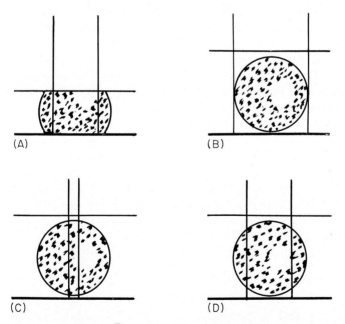

(A)

(B)

(C)

(D)

FIG. 8. Various conditions for photometric measurement of spherical cell nuclei (see text). The horizontal lines represent surfaces of the slide (below) and the coverslip; vertical lines represent, in profile, the margins of the light area that is measured in the photometric field, which is usually a central circular zone delimited by an iris diaphragm in the photometer mount.

First, nuclei have been measured by circumscribing the entire sphere with the photometer diaphragm (Fig. 8B) and computing the amount (M) as $M = EA$, where A is the area of the nuclear profile (i.e., πR^2), or more commonly relative values, ER^2, where R is the sphere radius. This result is usually somewhat inaccurate. Few biological structures are, in fact, perfectly circular in profile, and consequently peripheral background light (I_0) gets by the diaphragm in the I_s measurement to give higher transmission values. Furthermore, even if the profile is perfectly centerable in the iris of the photometer, the same error may arise from marginal diffraction if the refractive indexes of structure and background are not perfectly matched.

Second, one may measure the transmission through a small central cylinder of the sphere (Fig. 8C), which gives effectively the extinction, of thickness $2R$. $E/2R\mu$ then gives the arbitrary amount of dye per cubic micron, and this, multiplied by the volume of the sphere ($\frac{4}{3}\pi R^3$) gives the total amount in the nucleus. The condensed formula for dye mass then becomes $M = E(\frac{2}{3}\pi R^2)$. This method is accurate only in the rare case where the Feulgen-stained material is distributed in quite homogeneous fashion, so that the small cylinder is representative of the concentration of the whole nucleus. In the more common case distribution is in clumps of various sizes and the second method is likely to be even less accurate than the first.

The third procedure is designed to circumvent the above errors by the compromise of measuring a larger, and presumably more nearly representative, central plug, one-fourth to three-fourths the diameter of the nucleus (Fig. 8D). With this method the area measured can be considered a cylindrical plug with spherical segments on either end, cut through the center of a sphere. This assumption is not strictly accurate for high condenser numerical apertures, but the increased path length through a sphere of converging rather than parallel light is negligible for apertures of 0.3 or below (Caspersson, 1936). The total dye can be computed as $M = (E\pi C^2)/F$, where C is the cylinder radius and F that fraction of the total sphere volume included in the plug, and $F = (R^3 - H^3)/R^3$, where R is the sphere radius, and H is one-half the plug height. Also

$$F = 1 - (1 - C^2/R^2)^{3/2}$$

Table I gives values of F for various ratios of C/R. Table II gives, in terms of C and R, the mean optical path (m.o.p.), which is useful in computing concentration in the sphere.

Tissue sections, mounted in balsam, plastic media, or oil frequently flatten with age as the mounting medium dries. In such a case nuclei which were originally spherical become oblate spheroids. The extent of

TABLE I
VALUES OF F FOR DIFFERENT VALUES OF C/R[a]

C/R	0.00	0.01	0.02	0.03	0.04	0.05	0.06	0.07	0.08	0.09	
0.1	0.015	0.018	0.022	0.025	0.029	0.034	0.038	0.043	0.048	0.054	0.1
0.2	0.059	0.065	0.072	0.078	0.085	0.092	0.100	0.107	0.115	0.124	0.2
0.3	0.132	0.141	0.150	0.159	0.168	0.178	0.188	0.198	0.209	0.219	0.3
0.4	0.230	0.241	0.253	0.264	0.276	0.288	0.300	0.312	0.325	0.338	0.4
0.5	0.351	0.364	0.377	0.390	0.404	0.418	0.431	0.445	0.459	0.474	0.5
0.6	0.488	0.502	0.517	0.532	0.546	0.561	0.576	0.591	0.606	0.621	0.6
0.7	0.636	0.651	0.666	0.681	0.696	0.711	0.725	0.740	0.755	0.770	0.7
0.8	0.784	0.798	0.812	0.826	0.840	0.854	0.867	0.880	0.893	0.905	0.8
0.9	0.917	0.929	0.940	0.950	0.960	0.970	0.978	0.986	0.992	0.997	0.9
1.0	1.000										1.0
	.00	.01	.02	.03	.04	.05	.06	.07	.08	.09	

[a] Computed from $F = 1 - (1 - C^2/R^2)^{3/2}$; cf. Kasten (1956).

TABLE II
THE RELATION BETWEEN C/R AND MEAN OPTICAL PATH (P_r) THROUGH A SPHERE

C/R	0.00	0.01	0.02	0.03	0.04	0.05	0.06	0.07	0.08	0.09	
0.10	0.998	0.998	0.997	0.996	0.995	0.995	0.994	0.993	0.992	0.991	0.10
0.20	0.990	0.989	0.988	0.987	0.985	0.984	0.983	0.982	0.980	0.979	0.20
0.30	0.978	0.976	0.975	0.973	0.972	0.970	0.968	0.966	0.964	0.962	0.30
0.40	0.960	0.958	0.955	0.953	0.950	0.948	0.945	0.942	0.940	0.937	0.40
0.50	0.935	0.932	0.930	0.927	0.925	0.922	0.920	0.917	0.914	0.911	0.50
0.60	0.908	0.905	0.901	0.897	0.893	0.890	0.886	0.882	0.878	0.874	0.60
0.70	0.870	0.866	0.862	0.857	0.852	0.847	0.842	0.837	0.831	0.826	0.70
0.80	0.820	0.814	0.808	0.802	0.795	0.789	0.782	0.775	0.768	0.761	0.80
0.90	0.754	0.746	0.738	0.731	0.723	0.714	0.705	0.696	0.687	0.677	0.90
1.00	0.667										

flattening may be determined by scanning, i.e., by measuring the transmission of small regions of the nucleus from center to margin (Fig. 9), or by measuring the same nucleus with plugs of different diameter. Where a nucleus is appreciably flattened, M calculated from Table II becomes smaller with decreasing plug diameters. If flattening occurs, it usually affects all nuclei in one tissue section more or less proportionally. Thus, if C is always taken as a constant proportion of F (e.g., $C/R = 0.5$), the relative aspect of M values is maintained (Alfert, 1950).

For some determinations, such as the estimation of total protein per nucleus or nucleolus with protein stains, material above and below the nu-

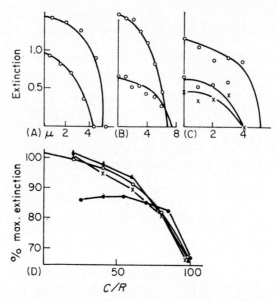

Fig. 9. Tests for shape and dye distribution in Feulgen-stained nuclei. A, B, and C were scanned by measuring areas 1 μ in diameter from the center outward. (A) Onion root (Navashin fixed). (B) *Tradescantia* ovary wall (acetic alcohol fixed). (C) Mouse liver (acetic alcohol fixed). In (C) values show flattening and increased dye concentration at the nuclear membrane. Solid lines have been computed for perfect spheres. (D) Mouse liver (formalin) scanned by concentric plugs of differing diameters. Solid dots show the expected values (disregarding distributional error), as given in Table III. One nucleus is flattened.

cleus may absorb light, and this absorption must be subtracted. For tissue sections of absorbing spheres in an absorbing background (Fig. 8C), measurements may be made as follows: Make three intensity readings, one through the sphere (I_s), one through the adjacent matrix (I_m) and one off the section (I_0). Compute extinctions, where $E_s = \log I_0/I_s$ and $E_m = \log I_0/I_m$. Find the mean optical path (p) through the sphere for the size of plug used by multiplying the relative path (p_r) obtained from Table II by the sphere radius. The section thickness (d) must be measured on nearby folds. The value of E_s can then be corrected to give only the sphere extinction (E_c), where $E_c = E_m - (1 - p/d)E_s$.

3. Spheroids

Most nuclei are not perfect spheres. Under the microscope many nuclei appear elliptical in outline. It is often difficult to tell without careful scanning whether such elliptical nuclei are prolate, oblate, or ellipsoidal. Where the degree of asymmetry is small it is usually simplest to average major and minor axes and to treat the nucleus as a sphere. Where it is large, but unknown, the two-wavelength method should be used. Some nuclei, e.g., of smooth muscle, or plant vascular elements, are obviously prolate spheroids. For these nuclei values of F can be obtained from Table III provided the plug diameter is always taken as half the minor axis.

4. Irregular Shapes

It is sometimes possible to obtain accurate results with specimens of other shapes, such as in smears or whole mounts of tissue cultures. In some cases these have been assumed to be disk shaped with M calculated as $M = EA$ (Korson, 1951). In many smears, however, nuclei may be flattened in varying degrees so that shapes may range from spheres to disks. In tissue cultures, cells often round up when preparing for division. In such cases either specimen thickness must be determined by focusing

TABLE III

VALUES OF F FOR PROLATE SPHEROIDS WHERE PLUG RADIUS IS HALF OF MINOR AXIS[a]

Ratio a/b	Values of F														
1.0	0.351	2.0	0.180	3.0	0.121	4.0	0.0907	6.0	0.0603	8.0	0.0455	10.0	0.0362
1.1	0.321	2.1	0.172	3.1	0.117	4.2	0.0863	6.2	0.0584	8.2	0.0444	10.5	0.0345
1.2	0.296	2.2	0.164	3.2	0.114	4.4	0.0823	6.4	0.0567	8.4	0.0433	11.0	0.0329
1.3	0.275	2.3	0.157	3.3	0.110	4.6	0.0787	6.6	0.0550	8.6	0.0422	11.5	0.0315
1.4	0.256	2.4	0.151	3.4	0.107	4.8	0.0754	6.8	0.0534	8.8	0.0412	12.0	0.0302
1.5	0.239	2.5	0.145	3.5	0.104	5.0	0.0722	7.0	0.0519	9.0	0.0403	12.5	0.0290
1.6	0.224	2.6	0.139	3.6	0.101	5.2	0.0694	7.2	0.0505	9.2	0.0393	13.0	0.0279
1.7	0.217	2.7	0.134	3.7	0.0985	5.4	0.0670	7.4	0.0491	9.4	0.0384	13.5	0.0268
1.8	0.200	2.8	0.129	3.8	0.0955	5.6	0.0647	7.6	0.0478	9.6	0.0376	14.0	0.0259
1.9	0.189	2.9	0.125	3.9	0.0929	5.8	0.0625	7.8	0.0466	9.8	0.0369	14.5	0.0250
2.0	0.180	3.0	0.121	4.0	0.0907	6.0	0.0603	8.0	0.0455	10.0	0.0362	15.0	0.0242

[a] Major axis $= a$; minor axis $= b$; plug radius $= c$.
Values were computed from approximate equation

$$F = \frac{2ab}{a^2 + b^2}\left[1 - \left(1 - \frac{a^2c^2 + b^2c^2}{2a^2b^2}\right)^{3/2}\right]$$

for plug through prolate spheroid with oblate spheroid caps of curvature intermediate between that of major (elliptical) and minor (circular) planes of the ellipsoid. Curvature of caps is that for a plane intersecting the ellipsoid at an angle of 45° to major and minor planes. Where $C = b/2$, then

$$F = \frac{2ab}{a^2 + b^2}\left[1 - \left(\frac{7}{8} - \frac{b^2}{8a^2}\right)^{3/2}\right]$$

(which is usually impossible to do with the necessary accuracy) or the two-wavelength method must be used. This method is independent of shape or distribution of the absorbing material. Any simplifying assumptions made about irregular-shaped specimens should always be checked with the two-wavelength method.

D. ABSORPTION CURVES

When absorption curves are measured with simple microphotometers it is usually most convenient to take a series of readings through the specimen at different wavelengths, and later the background readings. A pair of readings (I_s and I_0) through specimen and background may be taken together at each wavelength, but this requires repositioning the specimen for each point and is usually less accurate. If this method is used, stops may be placed on the stage to facilitate recentering. With the former method some time may elapse between I_s and I_0 for any one wavelength, so the photometer must be free from drift. The phototube should be illuminated only long enough to take the reading and the light beam interrupted between readings to prevent phototube fatigue. The scanning mirror, with scanning light off, makes a useful shutter for this purpose.

Instrument sensitivity varies with wavelength, due to variation in lamp output and phototube response (Fig. 2). Thus it is often necessary in obtaining absorption curves over large wavelength spans to vary the micro-ammeter response during measurement, so background readings do not go off the scale at peak sensitivity, or become too low for accuracy at regions of low response. Instrument sensitivity can be kept in the proper range throughout the wavelengths measured, by altering monochromator slit width or photometer gain, certain predetermined amounts at various points in the curve. Neutral density or other filters may also be placed in the light beam at certain wavelengths, but these must be accurately positioned to avoid any deviation in optical path.

For curve running, a 16-mm apochromatic objective of numerical aperture 0.3, makes an excellent condenser. Standard condensers are not adequately color corrected and are not as satisfactory. Care should be taken in aligning the condenser and substage mirror so that the monochromator light image does not shift with wavelength. Also the monochromator slits must be exactly aligned or slight shifts to shorter or longer wavelength distributions, and consequent change in extinction, may result from slight change in slit width.

E. ALL OR NONE ABSORPTION

In one special type of absorption measurement a value for total absorbing substance can be determined directly from the transmissions. This is where any particular region of a thin tissue section can be considered only as absorbing or nonabsorbing, with no intermediates. The measured transmissions then give an estimate of the section area occupied by absorbing material. The method has been applied, for example, to determination of collagen in muscle sections, where the collagen only was stained. A filter was used to illuminate the specimen which accentuated the collagen-dye absorption. Transmissions were determined for areas of pure collagen and pure muscle to find the 0 and 100% values for the measuring conditions used. A number of large microscope fields were then measured, and the transmissions were averaged to give an approximate figure for the section area occupied by collagen (Wang, 1949). The method could also be applied to opaque material, such as melanin granules, or the Gomori alkaline phosphatase reaction, but would obviously become inaccurate where the section was thick enough or the reaction intense enough to allow appreciable overlap of the opaque grains. With opaque material, monochromatic light is, of course, not necessary. The Beer-Lambert laws do not apply to such measurements, and transmissions only must be used.

V. The Two-Wavelength Method

The laws of absorption, which form the basis of the equations given above, hold only where absorbing molecules are randomly arranged, as in a perfect liquid. It has frequently been pointed out that nucleic acids, or attached chromophores, in cells and tissues may be sufficiently nonrandom to alter seriously the measured values (Commoner, 1949; Glick et al., 1951). This contention is easy to test provided the absorption curve of the chromophore in solution or from a homogeneous region is known (Ornstein, 1952; Patau, 1952; Mendelsohn, 1958a,b, 1961; Garcia, 1962). In Fig. 10A two Feulgen absorption curves are shown: one from a homogeneous nucleus and the other from a late prophase of the same volume and dye content where the dye is arranged in a few strongly staining chromosomes interspersed with clear areas. The peak of the latter curve is noticeably depressed. In Fig. 10B the same data are graphed, showing extinctions (E_0) of the homogenous area, plotted against those taken at the same wavelengths from an inhomogenous nucleus (E_i). At higher extinctions the disparity between the two curves increases.

Where any two areas containing the same pigment are to be compared, it can readily be seen that each may be measured at two (or more) wavelengths, and the ratios between extinctions determined. Where the ratios are dissimilar, distributional error is demonstrated (provided other photometric errors are inoperative). Further, the extent of disagreement is readily computed, and a correction for it may be made. This means that any irregular areas, such as Feulgen-stained metaphase plates (Patau and

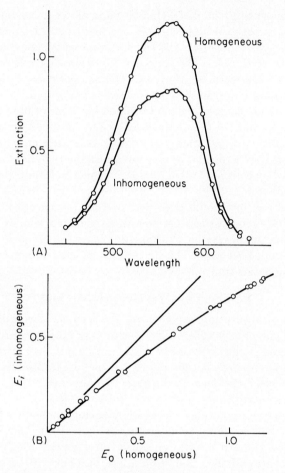

Fig. 10. Distributional error in Feulgen-stained grasshopper spermatocytes. Leptotene and diakinesis nuclei with the same size and dye content as determined with the two-wavelength method. (A) Absorption curves, showing flattening in diakinesis nucleus. (B) The relation between extinctions of the homogeneous leptotene nucleus and inhomogeneous diakinesis nucleus at each of the wavelengths measured.

Swift, 1953), lobed and distorted nuclei, or clumped cytoplasmic basophilia, may be measured. It is not necessary to determine the volume of such structures, since these cancel out of the calculations.

The two-wavelength technique is thus useful when material is too irregular in distribution to give valid results with the conventional measuring method. It also can readily demonstrate whether or not the distributional error is acting to distort any series of measurements. For example, mouse liver chromatin after acetic acid–alcohol fixation is clumped into irregular masses, but if liver is homogenized in sucrose before fixation, the nuclei appear completely homogeneous. Since Feulgen absorption curves of the two types of nuclei are almost identical, one can conclude that the clumping in the tissue blocks produces no measurable error.

The procedure for measuring irregular areas with the two-wavelength method is quite simple. Since the estimate of absorbing substance depends upon the difference between two low extinctions (or high transmissions), however, these must be determined with a high degree of accuracy, preferably by duplicate readings. The illuminated area must be homogeneous, the light as nearly monochromatic as possible, and all light scattering in the specimen should be practically eliminated by mounting with the proper refractive index medium. Further, all chromophores compared must have the same shape of absorption curve. Since hydrolysis conditions may alter the shape of the Feulgen absorption curve, where Feulgen sections are measured, they should all be on the same slide. In practice a homogeneous area is selected, and two wavelengths are chosen λ_1 and λ_2 such that the extinction (E_1) at one wavelength is half the extinction (E_2) at the other. Thus $2E_1 = E_2$ where $E_1 = \log I_0/I_s$ at λ_1 and $E_2 = \log I_0/I_s$ at λ_2. After the wavelengths have been properly chosen, inhomogeneous regions may be measured.

The total amount of absorbing material (M) in the measured area (A), regardless of its distribution, is given by the formula $M = KAL_1D$. Here K is a constant $(K = 1/e_1)$ where e is the extinction coefficient at wavelength 1 (λ_1); K may be disregarded for the relative, or arbitrary, determinations that are common results in the microspectrophotometry of cells. The actual computations are as follows: from the two transmissions T_1 at λ_1 and T_2 at λ_2, the respective light losses (L) are computed as $L_1 = 1 - T_1$ and $L_2 = 1 - T_2$; the ratio L_2/L_1 is computed, and from Table IV is found the corresponding value of D, which is the correction factor for distributional error. The reader should consult Garcia (1962) for details of these computations, with representative data showing the effectiveness in correcting for such extreme distributional differences as those of DNA in the nuclei of the three types of white blood cells.

Mendelsohn (1958b) has published tables from which L_aC (similar to L_1D) can be read for any pair of transmissions (T_1 and T_2) that are likely to be met in practice; these values are readily converted to L_1D by dividing by 0.868 (see legend, Table IV).

The value of M (computed as AL_1D or AL_2D) is a close approximation of a measure of the total number of absorbing molecules in the field and is comparable with the amount computed with one wavelength as EA (i.e., $E\pi R^2/F$) in Section IV, C, 1 if the absorbing material were so distrib-

TABLE IV
VALUES OF D FOR DIFFERENT VALUES OF L_2/L_1[a]

L_2/L_1	0.00	0.01	0.02	0.03	0.04	0.05	0.06	0.07	0.08	0.09	
1.0		4.033	3.461	3.134	2.907	2.734	2.595	2.479	2.380	2.294	1.0
1.1	2.218	2.150	2.089	2.033	1.982	1.935	1.892	1.851	1.813	1.777	1.1
1.2	1.744	1.712	1.683	1.655	1.628	1.602	1.578	1.555	1.533	1.511	1.2
1.3	1.491	1.471	1.453	1.435	1.418	1.400	1.384	1.368	1.353	1.339	1.3
1.4	1.324	1.310	1.297	1.284	1.271	1.259	1.247	1.235	1.224	1.213	1.4
1.5	1.202	1.191	1.181	1.171	1.162	1.152	1.143	1.133	1.124	1.116	1.5
1.6	1.107	1.098	1.091	1.083	1.075	1.067	1.059	1.053	1.045	1.038	1.6
1.7	1.031	1.024	1.017	1.011	1.004	0.998	0.991	0.985	0.979	0.973	1.7
1.8	0.968	0.962	0.956	0.950	0.945	0.940	0.934	0.928	0.923	0.918	1.8
1.9	0.914	0.909	0.903	0.899	0.894	0.890	0.884	0.880	0.876	0.871	1.9
2.0	0.867										

[a] Modified from values for C given by Patau (1952) where $D = 0.868C$.

uted that the error became negligible. When the two-wavelength method is used, for example, to measure representative regions of inhomogeneous cytoplasm where the object is not surrounded by blank areas, accurate determination of the size of A is of less consequence.

It is sometimes desirable to use both conventional and two-wavelength methods on the same material. Homogeneous areas (e.g., nucleoli or interphase nuclei) may be measured by the usual method, and inhomogeneous areas (mitotic figures, irregular cytoplasm) with the two-wavelength method. The two-wavelength method may be considered as giving an extinction corrected for distributional error, such that $E_c = L_1D$. This E_c is directly comparable to an extinction determined by the usual method at λ_2 for a homogeneous region. The two-wavelength method is also of importance to test the amount of error due to inhomogeneity that may be expected from any material. Regions may be measured by the two-wavelength method, and the value $1 - E_2/L_1D$ determined, where E_2 is the extinction at λ_2. This provides a direct measure of the magnitude of distributional error. Where $L_1D = E_2$ the error is negligible. If L_1D exceeds E_2, an error in calculation or measurement has been made.

VI. Photometric Variables

Microphotometers, of the type discussed here, appear misleadingly simple. A large number of variables influence the final results. It is obviously important to keep these at a minimum, so the instrument can provide information close to its greatest potential accuracy. It is also important continually to evaluate the magnitude of all variables, so that operative variation is not mistakenly ascribed to real variation in the materials investigated. Some photometric variables, such as amplifier noise, are essentially random, but others, such as distributional error, may consistently provide values that are too low or too high. Thus, although the usual effect of poor photometric technique is to increase the spread of values, data may be consistently skewed in either direction. In some cases it is even possible for treated and control values to be influenced differently. The application of tests for statistical significance to such measurements is thus occasionally inappropriate and may give the experimenter a false confidence in the data. Misleading statistical significance may be found, for example, between two sets of measurements where preparations vary in light-scattering properties, or extent of distributional error. Also, since distributional error, impure light error, and flare affect the higher extinctions more than the lower, these variables are particularly important in any series of measurements involving a wide range of pigment concentrations.

The major photometric variables are discussed in the following paragraphs. For convenience they may be divided into three classes: variables arising from properties of the specimen, from the instrument, and from the observer.

A. Variables from the Specimen

1. Light Scatter

Where the refractive index of the object is different from the medium in which it is mounted, light is reflected and refracted out of the measured path. The resulting "extinction" is too high because of nonspecific light loss, not associated with true light absorption by the pigment. The error obviously increases in magnitude with lower extinctions. For this reason extinctions below 0.1 are often too inaccurate to be trusted. In fixed and stained materials scatter usually need not be a problem. Material can be mounted in oils of proper refractive index, which in most cases effectively eliminates this error. Refractive index oils are obtainable commercially (e.g., Cargille Laboratories, New York) or may be prepared in the laboratory. Most fixed tissues have refractive indexes between 1.560 and 1.572. The refractive index can be matched reasonably closely by observing the specimen under dark field or with low numerical aperture bright field and looking for the Becke line, a bright diffraction band which moves from regions of lower to higher refractive index as the microscope tube is racked upwards. Almost no dark field image or Becke line should be evident in properly matched specimens. The amount of scatter is easier to evaluate in unstained tissue, or at a wavelength not appreciably absorbed by the specimen. Directions for refractive index matching are given by Shillaber

(1944). In some cases it is necessary to mount a specimen at one refractive index for measurements on cytoplasm, and at another for nucleoli, which often have higher density. A few cells, for example some protozoa and plant storage tissues, may contain inclusions of lower or higher refractive index than the cytoplasm. In such cases an adequate match is impossible.

Most commercial mounting resins are of too low refractive index for photometry of fixed tissue sections (Greco, 1950). A few (Canada balsam, Clarite X, Technicon) are of sufficiently high index to be useful for some measurements, where low dye intensities are not encountered. They should be used with a minimum of solvent which lowers their refractive index. Specific refractive index oils are more versitile and are always preferable.

Where absorption measurements are made on living or unfixed materials, matching refractive index may be more difficult, since usual oils may affect the specimen. It is occasionally possible to use comparatively nontoxic substances, however, as mounting media, such as sucrose or glycerin solutions, commercial white corn syrup (e.g., Karo), or paraffin oil. Light scatter is slight with many living cells, and their refractive index is much lower than after fixation.

If material with unavoidable light scatter must be measured, several solutions are possible, none of which is completely adequate. In some cases it is possible to obtain a difference spectrum by measuring unstained blank slides, and substracting the blank readings from values made on stained material (Pollister and Ris, 1947). In other cases, for example with Feulgen-stained tissues, I_0-readings may be made through unstained, but scattering, cytoplasm, instead of on an area away from the section. If, as is frequently the case, light scatter is from the cytoplasm only and not the nucleus, then extinction may be corrected by the factor $E_c = E_m - (1 - p/d)E_s$, discussed on page 222. It may also be possible to extrapolate scatter curves from wavelengths outside the absorption range of the pigment into the region of specific absorption, and then to substract the extrapolated values (Hyden, 1943). For single-point determinations it is also possible to take the background reading at a nearby wavelength off the region of specific absorption (Chance, 1951; Theorell and Chance, 1954). Several workers have considered the problem of obtaining accurate absorption curves on suspensions with strong light-scattering properties (Bateman and Monk, 1955), but as yet none of these methods has been applied to microphotometry.

Nonspecific light loss may also come from dirt on the slide or in the mounting medium, bubbles in the immersion oil, and other factors which may alter the optical path. Slides obviously should be kept clean. It is advisable to take all background readings in the same general area of any

slide and as close to the object reading as possible. The mounting medium
is occasionally thicker in some regions than others. This can alter condenser focus and affect background readings.

The magnitude of nonspecific light loss from all sources may be estimated by absorption curve analysis. Curves may be obtained from dark
and light regions of the same slide, and the extinction plotted as in Fig. 11.
For Feulgen preparations it is convenient to run the dark curve on an
uncut nucleus, and the light curve on an adjacent small fragment which
has been cut in sectioning. Error is demonstrated by these values except
in the unlikely case where light loss is exactly proportional to the extinctions. Where light loss is constant over the wavelengths measured (due to
reflectance of large surfaces, or dirt), values fall in a straight line that does
not extrapolate through the origin. Scatter, from specimens containing
many small refractive index changes in the light path usually becomes

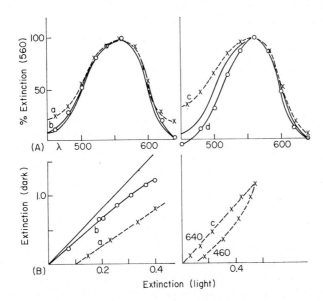

FIG. 11. (A) The effect of various photometric errors when Feulgen absorption
curves are run on dark and light portions of the same slide (here a large, darkly
stained *Tradescantia* ovary wall nucleus and an adjacent small nuclear fragment).
Solid lines, without points, indicate the absorption curve in the absence of major
variables. *a,* Reflectance error, due to surrounding starch grains, or to dirt on slide
in region of nucleus. The curve is flattened and elevated at the ends. *b,* The effect of
lens flare or distributional error. *c,* The effect of bad light scatter in the specimen
(here mounted in oil of very low refractive index). The curve is elevated more at the
shorter wavelength end. *d,* The effect of bad specimen flare (here produced by using
a numerical aperture of 0.9). (B) The same data with the extinctions of the dark area
plotted against those from the light area for each wavelength determined.

larger at shorter wavelengths, and thus elevates this end of the curve more than the longer (Fig. 11A).

In some cases where the condenser numerical aperture is too high, or the area illuminated by the monochromator too large, light can be deflected *into* the measured beam that should normally not be included. This results in a lowering of extinctions, so that the ends of the absorption curve may give values below zero, as in Fig. 11A. A somewhat similar error is produced by lens flare (see page 237).

2. Distributional Error

This can be divided for convenience into two types: distributional error due to nonrandom dye distribution, and error associated with variation in path length through the object.

In any specimen to be studied where the dye distribution is nonrandom, distributional error may be a serious variable. With fixed and stained preparations, however, one has merely to apply the two-wavelength method to determine the extent of the error. It is a rather surprising fact that error due to nonrandom dye distribution often proves on analysis to be small or negligible, even in material that appears markedly inhomogeneous to the eye. Its extent should obviously be investigated, however, for any new material.

A special type of distributional error may arise in crystalloid structures, where absorbing molecules are so oriented that absorption is greater along one plane of polarization than another (dichroism) (Commoner, 1949). Although such high molecular orientation is rare in biological material, this type of distributional error should be looked for in any highly oriented structure. Ultraviolet dichroism has been found in the nucleic acids of certain elongate sperm heads (Caspersson, 1941), although dyes bound to sperm nucleic acid are not dichroic (Pollister and Swift, 1950).

Absorption laws hold only for perfect solutions with plane parallel surfaces measured with parallel light. Where the solution is contained, for example, in a sphere, and the entire sphere is measured, an array of light intensities reaches the phototube varying from dark at the sphere center to light at the edge. The phototube summates this variety of intensities and provides a mean transmission for the sphere from which a mean extinction (E_m) can be computed. This extinction can be shown to differ from the true mean extinction ($\bar{E}$) that would be obtained if numerous small regions of the sphere were measured separately, an extinction obtained for each, and then all the extinction values averaged. The discrepancy between E_m and $\bar{E}$ becomes increasingly large with higher values of $\bar{E}$, as in Fig. 10A. It becomes negligible when plugs of diameter $\frac{2}{3}r$ or less are measured through the sphere center instead of the entire sphere.

Distributional error also occurs even with specimens having plane parallel surfaces, if the measured beam is not of parallel light. Light from a condenser is conical. The mean light path through a section with parallel sides is therefore greater than the section thickness, and the measured light is a composite of rays that have traversed the specimen at different angles. This also produces a discrepancy between E_m and $\bar{E}$. At numerical apertures of 0.3 or below, variations due both to increased path length and distributional error are negligible (below 1% at $E = 1.0$). At high condenser apertures both factors must be considered. The magnitude of error can be calculated (Uber, 1939; Blout et al., 1950), or estimated with the two-wavelength method.

3. Determination of Specimen Dimensions

For many determinations it is necessary to obtain the following dimensions: (1) section thickness; (2) cell, nuclear, or nucleolar diameters and volumes; and (3) diameter of measured area. It is important to estimate the accuracy obtainable with these measurements.

a. Section Thickness. Microtome settings are frequently very inaccurate, and usually cannot be relied on for photometry. Section thickness has been determined optically by careful focusing under oil immersion, on the upper and lower surfaces, using the scale on a fine-focusing knob (Pollister, 1948, 1965; Françon, 1961). (This scale may be inaccurate, particularly at the ends of the traverse.) In some tissues, for example of amphibians, pigment granules are useful objects on which to focus. A special optical system for thickness determination has been described (Thorell, 1947). Because of microscope depth of focus, this method is accurate only to about ± 0.3 μ, even under favorable conditions where several determinations are taken and then averaged. With cells of known mass, interferometry can provide accurate thickness estimates (Mellors et al., 1953).

Thickness is quite readily determined without special optics by measuring folds where the section is on edge. Careful focusing is necessary to find a region where the section is exactly perpendicular to the slide (i.e., the focal plane giving least thickness of the folded portion). It is usually simple to spread tissue slices incompletely, so that a number of folded areas occur in the section. Several things are apparent on careful viewing of such folds. Sections are often wedge shaped, so that thickness determinations on one region are not necessarily applicable in another. Section cuts are frequently quite irregular, with many local thin and thick areas. The size of such irregularities varies with tissues and cutting conditions, but they may be as great as ± 0.5 μ. Thus any estimate of section thickness should be the average of 10 or more determinations and photometric readings should be made immediately adjacent to the measured folds.

Where possible thicker sections are preferable, if necessary measured at wavelengths off the absorption maximum. Irregularities become proportionally larger with thinner sections.

b. Cell Dimensions. These are best determined by using an ocular micrometer in the photometer head. The instrument shown in Fig. 6 provides for size determinations at a magnification of 2000–5000 times. Images at these magnifications do not have sharp boundaries, so that linear dimensions involve a subjective factor, and probably can be determined at a numerical aperture of 0.4 only to ± 0.2 μ. More accurate size determinations may be obtainable especially with interference microscopes. In some instruments (Lison, 1950) the image may be projected for tracing on drawing paper, providing for convenient size measurements, particularly of irregular objects. Where determinations on nucleolar or nuclear diameter are used to compute volume, any error is obviously cubed. A diameter reading 0.2 μ too small thus provides a 5.6% error for a sphere of 10-μ diameter, and of 27% for a sphere of 2-μ diameter. Variation due to measuring error becomes much more significant with smaller structures.

c. Size of Measured Area. This dimension is of little consequence in measuring areas, for example of more or less homogeneously stained tissue sections. It is more important when measuring plugs through spheres, and very important in measuring isolated stained structures, such as smears, with the two-wavelength method. In sphere measurements the effect of an error in determining plug diameter can be computed from Table I. For example, a 5% error results in a variation of 3% in computed total dye per sphere, where the plug radius is half that of the sphere. Where the two-wavelength method is used, it is important to have the ocular micrometer and diaphragm both magnified several times and in sharp focus, so the diaphragm may be accurately set. The most accurate method of measuring area is undoubtedly that of Garcia (1962), by which the area is expressed in terms of each I_0 photometric reading as a fraction of the reading for a larger standard empty field.

d. Variation in Object Shape. In calculating total dye per nucleus or nucleolus using Table I or II, it is assumed that the measured object is a perfect sphere. This assumption seems justified with many tissues, e.g., mammalian liver parenchyma or kidney tubule cells, where nuclear volumes diviate from spheres in amounts that are small in relation to overall instrument accuracy. In other tissues, e.g., many tumors, nuclei may be markedly irregular in shape. Where a high degree of accuracy is needed, it is important to test simplifying assumptions that may be made with the two-wavelength method, or by scanning nuclei. Figure 9 shows results obtained in scanning nuclei. Of 10 nuclei examined 2 were flattened and 1 slightly elongated in the direction of the optical axis. The most aspherical of these nuclei would give a value 21% too low, were its total dye content calculated using Table II. This error in other tissues with less regular nuclei would obviously be much larger.

Large error may also be produced where a structure is assumed to be spherical but is actually cut in sectioning or overlain by another object. For Feulgen measurements it is important to cut tissue sections thick enough to provide a large number of uncut nuclei, but not too thick to allow unnecessary overlap. Such errors can be avoided only by careful observing and focusing. It is usually necessary to be able to focus on material in the section that is well above and below the nucleus measured to be sure it is uncut. Errors due to overlap may occur from out-of-focus objects even when some distance to the side of the measured area. Thus nuclei that are too close to other stained material may give values that are too large. For some tissues, such as spleen, in which nuclei are densely packed, Feulgen measurements may be very difficult. In such cases it may be necessary to homogenize a tissue, and study stained smears or suspensions. This was done for the tumor values shown in Fig. 12. Error

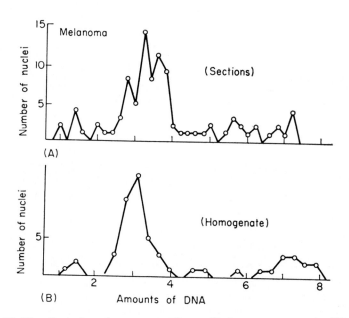

FIG. 12. The effect of specimen preparation on Feulgen measurements. (A) Values obtained from sectioned material, where overlap and irregular chromatin distribution were serious variables. (B) Part of the same tumor, measured after homogenizing in 30% sucrose. (From Bader, 1953; Swift, 1953b.)

due to cut nuclei and overlap was apparently responsible for much of the variation shown in Fig. 15A.

B. Variables from the Instrument

1. Noise

In any photometer there is fluctuation due to variation in light source output, in phototube sensitivity, and in amplifier gain. These fluctuations obviously reduce instrument accuracy and should be kept to a minimum. Line fluctuation can be reduced with constant-voltage transformers. Variable lamp output may be minimized by proper selection of light source (see page 203). The use for which an instrument is constructed should obviously influence the type of light-measuring equipment adopted. Where the two-wavelength methods is to be used, or extremely small areas measured, then sensitive amplifiers with high signal to noise ratios are recommended.

The effect of noise may be greatly reduced by taking the average of two or more readings on each object. Duplicate readings can be taken in the order I_s, I_0; I_0, I_s to cancel out any error due to slow drift in the instrument (Patau and Swift, 1953). Accuracy can be further increased if all values are arbitrarily discarded where the duplicate readings disagree by more than a certain percentage (Srinivasacher, 1953).

2. Instrument Alignment

All optical parts must obviously be carefully aligned. The importance of continual checks cannot be overstressed. A slight shift in monochromator axis, for example, may cause a wavelength shift of several millimicrons. Where the light path through a measured object is asymmetrical, conditions of absorption may be altered, lens flare greatly increased, and a less sensitive area of the phototube cathode may be illuminated. An instrument is easily tested for alignment (page 214). Poor alignment also shows up in the instrument tests discussed below.

3. Monochromator Dispersion

The Beer-Lambert laws hold only for monochromatic light. Too large a bandwidth may cause discrepancies that become greater at higher extinctions. The effect of impure light is to broaden and depress the peaks and to fill in the valleys of absorption curves. When a wide bandwidth is used a variety of intensities reach the phototube, some of which may be absorbed more than others. The photometer gives an average reading. Thus, at a given bandwidth, an extremely sharp absorption maximum may be severely depressed, where a broad absorption curve may be little effected.

The effect of bandwidth on absorption is readily tested by running absorption curves at varying slit widths on the pigments to be studied. Most dyes fortunately have broad maxima so that nominal bandwidths around 5 mμ can be used (Fig. 4). Where sharp maxima are to be measured, such as for chlorophylls (Fig. 16), narrower slit widths are required. Bandwidth is occasionally a problem at the red end of the spectrum. Dispersion of prism monochromators becomes much less in this region, and phototube sensitivity also decreased markedly.

4. Flare

Flare, as defined here, includes any stray light, in addition to the principal beam, that reaches the phototube. If the photometer is not light tight, room light may enter. This is easily checked by holding an opaque object in front of the light source and looking for phototube deflection. If the amount of background light is constant, it can readily be canceled out by the photometer zeroing adjustment. If it is variable, e.g., from a window, it should obviously be excluded.

Flare in the monochromator can be serious, since it may be the source of considerable light impurity. The monochromator should never be illuminated at more than full aperture. It is frequently necessary to place baffles of dull black material in the monochromator to minimize internal reflections. The extent of monochromator flare can be tested with line sources, such as mercury arcs, by measuring the light output on either side of an emission line. The intensity of output should drop to less than 0.2% at the wavelengths greater than two nominal bandwidths away from the emission line.

Flare in the microscope may also result in serious error (Naora, 1952; Ornstein and Pollister, 1952), and always occurs to some extent. It becomes much greater at higher condenser numerical aperatures. This is the major reason why condenser apertures should be kept low in microphotometers. An aperture of 0.3 is recommended for most photometry, although for objects below 2 μ in size, such as individual chromosomes, apertures up to 0.9 have been used (Caspersson, 1940). A few workers have used very high values, up to 1.3, on the assumption that matched condenser and objective apertures provide greatest definition. This is not necessarily justified, since the added flare produced with high apertures may reduce image contrast and thereby decrease definition (Osterberg, 1950). Optimal conditions for definition in most microscope systems appear to be a high objective aperture and a moderate aperture in the condenser (Berek, 1926). For photometry, such definition is important only for objects below

2 μ. Thus for most measurements a low aperture may be used, and flare becomes negligible. It may occasionally be desirable to determine cell dimensions with a wider aperture, and then stop down the condenser diaphragm for the absorption measurement.

Flare may be reduced by illuminating only a small central area of the microscope field with light from the monochromator. The size of the illuminated area is best controlled by the diaphragm at the monochromator exit lens. Some workers have illuminated only the exact region measured, using an inverted microscope as condenser (Naora, 1955). This makes alignment and focus exceedingly critical, makes necessary the mounting of material between two coverslips, and involves reconstruction of the photometer microscope. It is completely unnecessary except where exceedingly high condenser numerical apertures are used. Internal reflections are also reduced by placing a diaphragm in the microscope ocular, and by building the photometer bellows and head so that internal reflections are eliminated.

The extent of microscope flare is easily tested by "measuring" completely opaque objects with the photometer. For this purpose an iron-hematoxylin slide containing pycnotic nuclei is useful, but slides containing melanophores, dirt, or any small opaque objects, may be used. The area measured should be only slightly smaller than the object itself. The extinction obtained should be above 2.5, which indicates a flare error of less than 0.3%. Flare of 0.3% produces a negligible effect at extinctions below 0.5, but becomes rapidly larger at higher extinctions (i.e., 1.3% at 1.0, 3% at 1.5, and 7% at 2.0). For this reason, as well as the increased error produced by variations in scale readings, no extinctions above 1.5 should be trusted. It is preferable to adjust wavelengths so that all extinctions fall between 0.1 and 1.0. Flare, like distributional error, depresses higher extinctions more than lower. It thus can also be recognized by absorption curve analysis on homogeneous areas (Fig. 11A) or in measuring of step wedges, as described below.

5. Photometer Errors

The cathode of photomultiplier tubes is not uniformly sensitive. In tubes of the 931 A or 1 P 21 type, the cathode area of greatest sensitivity has projected dimensions of about 5 × 15 mm (Marshall et al., 1948). It is thus necessary to focus the photometer diaphragm on an area less than 5 mm across.

The photometer shown in Fig. 6 contains a lens above the diaphragm of 10-mm focal length and about 10-mm diameter. It serves to focus the measured image on the cathode, reducing the image by one-half. It is thus possible to measure areas up to slightly less than 10 mm across. With larger images, part of the area falls outside the sensitive area, and the phototube output is too low. Provision must be made for aligning the diaphragm lens and phototube, such that the phototube output is directly proportional to the diaphragm area. A graph of this relation is shown in Fig. 13. With areas that fall outside the sensitive area the output is too low. There are small local variations in sensitivity in the cathode of any phototube. The tube can usually be aligned empirically, however, so that the relation holds within 2%. For two-wavelength measurements these variations in sensitivity may produce certain errors. These can be partially corrected by placing a ground glass diffusion screen immediately in front of the phototube. Tubes of the 931 A type have a grid in front of the cathode, which should be adjusted approximately normal to the light path. Where pinpoints of light are measured, the grid wires may also produce small errors in the tube output. For this reason the light reaching the phototube should not cover too small an area, or care should be taken that light from small areas passes between grid wires.

Phototubes in general show a linear relation between incident light intensity and current output. They can, however, be overloaded by light of too great intensity, in which case the sensitivity decreases markedly, or the rate of fatigue (a slow decrease in response with time) is increased. Linearity of output is readily tested with neutral density filters which have been calibrated in other photometers, or by use of a step wedge (Fig. 14). This may be simply constructed from gelatin or cellophane sheets, from one to several thicknesses, mounted in standard mounting media on a glass slide. Cellophane is readily colored by soaking it in dye solutions. In making step wedges care must be taken to keep the thickness of mounting

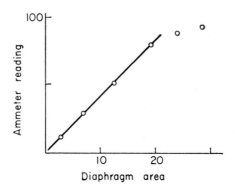

Fig. 13. The relation between phototube output and illuminated area of the cathode. Readings are too low when a portion of the measured area falls off the sensitive area of the cathode.

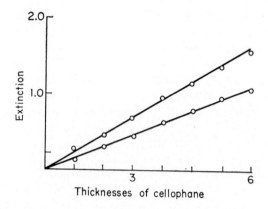

Fig. 14. Extinction values obtained by measuring a step wedge made from cello-phane soaked in formalin-regenerated Feulgen reagent. Upper line, values measured at 560 mμ; lower line, values measured at 520 mμ.

medium constant, or optical path differences may produce some error. In some cases amplifier gain may be nonlinear. This error is also demonstrated when step wedges are measured.

C. Variables from the Observer

Although microphotometers are intended to supply objective information, the accuracy of the determinations depends greatly upon the experience, skill, and judgment of the investigator. These factors can be evaluated to some extent by making duplicate readings on the same material to test observer reliability. Feulgen-stained adult rat or mouse liver makes a useful test object. In this tissue the amount of dye bound per nucleus reflects the multiple chromosome sets (polyploidy) of the nuclei, so that values fall into clearly defined groups, the means of which fit a 1:2:4 series. The actual precision with which the biological material fits this theoretical series, however, is unknown. It should not be assumed that all variation from the expected values is due to the instrument. Also, since pathological conditions may upset this relation, it is important that the animal be in a normal healthy condition. Figure 15A shows a set of readings made on a Feulgen-stained rat liver preparation during a student's first 3 days with a microphotometer. Figure 15B shows similar measurements, made by the same student on the same section after 3 weeks of experience. The reduction in variability is obvious. Although some individuals are capable of obtaining acceptable data immediately, most workers require practice. Experience is necessary for selecting and preparing material suitable for study, for accurate determination of object size, and in alignment and general handling of the instrument.

Table V shows replicate measurements on 10 mouse liver nuclei made by 10 different observers, all with some experience in microphotometry. The standard deviations for the values from any one investigator vary from 5% to 41%, indicating a much wider spread of values for some workers than others. Also the means of measurements in some cases show significant differences. As an indication of instrument reproducibility under more favorable conditions, Table VI gives values for 5 liver nuclei each measured 10 times over a period of 3 days by an experienced investigator. In this case all standard deviations fall within 3%.

VII. Testing the Instrument

The following five simple tests are suggested to demonstrate the presence of any major source of error in the photometer. It is recommended that test 1 be run each day before the photometer is used, and test 3 be made for any new dye, and on any new tissue that is to be studied.

Test 1. Determine the relation between diaphragm area and phototube reading on a uniformly lighted background area. The relation should be linear over the range of diaphragm size used for all routine measurements. It is convenient to set the photometer to read 100 at a diaphragm diameter of 5 mm. Then a 4-mm opening should read 64; 3 mm should read 36; and

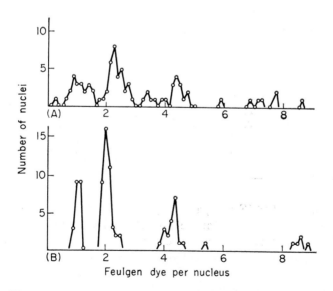

Fig. 15. The effect of observer experience on Feulgen measurements. (A) Values from adult rat liver obtained by a student during the first 3 days. (B) Values for the same section made by the same student after 3 weeks of experience.

TABLE V

MEASUREMENTS BY 10 DIFFERENT OBSERVERS ON THE SAME 10
FEULGEN-STAINED NUCLEI OF MOUSE LIVER

Nucleus	Observer									
	a	b	c	d	e	f	g	h	i	j
1	3.33	3.40	2.88	2.89	2.61	3.31	2.94	2.99	2.56	2.71
2	3.37	3.17	3.16	3.10	2.53	3.17	3.02	3.02	2.48	2.86
3	3.62	3.02	2.80	2.74	2.54	3.28	3.06	3.19	2.28	2.52
4	3.30	2.94	2.82	2.72	2.18	3.64	2.90	3.00	3.36	2.62
5	3.41	3.15	3.18	3.21	2.80	3.28	3.42	3.17	2.80	3.05
6	2.96	3.46	2.70	2.76	2.95	3.62	3.12	2.88	2.50	2.38
7	2.70	2.68	2.68	2.74	2.29	3.06	2.68	2.74	2.32	2.40
8	3.64	3.30	3.31	2.93	3.10	3.36	3.12	3.11	2.70	3.12
9	3.61	3.19	3.41	3.34	2.42	3.45	3.18	3.06	3.14	3.24
10	3.32	2.66	2.81	2.65	2.38	3.07	2.98	3.02	2.63	2.59
Mean	3.33	3.10	3.00	2.91	2.58	3.32	3.04	3.02	2.68	2.75
Standard deviation	±0.29	±0.28	±0.27	±0.24	±0.29	±0.21	±0.21	±0.14	±1.09	±0.28
Standard error	±0.10	±0.09	±0.09	±0.08	±0.10	±0.07	±0.07	±0.05	±0.36	±0.09

Nucleus	Mean	Standard deviation	Standard error
1	2.96	±0.30	±0.10
2	2.99	±0.30	±0.10
3	2.90	±0.42	±0.14
4	2.93	±0.42	±0.14
5	3.15	±0.22	±0.07
6	2.93	±0.39	±0.13
7	2.60	±0.24	±0.08
8	3.17	±0.27	±0.09
9	3.20	±0.32	±0.11
10	2.81	±0.28	±0.09

2 mm should read 16 (Fig. 13, and page 219). Nonlinearily is probably due
to misalignment of the phototube, nonuniformity of the illuminated area,
or nonlinearity of microammeter response (for example, associated with
overloading due to too high light intensities).

Test 2. Measure a small opaque object, such as an isolated nucleus
stained black with iron-hematoxylin. The extinction should be above 2.5.
If it is lower, check condenser numerical aperture, slide, and lens surfaces
for light-scattering films of dirt that might increase flare, and check internal

surfaces of the instrument that might produce reflections. Try the effect of reducing the size of the ocular diaphragm (page 231).

Test 3. Make a step wedge by soaking cellophane in the dye solution that is being studied. There should be enough steps on the wedge to produce extinctions up to 2.0 at the wavelength of maximum dye absorption. Care must be taken to avoid uneven thickness of preparations due to varying amounts of the mounting medium. Obtain extinction values at several wavelengths, as in Fig. 14. Nonlinearity may be associated with lens flare, monochromator flare, poor dispersion, or specimen flare from the slide. In Fig. 14 nonlinearity was produced by monochromator flare, causing the passing of a small amount of bluish light. When a green filter was added to the optical path and the wedge measured again at 560 mμ, the response was linear.

Test 4. Run absorption curves on adjacent lightly and darkly stained regions of the same slide. Plot extinctions as in Fig. 11. This test demonstrates the extent of specimen scatter, irregularity of background regions, distributional error, insufficient monochromator dispersion, or instrument flare.

Test 5. Measure Feulgen-stained rat or mouse liver parenchymal nuclei from a normal healthy adult. Values should be distributed as in Fig. 15B. Means of the classes should fall into a 1:2:4:8 ratio within about 5%. An

TABLE VI

REPLICATE READINGS ON 5 FEULGEN-STAINED NUCLEI OF MOUSE
LIVER MADE BY THE SAME INVESTIGATOR

Readings	Nucleus				
	1	2	3	4	5
1	2.92	3.28	3.23	3.14	3.29
2	3.06	3.22	3.15	3.00	3.39
3	3.02	3.12	3.15	3.03	3.31
4	2.92	3.16	3.26	3.03	3.43
5	2.92	3.05	3.16	3.01	3.27
6	2.98	3.15	3.13	3.03	3.41
7	2.92	3.24	3.11	2.99	3.36
8	2.92	3.24	3.10	3.19	3.37
9	2.91	3.17	3.08	3.00	3.37
10	2.59	3.10	3.21	2.93	3.34
11	2.88	3.16	3.18	3.30	3.20
Mean	2.94	3.17	3.16	3.06	3.34
Standard deviation	±0.05	±0.07	±0.06	±0.11	±0.07
Standard error	±0.02	±0.02	±0.02	±0.03	±0.02

occasional interclass value is to be expected from nuclei that were under-going DNA (deoxyribonucleic acid) synthesis when the tissue was fixed.

VIII. Examples of Microphotometer Use

Examples of uses for the microphotometer are the following:

1. Determination of the differences in pigment concentration in individual chloroplasts from living cells of the alga *Chlorella*. Figure 16 shows absorption curves made on chloroplasts of three different cells. Marked individual variation is apparent.

2. Does Beer's law hold for nucleic acid staining with the dye azure B (Flax and Himes, 1952)? Absorption curves were run on nuclei from tissue sections previously treated with ribonuclease. Figure 17 shows absorption curves from two *Tradescantia* nuclei, one in which the DNA was highly concentrated (maximum E of 0.90), and one in which it was more dilute (maximum E of 0.32). The curve shapes, when plotted on a percent scale are different, indicating Beer's law does not hold for the dye–DNA complex. Similar data are shown for dye–RNA binding in clam oocytes. Here curve shapes are practically identical for two curves with maximum E values of 0.13 and 0.42, so that Beer's law can be assumed to hold.

3. To determine the time of optimal color development for the Millon reaction, pieces of silk and denatured egg white were sectioned and mounted on slides, their tyrosine concentrations were determined by measuring the ultraviolet absorption at 280 mμ, and intensity of the Millon reaction was followed by periodic measurement of the same regions

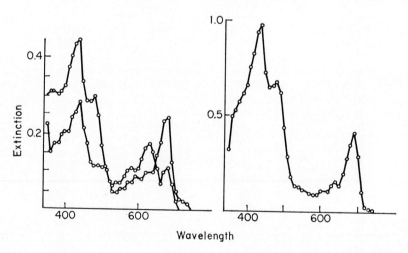

FIG. 16. Absorption curves of chloroplasts from three living cells of the alga *Chlorella*.

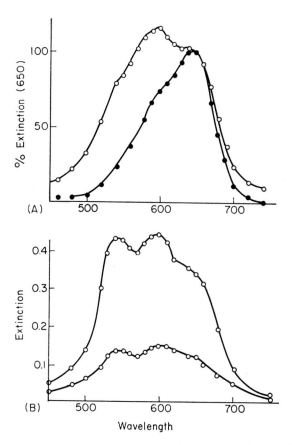

Fig. 17. (A) Absorption curves run on nuclei stained with azure B after ribonuclease treatment. In one nucleus the DNA was highly concentrated, and in the other
more dilute. The curve shapes are markedly dissimilar, indicating that Beer's law is not
followed. (B) Absorption curves run on concentrated and dilute regions of clam oocyte
cytoplasm. In this case curve shapes are similar, so that Beer's law can be considered
as holding for the conditions used.

at 500 mμ for various intervals in the Millon reagent (Fig. 18) (Rasch and
Swift, 1960).

4. To determine the relative amount of dye bound to Feulgen-stained
nuclei. Examples are given in Table VII of the calculations made on
Carnoy-fixed whole rat testis nuclei measured at 560 mμ. Results indicate
spermatids bind about one-fourth the dye of primary spermatocytes.

5. Determination of the total Millon dye bound by proteins of rat
liver nucleoli. Sections were cut at 6 μ, thick enough to allow whole nucleoli, but thin enough to cut through most nuclei. Tetraploid cells con-

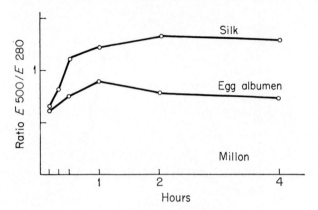

Fɪɢ. 18. Determinations of the optimal conditions for a histochemical test (here the Millon reaction, run on sections of two test proteins).

taining single nucleoli were chosen for measurement where the nucleolus was entire, but it was assumed the top and bottom had been sliced off the nucleus. Since the nucleus was also stained, absorption due to material above and below the nucleolus had to be subtracted. Section thickness was determined on folds adjacent to the measured areas (Table VIII).

6. Determination of nucleolar and cytoplasmic dye in HeLa cells in tissue culture. Whole cells on coverslips were stained for RNA (ribonucleic acid) with azure B. Flattened cells with single round or oval nucleoli were chosen for measurement, and nucleoli and cytoplasm were considered as

TABLE VII
AMOUNTS OF FEULGEN DYE BOUND PER NUCLEUS IN CELLS OF RAT TESTIS

$2R$	$2C$	I_s	I_0	E	$\dfrac{F}{C^2} (\times 10)$	$\dfrac{E}{(F/C^2)}$
		Primary Spermatocytes				
8.8×7.6	4	69.1	104	0.178	0.834	2.11
9.2×8.0	4	69.5	103	0.171	0.765	2.25
8.6×7.8	4	71.4	108	0.188	0.937	2.01
7.8×7.0	4	66.7	108	0.208	1.01	2.06
		Spermatids				
5.6×4.8	3	50.2	62.5	0.097	2.03	0.48
4.8×4.6	3	48.0	63.7	0.123	2.43	0.51
5.6×5.0	3	51.2	63.4	0.093	1.96	0.48
5.4×4.8	3	49.0	64.0	0.117	2.10	0.55

TABLE VIII
DETERMINATIONS OF TOTAL MILLON DYE BOUND PER NUCLEOLUS IN RAT LIVER CELLS[a]

Nucleolus diameter $(2R)$	Plug diameter $(2C)$	Optical path $(P_r \times 2R = p)$	E(nucleus) (E_m)	E(nucleolus) (E_s)	E(corr.) (E_c)	Total amount (M)
3.0	2.0	$0.885 \times 3 = 2.65$ $1 - \dfrac{2.65}{6.1} = 0.565$	0.185 0.185×0.565 $= 0.105$	0.274 $0.274 - 0.105 = 0.169$		0.288
2.8	2.0	$0.862 \times 2.8 = 2.41$ $1 - \dfrac{2.41}{6.1} = 0.605$	0.193 0.193×0.605 $= 0.117$	0.287 $0.287 - 0.117 = 0.170$		0.258
3.2	2.0	$0.898 \times 3.2 = 2.87$ $1 - \dfrac{2.87}{6.1} = .471$	0.168 0.168×0.471 $= 0.079$	0.269 $0.269 - 0.079 = 0.190$		0.362

[a] Mean section thickness 6.1 μ.

flat plates. The extinction of the cytoplasm overlying the nucleolus was found to be negligible. Extinctions were measured at 600 mμ through an area of 2- or 3-μ diameter in the nucleolus, and in 3 areas, each 5-μ in diameter, in the cytoplasm of each cell. Values from these readings were averaged. Camera lucida drawings were made of each cell, the areas were determined with a planimeter, and the total amount of dye was computed as extinction $\times$ area ($M = EA$) (Table IX).

TABLE IX
DETERMINATION OF TOTAL AZURE B DYE BOUND TO NUCLEOLI AND CYTOPLASM OF HeLa CELLS IN TISSUE CULTURE

Nucleolus			Cytoplasm			
E	Area	Total amount	E	$\bar{E}$	Area	Total amount
0.342	5.2	1.78	0.183 0.170 0.208	0.187	285	53.3
0.287	6.8	1.88	0.098 0.124 0.130	0.117	380	44.5
0.365	4.8	1.75	0.215 0.230 0.193	0.213	245	42.8

TABLE X
Two-Wavelength Measurements on Feulgen-Stained Lily Nuclei[a]

Curve for wavelength selection

λ	E	$E_1 \ (\lambda = 490)$	$E_2 \ (\lambda = 519)$	E_2/E_1
480	0.285	—	—	—
490	0.399*	—	—	—
495	0.458	0.375	0.748	1.99
500	0.528	0.292	0.584	2.00
510	0.662	0.419	0.839	2.00
515	0.734	0.348	0.703	2.02
517	0.764	—	—	—
518	0.780	—	—	—
519	0.796*	—	—	—
520	0.812	—	—	—

		I_s	I_0	T	$\bar{T}$	L	
Zygotene	λ_1	45.0	58.2	0.774	0.773	0.227	$L_2/L_1 = 1.56$
Field diameter $= 5$		44.9	58.3	0.771			$D = 1.143$
	λ_2	52.0	80.6	0.645	0.646	0.354	$L_1D = 0.260$
		51.8	80.3	0.647			$C^2 = 6.25$

$$E_2 = 0.190 \qquad\qquad M = 0.260 \times 6.25 = 16.2$$
$$\% \ de = 1 - \frac{0.190}{0.260} = 27.0$$

		I_s	I_0	T	$\bar{T}$	L	
Metaphase II	λ_1	36.2	45.5	0.796	0.794	0.206	$L_2/L_1 = 1.66$
Field diameter $= 4$		36.0	45.5	0.792			$D = 1.059$
	λ_2	40.9	62.2	0.658	0.658	0.342	$L_1D = 0.218$
		40.8	62.0	0.658			$C^2 = 4$

$$E_2 = 0.182 \qquad\qquad M = 0.218 \times 4 = 8.72$$
$$\% \ de = 1 - \frac{0.182}{0.218} = 16.5$$

[a] Duplicate readings were made on each nucleus and the transmissions were averaged ($\bar{T}$). Total amount (M) was calculated as $M = L_1DC^2$, where C is the radius of the measured area. The factor π was omitted (see page 225).

7. Determination of Feulgen dye bound to prophase and metaphase chromosomes in a section of lily anther. Here the two-wavelength method was used because of the highly irregular dye distribution (Table X).

8. Determination of amounts of cytoplasmic dye per cell in rat liver. Tissue sections were stained for RNA with azure B. Section thickness was

TABLE XI
DETERMINATIONS OF CYTOPLASMIC AZURE B BOUND PER CELL IN SECTIONS OF RAT LIVER[a]

Area	I_{s1} I_{s2}	I_{01} I_{02}	L_1 L_2	L_2/L_1 D	(E_2) L_1D
1	48.3	63.1	0.234	1.56	(0.196)
	46.0	72.3	0.364	1.143	0.268
2	50.0	63.0	0.206	1.68	(0.185)
	47.2	72.4	0.374	1.045	0.215
3	46.1	63.0	0.268	1.68	(0.259)
	40.0	72.6	0.450	1.045	0.280
4	46.0	63.1	0.271	1.70	(0.269)
	39.0	77.4	0.461	1.031	0.279
5	45.3	62.8	0.280	1.66	(0.272)
	38.7	72.3	0.465	1.059	0.296

[a] Sample measurements and calculations are given for five areas 5 μ in diameter, taken through the cytoplasm.

$\lambda_1 = 515$ mμ; $\lambda_2 = 534$ mμ.
Mean section thickness = 5.9 μ.
Mean L_1D = 0.267.

Conc. $= \dfrac{E}{d} = \dfrac{0.267}{5.9} = 0.0453.$

Nuclear-cytoplasmic ratio = 15.0.
Mean nuclear volume = 265 μ^3.
Mean cytoplasmic volume = 15.0 $\times$ 265 = 3980 μ^3.
Dye per cell = 0.0453 $\times$ 3980 = 180.

determined on folds adjacent to measured areas. For each section 20 areas, each 5 μ in diameter, were chosen at random through parenchymal cell cytoplasm. Since the dye showed irregular distribution, measurements were made with the two-wavelength method. Nuclear–cytoplasmic ratios were estimated from 1000 point hits with the Chalkley (1943) method. Nuclear volume was determined for 50 nuclei taken at random from all polyploid classes, and the cytoplasmic volume was computed. Total amount of dye per parenchymal cell was calculated as $M = EV/d$, where (d) is section thickness, and (V) is cytoplasmic volume (Table XI).

REFERENCES

Alfert, M. (1950). *J. Cellular Comp. Physiol.* **36,** 381.
Alfert, M. (1952). *Biol. Bull.* **103,** 145.
Anderson, W. T. (1951). *J. Opt. Soc. Am.* **41,** 385.
Bader, S. (1953). Ph.D. Thesis, Univ. of Chicago, Chicago, Illinois.
Bateman, J. B., and Monk, G. W. (1955). *Science* **121,** 441.
Berek, M. (1926). *Sitzber. Ges. Befoerder. Ges. Naturw. Marburg* **61,** 251.
Blout, E. R., Bird, G. R., and Grey, D. S. (1950). *J. Opt. Soc. Am.* **40,** 304.
Caspersson, T. (1936). *Skand. Arch. Physiol.* **73,** Suppl. 8. 1–151.
Caspersson, T. (1940). *Chromosoma* **1,** 562.
Caspersson, T. (1941). *Chromosoma* **2,** 247.

Chalkley, H. W. (1943). *J. Natl. Cancer Inst.* 4, 47.

Chance, B. (1951). *Rev. Sci. Instr.* 22, 619.

Chance, B. (1954). *Science* 120, 767–768.

Commoner, B. (1948). *Ann. Missouri Botan. Garden* 35, 239.

Commoner, B. (1949). *Science* 110, 31.

Deeley, E. M. (1955). *J. Sci. Instr.* 32, 263–267.

Eastman Kodak Co. (1945). "Wratten Light Filters." Rochester, New York.

Flax, M. H., and Himes, M. H. (1952). *Physiol. Zool.* 25, 297.

Françon, M. (1961). "Progress in Microscopy." Row, Peterson, New York.

Garcia, A. M. (1962). *Histochemie* 3, 178–194.

Garcia, A. M. (1965). *J. Histochem. Cytochem.* 13, 161–167.

Garcia, A. M. (1968). *Ann. N.Y. Acad. Sci.* (in press).

Glick, D., Engström, A., and Malmström, B. G. (1951). *Science* 114, 253.

Greco, J. P. (1950). *Stain Technol.* 25, 11.

Hiskey, C. F. (1955). *Phys. Tech. Biol. Res.* 1, 74–129.

Hyden, H. (1943). *Acta Physiol. Scand.* 6, Suppl. 17, 1.

Jensen, M. J. (1961). *Histochemie* 2, 342–347.

Kasten, A. (1956). *Physiol. Zool.* 29, 1.

Kasten, F. (1960). *Intern. Rev. Cytol.* 10, 1–100.

Korson, R. (1951). *J. Exptl. Med.* 93, 121.

Lison, L. (1950). *Acta Anat.* 10, 333.

Marshall, F., Coltman, J. W., and Bennett, A. I. (1948). *Rev. Sci. Instr.* 19, 744.

Mellors, R., Kupfer, A., and Hollender, A. (1953). *Cancer* 6, 372.

Mendelsohn, M. (1958a). *J. Biophys. Biochem. Cytol.* 4, 407–414.

Mendelsohn, M. (1958b). *J. Biophys. Biochem. Cytol.* 4, 415–424.

Mendelsohn, M. (1961). *J. Biophys. Biochem. Cytol.* 11, 509–513.

Mendelsohn, M. (1966). *In* "Quantitative Cytochemistry" (G. L. Wied, ed.). Academic Press, New York.

Michaelis, L. (1947). *Cold Spring Harbor Symp. Quant. Biol.* 12, 131.

Moses, M. J. (1952). *Expt. Cell Res. Suppl.* 2, 75.

Naora, H. (1952). *Science* 115, 248.

Naora, H. (1955). *Exptl. Cell Res.* 8, 259.

Ornstein, L. (1952). *Lab. Invest.* 1, 250.

Ornstein, L., and Pollister, A. W. (1952). *Science* 116, 203.

Oster, G. (1953). *Anal. Chem.* 25, 1165.

Osterberg, H. (1950). *J. Opt. Soc. Am.* 40, 295.

Patau, K. (1952). *Chromosoma* 5, 341.

Patau, K., and Swift, H. (1953). *Chromosoma* 6, 149.

Pollister, A. W. (1948). *Cold Spring Harbor Symp. Quant. Biol.* 12, 147–157.

Pollister, A. W. (1952). *Lab. Invest.* 1, 106.

Pollister, A. W. (1955). *In* "Radiation Biology" (A. Hollaender, ed.), Vol. 2, pp. 203–248. McGraw-Hill, New York.

Pollister, A. W. (1965). *J. Morphol.* 116, 89–98.

Pollister, A. W., and Moses, M. J. (1949). *J. Gen. Physiol.* 32, 567.

Pollister, A. W., and Ornstein, L. (1959). *In* "Analytical Cytology" (R. Mellors, ed.). McGraw-Hill, New York.

Pollister, A. W., and Ris, H. (1947). *Cold Spring Harbor Symp. Quant. Biol.* 12, 147.

Pollister, A. W., and Swift, H. (1950). *Science* 111, 68.

Rasch, E., and Swift, H. (1960). *J. Histochem. Cytochem.* 8, 4–17.

Shillaber, L. P. (1944). "Photomicrography." Wiley, New York.

Srinivasacher, D. (1953). Ph.D. Thesis, Univ. of Wisconsin, Madison, Wisconsin.

Stockbarger, D. C., and Burns, L. (1933). *J. Opt. Soc. Am.* **23,** 379.

Swift, H. (1950a). *Physiol. Zool.* **23,** 169–184.

Swift, H. (1950b). *Proc. Natl. Acad. Sci. U.S.* **36,** 643.

Swift, H. (1953a). *Intern. Rev. Cytol.* **2,** 1.

Swift, H. (1953b). *Texas Rept. Biol. Med.* **11,** 755.

Swift, H. (1966).

Theorell, H., and Chance, B. (1954). *Acta Chem. Scand.* **5,** 1127.

Thorell, B. (1947). *Acta Med. Scand. Suppl.* **200,** 1.

Uber, F. (1939). *Am. J. Botany* **26,** 799.

Vendrely, R. (1955). *In* "The Nucleic Acids" (E. Chargaff and J. N. Davidson, eds.). Academic Press, New York.

Vialli, M., and Perugini, S. (1954). *Riv. Istochim. Norm. Patol.* **1,** 149.

Walker, P. M. B., and Richards, B. M. (1959). *In* "The Cell" (J. Brachet and A. E. Mirsky, eds.), Vol. 1, pp. 91–138. Academic Press, New York.

Wang, H. (1949). *Anat. Record* **105,** 537.

Wied, G., ed. (1966). "Introduction to Quantitative Cytochemistry." Academic Press, New York.

CHAPTER 5

Fluorescence Microspectrophotometry of Supravitally Stained Cells[1]

SEYMOUR S. WEST

I. Introduction

Cytochemists have long been aware of the desirability and need to conduct their investigations on living, functioning cells. Unfortunately, the extremely small quantities of substance present in cells have, in the past, precluded such investigations. Generally available analytical tech-

[1] This work was supported, in part, by U.S.P.H. Grants A-2301, DE-2670, and JPL (NASA) Contract 951925.

253

niques are not sufficiently sensitive. Consequently, the chemical composition and the chemical activity of the structures composing cells and tissues are investigated in fixed microscopic preparations. These studies are paralleled by experimental investigations conducted on substances isolated or extracted from cells and tissues. These methods have yielded and will, no doubt, continue to yield much valuable information. But, in the absence of direct experimental evidence, this information is applicable to the living cell only by inference.

The large and rapidly growing body of knowledge derived from fixed microscopic preparations and from *in vitro* biophysical chemical, and biochemical investigations adds emphasis to the long-appreciated need for investigating these characteristics of the cell in the living cell itself. Of particular importance is the identification and localization of the various intracellular constituents, either directly or by the product of their interaction with chemicals (i.e., dyes) introduced into the cell. It is also necessary to know whether the molecular structure and physical-chemical behavior of isolated intracellular constituents is the same as in the intact cell. Equally important is the measurement of the concentrations of given intracellular constituents *in situ*, the changes in concentration in various functional states, and the bearing on cell physiology. Worthy of reemphasis is the importance of obtaining cytochemical data that are directly comparable with data obtained from model systems.

For these reasons, new cytochemical methods capable of overcoming the limitations of classical techniques have been sought. Television fluorescence microspectrophotometry (West, 1965) is one such method. It is capable of dealing quantitatively with the extremely small amounts of substance present inside a living cell. It can produce data that can be compared directly with those derived from *in vitro* studies on model systems. It preserves intercellular differences as well as the morphology of the cell. Selected biochemical components of the cell may be identified, localized, and studied in their native state and *in situ*. With the aid of appropriate fluorescent vital dyes the spectrum of intracellular substances made available for study can be broadened and the possibilities for investigations in depth on a given intracellular constituent increased. Direct comparison of the data obtained from living cells with that obtained from *in vitro* model systems is possible.

Although certain intrinsically fluorescent substances, notably riboflavin and vitamin A, have been detected and identified in living cells by photographic microspectrofluorophotometry, the use of fluorescent vital dyes has much to recommend it. Highly conjugated planar dye molecules in solution may interact to form molecular complexes that have physical properties different from the dye in monodispersed form (Rabinowitch and Epstein, 1941; Förster, 1951; Zanker, 1952). The phenomenon of metachromasy is one result of such behavior. Aggregation of the dye molecules is accompanied by the following behavior:

1. Beer's law is not obeyed.

2. Absorption and fluorescence spectra are altered as a function of environmental conditions. These include concentration, pH, solvent, temperature, and the particular polymer to which the dye is bound (Bradley and Wolf, 1959, 1960; Stone and Bradley, 1961, 1967; Stone, 1967; Weill and Calvin, 1963).

3. Dyes may exhibit induced optical rotatory dispersion (induced Cotton effect) when bound to certain asymmetric polymers (Blout and Stryer, 1959; Neville and Bradley, 1961; Stone and Moss, 1967; Eyring et al., 1968).

4. Other properties such as viscosity (Drummond et al., 1966) are also found to vary.

At present, only some of these aspects of the behavior of dye–polymer complexes can be observed with the microscope in cells stained with metachromatic dyes. These include fluorescence and absorption spectra. A microscope spectropolarimeter is being developed (West, 1967). Hopefully, the studies of the polymer chemists will stimulate further additions to microscope technique to permit comparison between in vivo and in vitro data over a broad range of phenomena. The complexity of biological macromolecules makes it doubtful that they can be completely characterized on the basis of only one kind of phenomenological investigation. But all the above-listed phenomena are interrelated. As the data and insights of the polymer chemists accumulate, it should be possible to infer some of the unmeasurable behavioral aspects from the measurable when dealing with stained cells.

The emphasis on stained cells is due to the fact that it is always the dye and the changes in the dye that are detected and measured by the cytochemist. Dyes are relatively simple molecules, which can be prepared in pure form. Understanding their behavior can be extended to the limits afforded by modern chemistry. When dye is bound to a biological macromolecule, certain conclusions can be drawn with respect to the macromolecule in the light of the observed alterations in the behavior of the dye. The problem presented by the macromolecule has been reduced to a study of a simpler dye molecule. The extent to which this provides understanding of the behavior of the macromolecule will depend upon the nature of the macromolecule, the nature of the dye-macromolecule interaction, the nature of the dye, the kinds of experiments that are performed, and the kind of observations that are made. In the case of the living cell, physiological requirements place limits on the extent of experimental variation of environmental parameters. Much broader limits exist for *in vitro* studies. Thus, if appropriate cytochemical investigations are conducted, the polymer chemist may not only provide data for comparison, but may also provide direct extension of the cytochemical results.

Spectroscopy is of particular interest. Absorption and fluorescence spectra may serve to identify and characterize a compound or molecular species even when it is present in a mixture, and without prior chemical separation. Alterations in the molecular state of planar dye molecules in solution, or when bound to polymers that lead to changes in the optical properties are associated with the formation of dimers and higher polymers of the dye. Polymer formation results from the interaction of the energy levels of adjacent dye molecules (Rabinowitch and Epstein, 1941). The new energy levels are different from those of the monomer. Hence, the position and intensity of the absorption and fluorescence bands in a given spectrum reflect the relative amounts of monomer and polymer. The relative proportions vary with concentration, temperature, ionic strength, dielectric constant, binding substrate(s), and other environmental parameters.

Fluorescence microspectroscopy is one method for placing these characteristics of fluorescent metachromatic dyes at the disposal of the cytochemist. Over and above the already listed characteristics of such dyes is the fact that they are truly vital dyes and are also fluorescent. As vital dyes they permit the cytochemical investigation of living cells. As fluorescent dyes they provide extremely high sensitivity in terms of absolute quantity of substance. The dye, as a foreign substance in the cell, is cytochemically useful and informative in such small quantities as to have little or no measurable effect on cell physiology in acute experiments. For chronic experiments, however, mutagenic (Orgel, 1961) and possible phototoxic effects must be taken into account. In principle, absorption spectroscopy provides comparable information. However, in terms of absolute quantity, it is less sensitive by several orders of magnitude. Large intracellular quantities of dye are required for minimum detectable signal, and, aside from possible toxic effects, the very interesting behavior at low intracellular dye concentrations is simply not detectable.

The fluorescence emitted by a fluorochrome-stained cell may be photosensitive and fade upon irradiation with fluorescence-exciting light. When fading occurs it is not necessarily uniform across the fluorescence spectrum. Consequently, any spectroscopic recording method that requires long exposure times such as photography or scanning with a single multiplier phototube will generally result in distortion of the intensity values as one passes from one end of the spectrum to the other. Also the degree of fading after a given interval of irradiation varies with the intracellular dye content and the type of cell. Thus, it does not appear to be either practical or useful to try to take account of the fading by measuring exposure time or similar procedure. Further, *in vitro* studies display different fading behavior from that observed with supravitally stained cells and so cannot be used to correct the spectra from cells.

Thus, an extremely high sensitivity and rapid means for recording the fluorescence emission spectra from cells must be provided. A television system employing an image-intensifier orthicon satisfies these requirements and places fluorescence spectroscopy of individual fluorochrome-stained cells, or portions thereof, at the disposal of the cytochemist.

ACRIDINE ORANGE, A METACHROMATIC DYE

A large number of metachromatic fluorochromes can be used as cytological stains (Richards, 1955; Price and Schwartz, 1956; Reichert Optische Werke, 1963). Many of them can also be used as vital dyes. There is, as yet, insufficient information (as measured by fluorescence microspectroscopy) available as to which of these dyes would be most useful or have particular merit for a given cytochemical investigation. The *in vitro* systems, though providing important clues, do not necessarily display all the effects that can be observed in cells. Also, it is necessary to establish the fact that data from living cells can be expressed in the same terms as those used for solution studies before one can proceed to exploit further the properties of metachromatic dyes as cytochemical agents. Thus, acridine orange (AO), a diaminoacridine (Albert, 1951; Venkataraman, 1952), was chosen for these preliminary studies since the literature already contains the results of a number of physical chemical investigations.

Acridine orange is a planar dye molecule which is fully dissociated in the neighborhood of pH 7, existing as the cation (Strugger, 1949, page 60; Zanker, 1952). The formula shown depicts one of two equivalent resonating structures.

Systems of numbering acridine ring.

Zanker (1952) studied the absorption and fluorescence spectra of acridine orange in aqueous solutions. As a monomer, at low concentrations (pH 6.0), it has an absorption maximum at 490 nm and a fluorescence peak at 535 nm. As a polymer at higher concentrations, acridine orange has an absorption peak at 455 nm and an emission peak at 660 nm. The absorption peak of the monomer does not change its position with dilution, but that of the polymer does. The corresponding fluorescence spectra show slight alterations of peak position. In both cases, the relative heights of the maxima vary with dilution. These results are shown in Figs. 1 and 2 reproduced from Zanker's paper. Note that the long wave-

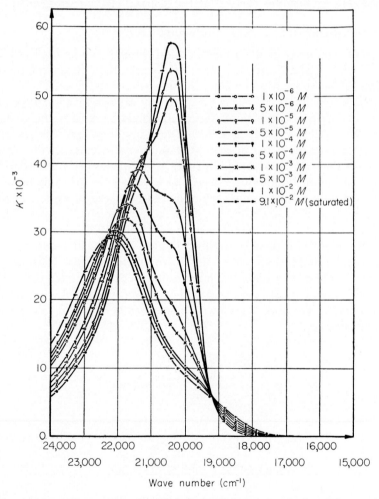

FIG. 1. Absorption spectra of acridine orange in aqueous solution. Solvent: citrate-phosphate buffer, pH 6.0, 20°C. (From Zanker, 1952.)

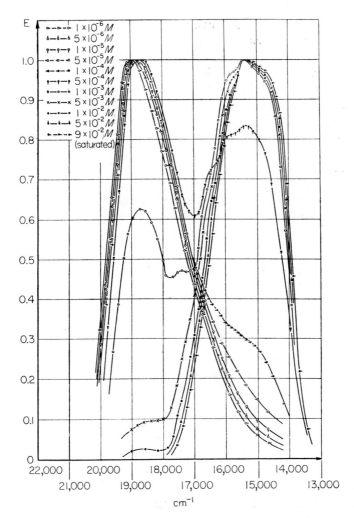

FIG. 2. Fluorescence spectra of acridine orange in aqueous solution. Solvent: citrate-phosphate buffer, pH 6.0, 20°C. (From Zanker, 1952.)

length absorption peak (490 nm) can be identified with the short wavelength fluorescence peak (535 nm) and the short wavelength absorption peak (455 nm) can be identified with the long wavelength fluorescence peak (660 nm). On the basis of these results, Zanker proposed a stacked-coin model for the structural configuration of the AO polymer. Low temperature studies (Zanker, *et al.*, 1959) confirmed these conclusions.

Studies (Loeser *et al.*, 1960; Bradley and Wolf, 1960) of the absorption and fluorescence spectra of solutions of nucleic acid (NA) and AO show that at least two distinct complexes may be formed. When the ratio of dye to NA is small (moles of dye per moles of phosphate or nucleotides) the complex formed has an absorption maximum at 502 nm (complex II) (Steiner and Beers, 1961) compared to the 490 nm maximum of the dye alone in the monomeric state. Complexes of this kind are easily recognized when less than 15–20% of the phosphate residues interact with the dye (actually when the binding is in the order of one acridine orange molecule for every 5 nucleotides or less). Complexes of this type are relatively stable with respect to variation in ionic strength, temperature, and dielectric constant (Loeser et al., 1960). When the amount of AO is increased relative to the NA, another complex is formed that absorbs at approximately 465 nm (complex I) (Steiner and Beers, 1961) and is less stable than the first with changes in ionic strength, temperature, and dielectric constant of the solution. It can be readily shown that both absorbing species can coexist in solution under the proper conditions and can be distinguished from one another. The second type of complex seems more nearly amenable to treatment in terms of the stacked-coin model (Michaelis, 1950).

Modifications also exist in the fluorescence emission spectra of the two kinds of complexes. The 502 nm absorbing species (complex II) has an emission maximum at 540 nm while the complex absorbing at 465 nm (complex I) characteristically has an emission maximum at 660 nm.

These results may be summarized as follows:

1. Two molecular complexes result from the interaction of NA with AO, the relative amount of each depending on the solution conditions.

2. At low dye to nucleotide ratios a relatively stable complex is formed, absorbing at 502 nm and emitting at 540 nm (complex II).

3. At high dye to nucleotide ratios a second complex is formed, absorbing at 465 nm and emitting at 660 nm (complex I), whose emission is markedly sensitive to changes in dielectric constant, temperature, and ionic strength.

4. Formation of the 465 nm absorbing species, as the ratio of dye to NA increases, is at the expense of the complex absorbing at 502 nm, although the fluorescence emission characteristics of the 502 nm complex seem to be unaltered. There are reports in the literature that disagree with the latter half of the above statement (Oster, 1951), but the concentration ranges of dye and substrate are not comparable to those reported here.

5. The spectra of the complexes do not distinguish between RNA and DNA.

6. In the case of NA-AO complexes the absorption and emission maxima characteristic of the polymer are the same as those for the dye alone in aqueous solution. This is coincidental. If the dye molecules are bound to fixed sites on the macromolecule, then the spacing of these sites

is such as to produce similar dye to dye interaction and, hence, similar spectra. Indeed the strength of the dye to dye interaction varies with the dye and the particular polymer.

Peacocke and Skerrett (1956) have shown that DNA combines with proflavine (a diaminoacridine) in at least two different ways. Holding the DNA concentration constant and increasing the dye concentration, they observed that two distinct binding processes are involved: (I), a stable, strong binding between proflavine and DNA that is found when less than 22% of the available sites on the DNA molecules are bound with the dye, and (II), a weak binding of a different kind that is found when more than 22% of the available sites are bound. They interpreted process (I) as the direct combination of single dye cations with the binding sites on the DNA. Process (II) was considered to be the combination of dye aggregates with the DNA, and it reached saturation when all the remaining binding sites were occupied. Processes (I) and (II) correspond to the formation of complexes (II) and (I), respectively. RNA-diaminoacridine complexes behave similarly (Loeser et al., 1960).

In view of the above evidence that AO–DNA complexes are spectroscopically indistinguishable from AO–RNA complexes, the discussion of AO–DNA complexes (see below) is assumed to be applicable to AO–RNA complexes whenever RNA is found to form a complex with the dye. Some investigators have suggested that AO–RNA and AO–DNA complexes may be distinguished from each other spectrophotometrically (Beers et al., 1958). However, in similar studies by Loeser et al. (1960) over even greater concentration ranges, AO–RNA and AO–DNA complexes were found to be spectrophotometrically indistinguishable.

Since the concern here is with the staining of cells with AO, it is important to consider the effect of the intracellular environment. AO has a pK of 10.45 (Zanker, 1952), exists as the cation at lower pH values, and is 100% ionized in the neighborhood of pH 7. In solutions, buffered to approximately pH 7, the phosphoric acid residues on the NA molecule are ionized (Levene and Simms, 1925) and form complexes with the dye. For the cell, the intranuclear pH is 7.6–7.8, while the pH of the cytoplasm is 6.8 (Langridge et al., 1957). Thus, one can expect, at least with regard to the nucleic acids, that spectroscopic data from AO-stained cells will resemble that from AO–NA complexes in solution.

II. Historical

A. VITAL STAINING

Vital staining, first introduced by Ehrlich (1909), aroused great interest as a means of staining cells *in vivo*. The method, however, proved to be limited. The vital stains used by Ehrlich acted upon the cells of one system of the body—the reticuloendothelial—and to lesser degree on the fibrocytes of connective tissue. Nuclei were not stained. The method was used to investigate the origin and identify the histiocyte (Evans and Schulemann, 1914). It was through the use of these vital stains that the concept of the "reticuloendothelial system" was arrived at by Aschoff (1924). After 1920 the method was rarely used.

At the end of the 1920's a new class of vital dyes was introduced by Ellinger and Hirt (1929, 1930, 1931). These authors, though concerned primarily with the study of kidney and liver function, reported that the nuclei of the cells of these organs stained *in vivo* with the fluorescent dye acriflavine. In contrast, detectable staining of nuclei *in vivo* with nonfluorescent dyes could be accomplished only by subjecting cells to harmful treatments (Nassonov, 1930, 1932; Alexandrov, 1932–1933; Kamnev, 1934). Ellinger and a number of other workers went on to use fluorescent dyes in a series of *vital* studies on the function of kidney, liver, and other parts of the body. Ellinger's review article (1940) covers the early work on intravital fluorescence microscopy thoroughly. Tonutti (1946) and Zeiger and Harders (1951) reported on the vital staining of nervous tissue with acridine orange. During this same period a great deal of work was carried out by microbiologists and others to establish the fluorescent dyes and acridine orange, in particular, as truly vital dyes. This work has been reviewed by Strugger (1949) in a monograph. Especially noteworthy are the observations of Strugger (1940) that vital staining of chromosomes with acridine orange does not interfere with mitosis. Vital and supravital studies on animal cells were also reported by Schümmel feder (1950) and Stockinger (1958). Zeiger and Harders (1951) and Zeiger and Wiede (1954) extended the application of vital fluorochroming to nervous tissue and frog liver, respectively.

Though Strugger was aware of the potential of acridine orange as a cytochemical agent, credit should be accorded to DeBruyn and his co-workers (1950) for first relating the staining of the nucleus with acridine orange and other fluorochromes to particular intranuclear biochemical constituents. These investigators conducted a systematic histological investigation of the *in vivo* staining properties of the diaminoacridines. The dyes were administered orally or parenterally. Many tissues of the body were examined for fluorescence. The fluorescence pattern of nuclei stained *in vivo* was well defined and resembled the chromatin pattern after staining fixed material with ordinary dyes.

In a later study (DeBruyn, 1953) the diamioacridines were shown to stain the nucleoproteins of the nucleus without distinguishing the ribonucleoprotein from the deoxyribonucleoprotein. A cell which had been stained *in vivo* with a diaminoacridine (proflavine hydrochloride) was fixed after fluorescence examination and restained with either the methyl green-pyronin or the Feulgen methods. With the exception that the diaminoacridines always stained the nucleolus so that it was indistinguishable from the rest of the chromatin, the fluorescence staining pattern corresponded exactly to that obtained with the Feulgen and methyl green-pyronin methods. These workers also found that other basic fluorescent dyes failed to stain the nucleus *in vivo* and concluded that *in vivo* staining of the nucleus is peculiar to the diaminoacridines. Nevertheless, Briggs (1952) following the work of Hertwig (1924) and Dalcq (1931) was able to inactivate frog sperm nuclei with a number of thiazines (toluidine blue, methylene blue, and thionine). Hertwig and Dalcq both had used trypaflavine. Briggs found, as had Hertwig and Dalcq before him, that frog eggs fertilized with the stained sperm gave rise to haploid tadpoles. Minimum dye uptake of the sperm required for complete inactivation was approximately 6.7×10^{-18} mole per sperm cell. Also, damage to sperm nuclei did not occur in the dark, a finding previously reported by Drebinger (1951).

DeBruyn *et al.* (1950) also found that the diaminoacridines varied considerably with respect to toxicity, duration of nuclear staining after administration of the dye, and brightness of fluorescence of individual tissues. Acridine orange was the least toxic of the dyes tested. No toxic or degenerative changes were observed for *any* of the diaminoacridines at low dose levels, yet adequate nuclear staining was observed. Rabbit leukocytes in tissue cultures stained *in vivo* with diaminoacridines survived as well as those from control cultures. Moreover, the rate of regeneration of the liver in the rat was the same in animals with or without injections of diaminoacridines. Species differences were not observed in the rabbit, guinea pig, rat, and mouse.

Krebs and Gierlach (1951) used acridine orange as a vital fluorochrome in radiobiology and Krieg (1954) studied yeast cell morphology in similar fashion.

B. METACHROMASY

Tissues or cells, fixed or unfixed, stained with fluorochromes (fluorescent dyes) may show fluorescence colors different from the fluorescence color of the dye in dilute solution. Indeed, within a single preparation various structures may fluoresce with different colors. Similarly, some dyes observed by absorption can stain different histological elements with different colors. This effect is called metachromasy. Fluorescence metachromasy is related to absorption metachromasy in the case of fluorescent substances. A brief review of metachromasy is given below. Detailed reviews can be found in Schubert and Hamerman (1956) and Bergeron and Singer (1958).

As early as 1875, approximately 20 years after the introduction of synthetic dyes, Cornil (1875a,b), Heschl (1875), and Jürgens (1875) reported that certain dyes stained amyloid with a different color from that of the dye in dilute solution. Shortly thereafter, Ehrlich (1879) found that alteration of the color upon binding of the dye could be used to identify granulated cells of connective tissue and eosinophilic leukocytes. He termed the effect *metachromasy* and called the color that was different from that of the dye in dilute solution *metachromatic*. The substance which stains in the metachromatic color was called a *chromotrope*. These and other early investigators offered a number of possible explanations for metachromasy.

In most of the early work color was judged visually. The stained material was heterogeneous, and the light sources were not standard. Results were not uniform among the workers and were difficult to compare or reconcile with each other. Spectroscopic analysis was employed by Lison (1935) to study the effects of various environmental parameters on the absorption spectra of solutions of metachromatic dyes and dye–chromotrope systems. He noted that metachromasy was a reversible phenomenon but could find no stoichiometric relationship between dye and chromotrope. Scheibe (1938), though not the first to suggest the importance of aggregation in the metachromatic phenomenon, conducted a series of detailed investigations from which he concluded that new absorption bands in a dye spectrum were due to the formation of dye polymers, a reversible process, in which he believed van der Waals forces were involved. Rabinowitch and Epstein (1941) also attributed the metachromasy of dyestuffs in solution to polymerization. They determined the spectra of dye solutions at different temperatures and concentrations in water and in ethanol–water mixtures. They rigorously explained deviations from Beer's law as due to the formation of dimeric ions of the dyes. Dimerization did not occur in pure ethanol and was reduced in ethanol-water mixtures. Other properties of dyestuff solutions (oxidation-reduction potentials, conductivity, osmotic pressure, etc.) were in accord with the dimerization hypothesis. Sheppard (1942) and Sheppard and Geddes (1944a,b) also supported the dimerization hypothesis. In the earlier paper, Sheppard made the observation that the molecules of the substrate are the centers of orientation which attract the polar groups of the dyestuffs. This and aggregation of the dyestuff appear to be requirements for metachromasy. Bank and Bungenberg de Jong (1939), Wiame (1947), and Michaelis (1947, 1950), all stressed the importance of the substrate in the phenomenon of metachromasy. However, they could not explain the observed dye-substrate interactions satisfactorily. Singer (1954) suggested that clustered binding could account for results observed with model systems (agar gel). Morthland, DeBruyn, and Smith (1954) investigated solutions of mixtures of nucleic acids and aminoacridines and other basic dyes with absorption spectrophotometry. In several cases they noted that DNA had a greater effect on the dye spectra than did RNA. However, the sources of DNA and RNA were not stated, nor were the concentrations of the nucleic acids derived from phosphorus determination. They concluded that the amino groups in the 3 and 6 position on the acridine orange molecule interact with the phosphoric acid groups of the nucleic acid molecule, and they proposed a model wherein the planar dye molecules are interleaved between the nucleotides. Lerman (1961, 1963, 1964) has also proposed that acridines and related compounds bind to DNA by intercalation. Bradley (1961) stated that if it is assumed that coupling occurs between dye molecules held to fixed sites on the polymer, then dye aggregation should depend on the intersite spacing on the polymer. Thus, dye aggregation should vary with polymer conformation and provide a means for investigating polymer structure. He went on to state that by using a combination of statistical and quantum mechanical methods, it should be possible to relate all of the absorption, emission, equilibrium constant, and optical rotation observations in a unified way. With these considerations in mind, Bradley and his co-workers have been studying the optical properties of dye–polymer complexes (Stone and Bradley, 1961, 1967; Neville and Bradley, 1961; Stone, 1964, 1967; Stone and Moss, 1967). Statistical treatment of the aggregation phenomenon (Bradley and Wolf, 1959) has resulted in the proposal that dye aggregation on a given polymer can be described in terms of a "stacking coefficient" which is proportional to the free energy of interaction of a pair of neighboring dye molecules. There is evidence that the value of the stacking coefficient is related to the conformation of the polymer. The more highly ordered the polymer, the smaller the stacking coefficient, i.e., the more random the binding sites of the dye on the polymer. Native DNA has a stacking coefficient of 1.25 which increases to 6.2 upon helix-coil denaturation. RNA has a stacking coefficient of 3, while certain acid polysaccharides have stacking coefficients greater than 800. This means that aggregation of dye on the polymer will occur at very small dye to polymer ratios when the stacking coefficient is large. On this basis, deep red (peak emission approximately 700 nm) granules observed in AO-stained cells, with very low intracellular dye content, can be considered to have a large stacking coefficient and, hence, cannot be considered a nucleic acid (West, 1963).

Goessner (1949) used RNase to show that the red fluorescence in acridine orange-stained fixed material was due to the presence of RNA. von Bertalanffy and Bickis (1956) investigated acridine orange staining to detect RNA in fresh smears, fresh frozen sections, and conventionally fixed tissues. They concluded that, under supravital conditions, acridine orange staining allows identification of RNA in the cytoplasm. Armstrong (1956) studied the staining properties of acridine orange in a variety of fixed tissues and noted marked differences in the affinity of various tissues, cells, and cell components for the dye in the pH range 1.5–6. The most remarkable results occurred between pH 3.6 and 5.2, when a wide range of spectral colors were seen together in one section. He identified the red fluorescence with RNA and the greenish-yellow fluorescence with DNA. Armstrong and Niven (1957) and Mayer (1963) used this method of differentiating DNA from RNA to study the intracellular phase of virus infection. Bergeron and Singer (1958) noted the similarities between the metachromasy of dye in solution and that of stained membrane substrates and suggested that a common explanation is possible. They also emphasized the fact that certain substrates suppress metachromasy at dye concentrations in which the color of the dye in solution would ordinarily be metachromatic. Similar observations were reported from solution studies by various workers. These have been reviewed by Steiner and Beers (1961).

The results obtained by Armstrong and by Armstrong and Niven refer only to fixed material. It had already been noted by DeBruyn et al. (1953) that living or unfixed cells exhibited markedly different staining behavior with diaminoacridines from that shown by fixed material. The cytoplasm of living cells stained with diaminoacridines was very faintly and diffusely fluorescent, at best. The chromatin of the nucleus was brightly fluorescent and well defined. Direct comparison with Feulgen and methyl green-pyronin staining established that the intranuclear fluorescent material was a complex formed between the dye and the nucleic acids. However, whereas the Feulgen and the methyl green-pyronin methods distinguish RNA from DNA, the amino acridines do not; i.e., the nucleic acids cannot be distinguished from each other in the fluorochromed preparations. It is worth noting that the in vivo staining was accomplished by subcutaneous injections of the dye solutions into the living animal. The observed staining is then the result of subjecting the cells to dilute solutions of the dye. Using tissue culture Wolf and Aronson (1961) also noted that the cytoplasm of either fixed material or damaged cells stains red at low dye concentrations whereas for living undamaged cells the observed fluorescence is essentially confined to the intranuclear material.

They also studied the photodynamic effect of acridine orange and observed that cell damage and mortality in culture, upon irradiation, were roughly proportional to the concentration of the dye solution. They suggested that the difference in behavior between the living and fixed material could possibly be attributed either to denaturation of the cytoplasmic RNA (a less stable substance than the intranuclear DNA) or to the new availability of binding sites on the RNA due to the dissolution of previously existing complexes or, perhaps, to a combination of these factors. They also noted that once these phototoxic changes have been initiated by a short interval of fluorescence-exciting radiation, the ensuing degeneration and death of the cell is ordinarily an irreversible process. Continued irradiation is not necessary. Observations identical with these have been made on supravitally stained cells by the author. Beers, Hendley, and Steiner (1958) concluded from studies of complexes of acridine orange with DNA or RNA in solution that the AO–DNA complex produced only green fluorescence and the AO–RNA complex produced only red fluorescence. In this paper they referred to the work of Armstrong and Niven (1957), stating that the green fluorescence of nuclei stained with acridine orange is, no doubt, due to the formation of AO–DNA complexes. It has already been noted above that DeBruyn et al. found that nucleoli were not distinguishable from the rest of the chromatin of the nucleus after staining with acridine orange. Identical results were also obtained by Wolf and Aronson. Loeser, West, and Schoenberg (1960) and Ranadive and Korgaonkar (1960) found that AO–DNA complexes are spectroscopically indistinguishable. West (1963) has spectroscopically examined the fluorescence emission from acridine orange-stained fixed cells treated in accordance with the technique developed by Dart and Turner (1959). Although only a small number of cells were examined, it is worthy of note that in only one instance was the fluorescence emission spectrum of the red fluorescing component in the cytoplasm characteristic of the AO–RNA complex or AO–DNA complex as observed either in solution studies or in the spectra of individual supravitally stained cells. Indeed, the shift in the fluorescence emission spectrum is sufficiently large to be visually observed once the observer is aware that this color difference may be of significance. In the case of the AO–nucleic acid complexes, the long wavelength emission appears to be a yellow orange or a reddish orange, whereas, in the case of cytoplasmic staining, either supravitally with very high dye concentrations or for fixed material under the conditions specified by Dart and Turner, the red fluorescing cytoplasm is a deep brick red. But one should not extrapolate to the results obtained with fixed material treated differently from this without conducting the appropriate spectroscopic studies and parallel investigations on equivalent model systems in solution.

C. Fluorescence Microspectroscopy

Microspectroscopy, with the spectroscope placed behind the microscope eyepiece, has been used by only a few investigators. The conventional means for obtaining a spectrum is to record the spectrum on a photographic plate and then obtain a graph of the spectrum which shows amplitude as a function of wavelength with a densitometer. This is a rather difficult and taxing procedure if corrected spectra are desired. Similarly, a phototube or multiplier photocell may be placed in an image plane, wherein the spectrum comes to a focus. Then the spectrum is traversed relative to an aperture in the image plane placed in front of the photodetector. This can be accomplished by moving the phototube and its accompanying aperture relative to the spectrum; or, conversely, the spectrum can be scanned by using a monochromator and causing the spectrum to pass across the fixed exit slit and phototube, or a rotating helical aperture can be interposed between a spectroscope and photocell. Yet another approach is to image the spectrum on the photocathode of a television camera tube (e.g., Vidicon, Image Orthicon, Image Dissector) and scan the spectrum electronically. Photoelectric spectroscopy completely circumvents the photographic process and makes it relatively easy to obtain corrected spectra. However, unless special instrumentation is employed, a simple experimental setup using readily available components provides only slow scanning speeds for low intensity radiation. And, the fluorescence emission from fluorochrome-stained cells is rather a weak phenomenon. Also, the rapid fading of the fluorescence requires exposures of approximately one second or less.

A fluorescence microscope was first demonstrated by Köhler (1904) three years after he developed the ultraviolet microscope. Lehman (1913) constructed a fluorescence microscope and suggested the possibility of using it for fluorescence microspectrographic analysis. Stübel (1911) reported the intrinsic fluorescence of animal tissues and Wasicky (1913) recognized the potentiality of fluorescence microscopy for pharmacological investigations. Policard (1925a,b) attempted to identify hematoporphyrin in tissue sections by means of the method suggested by Lehman. These were all visual observations. Qualitative, subjective examination of the spectrum is, at best, of very limited usefulness. It requires that the component of interest exist in an isolated portion of the spectrum or it may be masked. When this requirement can be met, it can be used to advantage. Thus, Keilin (1925) discovered the cytochromes using absorption spectroscopy (spectroscope placed behind the microscope eyepiece).

Despite the difficulties of photographic spectroscopy, photographic fluorescence microspectroscopy has been used effectively by a number of workers. Borst and Königsdörffer (1929) localized porphyrin in tissue sections by means of fluorescence microspectroscopy. Fikentscher (1931) used the same apparatus for localizing porphyrin in the skeleton. Fischl and Schwenk (1932) introduced intravital fluorochroming. von Euler, Hellström, and Adler (1935) localized and identified riboflavin in the pigment epithelium of the eyes of fishes and mammals by comparison with spectra obtained from riboflavin solutions. Their apparatus incorporated a small camera for photographing the fluorescence spectrum. DeLerma (1940, 1942, 1949) and Sjöstrand (1944, 1946a,b) quantitatively analyzed the photographically recorded spectra and produced graphs of fluorescence intensity as a function of wavelength. By direct comparison with fluorescence spectra recorded from solutions, they were able to identify the substances in cells and tissues whose fluorescence spectrum was recorded with the microspectrograph. An excellent review of photographic fluorescence microspectrofluorophotometry has been provided by DeLerma (1958). Sjöstrand stated that the fluorescence microspectrographic method was not to be outdone by any other known method of direct analysis suitable for tissue sections, provided fluorescing substances were being dealt with.

Photoelectric fluorescence microspectrophotometry was used by Norden (1953) to study the behavior of 3,4-benzpyrene in mouse skin. Fluorescence spectra were obtained by changing the wavelength setting of a monochromator. Scheibe and Eder (1956) using a similar method obtained fluorescence spectra from fixed frog-heart sections stained with acridine orange. They reported emission peaks at approximately 534 nm and 640 nm, the relative heights being concentration dependent. Olsen (1960) used a rapid-scanning fluorescence microspectrophotometer to study fluorescent structure in connection with the photochemistry of living cells. The apparatus uses a direct vision prism and a rotating linear spiral slit. The spiral slit is rotated at 2 rps. Spectra are recorded from an oscilloscope display. Runge (1966) described a fluorescence microspectrophotometer useful for spectroscopic examination of porphyrins. Spectra are displayed on a strip chart recorder. The system uses a direct vision spectroscope and a scanning mirror. The scanning mirror traverses the spectrum across a slit placed in front of the phototube. Analysis of various instrumental factors are included in this paper. Rigler (1966) has made use of a recording fluorescence microspectrophotometer for an extensive study of the interaction of acridine orange with intracellular nucleic acids and nucleoproteins. Using fixed material he related the short wavelength fluorescence band to the presence of a helical molecular configuration and the long wavelength fluorescence band to the presence of random coil molecular configuration. Norden, Scheibe, and Rigler have presented their data as corrected spectra.

One further note should be added with regard to fluorescence microspectrophotometry. Living material does not absorb appreciably in the visible region of the spectrum. In the ultraviolet, the bands with maxima at 260 nm (nucleic acids) and 280 nm (proteins) are most useful and have been investigated with monochromatic illumination, a method that is much easier to quantitate than a record of an entire spectrum. For stained, fixed material (Feulgen preparations, for example) absorption photometry at a single wavelength is again the method of choice. However, when cells or tissues are caused to fluoresce, the spectra of the emitted fluorescence may be complex, as in the case of metachromatic fluorochromes. It has already been pointed out that the complexity of the spectrum is due to the formation of different molecular species, though the dye is the same. Even with complete knowledge of the behavior of the dye in solution, both alone and bound to various substrates, the complexity of the cell is such that it is not possible to predict *a priori* the shape that the fluorescence spectrum will take. Analysis at a single wavelength with the broad spectral bandpass provided by optical filters may be completely inadequate as an analytical tool. Such measurements are insensitive to the presence of interfering fluorescing species or alterations in the nature of the spectrum even when only a single species is present. Thus, detailed analysis of spectra is a prerequisite for more exact identification of substances and for theoretical insight into the nature of the substances identified by the spectra. Where chemical specificity is provided (Ruch, 1966) a simple microfluorometer is adequate.

III. Staining Procedure

A. GENERAL CONSIDERATIONS

Before entering into any staining procedure for histo- or cytochemistry, it is necessary to make clear the purposes of the procedure. Thus, one may provide a list of criteria for an ideal histo- or cytochemical procedure. These are:

1. Identification
2. Localization
3. Physical-chemical and biochemical significance
4. Sensitivity and contrast enhancement
5. Vital or lethal procedure (effect upon cell physiology)
6. Subjective or objective detection

1. Identification

An ideal staining procedure would provide specific, unequivocal identification of a given biochemical constituent of a cell. Almost all known methods fall short of this ideal in some respect. For example, most cytochemical methods do not display species differences, but rather identify a class of substances. Conversely, methods that are capable of displaying species differences, such as fluorescent antibody techniques (Goldman, 1968), may not provide much direct chemical information with regard to the complexing substrate. In a chemical sense, the completeness of the identification of the stained substrate will depend upon the extent of knowledge of the chemistry of the dye employed and whether its interaction with the suspected intracellular component can be studied *in vitro*.

2. Localization

Cellular metabolism and its regulation depend upon the biochemical behavior of the intracellular constituents and their geographical location within the cell. Reagents that cannot mix with each other cannot react. Also, if one of a pair of reagents is transported in limited quantities to the site where the reaction occurs, this may serve to control the reaction. The cell is much more complex than these simple examples would indicate, but they do demonstrate the importance of cell morphology in cytochemical studies. Thus, one of the important aspects of cytochemistry, long recognized by cytologists and cytochemists, is ability to localize particular substances with respect to the morphology of the cell. Indeed, this is one of the prime criteria in evaluating a cytochemical technique.

3. Physical-Chemical and Biochemical Significance

Ideally, the cytochemical reaction should be such as to permit its expression by means of a chemical equation. The staining procedures should be in keeping with this goal. The reagents of interest are the intracellular constituent(s) and the dye or other cytochemical reagent. For example, let us suppose p moles of an intracellular polymer P combines with d moles of dye D to give a moles of complex A at equilibrium, as shown in Eq. (1).

$$p\mathrm{P} + d\mathrm{D} \rightleftharpoons a\mathrm{A} \tag{1}$$

The criterion of equilibrium is that for any infinitesimal variation of the system associated with a reaction either to the right or left in Eq. (1) there be no change in free energy, pressure and temperature remaining constant. Equation (1) represents a reversible reaction and has a *thermo-*

dynamic equilibrium constant associated with it, K_a given by

$$K_a = \frac{C_A^a}{D_P^p C_D^d} \frac{f_A^a}{f_P^p f_D^d} \tag{2}$$

where C_A^a, C_P^p, C_D^d, are the concentrations of A, P, D, respectively, and f_A^a, f_P^p, f_D^d, are the activities of A, P, D, respectively.

The first term on the right side of Eq. (2) is called the *concentration equilibrium constant*, K_c, of a reaction and is equal to K_a if the f's are assumed equal to unity. The change of free energy ΔF° is related to K_a as shown in Eq. (3).

$$\Delta F^\circ = -RT \ln K_a \tag{3}$$

(Rigorous derivations and extensions to other thermodynamic quantities are to be found in Maron and Prutton, 1965; Edsall and Wyman, 1958; and Mahler and Cordes, 1966.)

Equation (3) is of fundamental importance and is called the *reaction isotherm*. (Measurements of phenomena under equilibrium conditions are labeled isotherms with an adjective describing the phenomenon, e.g., *absorption isotherm.*) The free energy, ΔF°, and the equilibrium constant, K, are functions of pressure and temperature.

Referring back to Eq. (1), note that the solvent does not appear in the expression. Even in Eq. (2), which is expressed in terms of concentration, the solvent does not really play a role. Thus, if cytochemistry is to produce data useful for quantitative theoretical chemical analysis and prediction, staining reactions must be quantitatively expressed in terms of the active components. Further, unless kinetic studies are frankly and explicitly undertaken, reactions must be allowed to achieve equilibrium and temperature must be controlled. These are minimum conditions. There may be other experimental variables that must be controlled to achieve equilibrium. For example, many of the fluorochromes are photochemically active. Uncontrolled illumination during the course of a staining reaction may produce a set of irreversible reactions. Reversibility is a necessary condition for equilibrium.

In dealing with cells, it is difficult to express a staining reaction strictly in accordance with the dictates of Eqs. (1) and (2). The intracellular amounts of substances of interest are generally not known, nor are their activities. However, it is possible to make some assumptions so that a relationship of the kind expressed by Eq. (2) may be approximated. These assumptions are:

a. The activity of water is taken as unity.

b. In an essentially homogeneous population of cells, the quantity of intracellular constituents present per cell is essentially constant. In the case of the nucleic acids in peripheral leukocytes (used as a model system here), this is probably a fairly good assumption. Thus, a given intracellular constituent may be quantitated simply by counting cells.

c. Assume $K_c = K_a$ (f's $= 1$).

Implementing these assumptions and these goals requires:

a. That living or unfixed cells be utilized. This is to avoid the effects of environmental alterations (fixation, etc.) on intracellular constituents, which are generally not well understood.

b. That the staining reaction be carried out at a given, constant temperature within the physiological range.

c. That the staining reaction be permitted to go to equilibrium. Equilibrium must be determined by measurement.

d. That the staining solution be specified on a dye per cell basis, i.e., moles of dye per cell. This can be accomplished by introducing counted numbers of cells into measured volumes of staining solution of known concentration. After equilibrium between cells and staining has been attained, dye remaining in solution is measured. The difference between initial and final values divided by the number of cells is the dye uptake per cell, on the average. If it is not possible or desirable to count cells, then some other means of quantitating the amount of biological material, or the amount of substance of interest that it contains, must be determined if reproducible staining characteristics are to be achieved.

e. Determine intracellular fate of the dye. Individual cells should be examined visually, by fluorescence microspectrophotometry, or by other physical-optical means. Intercellular differences, although exhibited by very few cells out of the total population, may be of great biological importance—to say nothing of identification and localization within the cell itself, which have already been emphasized.

4. Sensitivity and Contrast Enhancement

An ideal staining technique should be sensitive enough to detect the very small quantities of a given material in a cell and to make them clearly distinguishable from their surroundings. This is of particular importance when instrumental detection is to be employed. The chosen fluorochrome should permit optical filtering that will reduce the background to levels that permit detection of the smallest signal of interest. Filter combinations that are perfectly satisfactory for visual observation are frequently quite unsatisfactory for instrumental measurements. Where the excitation and emission spectra of a given dye are such that adequate filter combinations cannot readily be obtained, then consideration should be given to monochromators for excitation and emission, even though measurements at only a single fluorescence wavelength interval are desired.

5. Vital or Lethal Procedure

Ideally only vital or supravital procedures should be employed. Any procedure that interferes markedly with the physiology of a cell may introduce great difficulties in interpreting the results in terms of cell physiology and its underlying physical-chemical and biochemical behavior. Another way to express this is to realize that a functioning cell, given an opportunity, controls its own internal environment. Procedures that interfere minimally with the cell physiology will display substances of interest in their functional, native state and with proper localization. Thus, the burden of controlling a great many of the variables in any given experimental procedure is borne by the functioning cell. In fixed material the entire burden of controlling all significant variables rests upon the investigator. Disagreements between results and difficulties in interpretation may be the result of failures to adequately control all significant variables. This is not surprising when one considers the complexity of a cell, the multiplicity of its intracellular constituents, and the variety of responses these constituents display toward alterations in their environment.

6. Subjective or Objective Observation

The requirements placed upon any staining procedure will vary, depending upon whether objective or subjective detection is intended. The eye is not capable of quantitating intensities or assessing spectroscopic composition with any degree of precision or accuracy. Indeed, where spectra are concerned, the psychological response may be far different from the actual physical composition of the spectrum being observed. For example, in an additive color system the eye will see some shade of yellow when only red and green are present. Techniques designed for visual observation are primarily useful for the enhancement of contrast to display morphological detail. A refinement is to use a reaction giving a colored product that identifies a given substance. The quantitation of such substances in terms of amount or spectral alterations cannot readily be accomplished by simple visual observation. In contrast, objective, i.e., instrumental detection is capable of quantitating the amount and other physical-optical properties of a detected substance. Staining of one kind or another is still necessary both to enhance contrast and to permit the detector to select a given substance for measurement. However, any instrument has a great deal of difficulty with morphology. While imaging systems of various kinds are available (television, flying-spot scanning, etc.), none of these are capable of dealing with the subtleties of cell morphology. Even very simple morphological decisions may represent a tremendous instrumental effort. It is, therefore, important that facility be provided for the human observer to examine the morphology and the source of the signal when an objective detector is used for cytochemical investigations.

The cytochemical staining procedure and the method of detection and analysis cannot well be separated from each other if the criteria listed above are to be satisfied in any measure. Thus, the staining procedure described below has been developed with a view toward fluorescence microspectrophotometric detection and analysis. This requires that the development of the technique occur with the aid of the spectroscopic analysis. Visual or simple filter photometry will generally be insensitive to the qualitative and quantitative behavior of complex spectra. Cytochemical interpretation may be misleading. Spectroscopic evaluation is necessary. However, once such spectroscopic analyses have been properly carried out for the given reaction, then extensions to meaningful measurements with simple instrumentation are entirely possible.

B. EQUILIBRIUM STAINING TIME

When vital dyes, such as acridine orange, are utilized, cells will suffer no damage even though immersed in the staining solution for long periods of time. This is true only if the dye concentration in the staining solution is not excessively high and if the staining reaction is carried out in the dark (low-actinic glassware). Proper dye concentrations cannot be stated in absolute terms since, as will become clear below, it is the ratio of dye to cells that is important. Also, a ratio of dye to cells satisfactory for one type of cell may be excessive for another because it contains a smaller quantity of the substance (DNA is one example) that binds the dye. The proper dye concentration for a particular experimental situation is easily determined in trial experiments.

For the same reasons it is neither possible nor desirable to provide an absolute staining time for equilibration. However, for a fixed number of cells and a given staining solution volume, equilibration time varies inversely with dye concentration, i.e., the higher the dye concentration the shorter the equilibration time. It is only necessary, therefore, to determine the equilibration time for the smallest dye to cell ratio that will be used with a given staining solution concentration. Since the cells are not damaged by the staining solution (at least in acute experiments), allowing for staining times appreciably longer than the maximum equilibration time will assure that all measurements on cells are made after equilibrium between cells and dye has been attained. It should be borne in mind that reaction rates increase with temperature and vice versa. Staining carried out at a temperature different from that at which the equilibration time was determined requires determining a new equilibration time. The exact dependence of equilibration time on temperature is not known, hence, the need for a new determination.

The staining procedures given here merely exemplify how the goals set forth above can be implemented. Variations may suggest themselves to the reader in keeping with the needs of a particular problem. It is worth emphasizing that staining concentrations must be expressed on a per cell basis, that living or unfixed cells should be used for greatest ease in reproducing and interpreting the results, and that the staining reaction must be carried to equilibrium. The emphasis placed upon attaining chemical equilibrium is not meant to imply that kinetic studies are unimportant. Indeed they are. But they present another set of experimental problems that must be expressly provided for (Guilbault, 1967).

C. Detailed Staining Procedure

1. Glassware

All glassware that is not fused silica must be coated with Desicote (Beckman) or Siliclad (Clay-Adams). Low-actinic glassware should be used for long-term storage of dye solution and for staining cells. Twelve milliliter glass-stoppered low-actinic glass centrifuge tubes have been found convenient for carrying out the staining.

2. Acridine-Orange Solutions

Acridine orange (AO) (National Aniline Division, Allied Chemical Company) was recrystallized as the hydrochloride from hot water and ethanol and proved to be homogeneous by filter paper chromatography. [Later, studies conducted with acridine orange solutions made directly from the dye as supplied by the manufacturer (National Aniline) produced results equivalent to those obtained with the purified dye.]

Buffered physiological saline was used as solvent for all dye solutions with the exception of the concentrated stock solution. Physiological saline was buffered to pH 7 with McIlvaine's citrate-phosphate buffer (Hodgman, 1955–1956). The use of a two-solution buffer permitted slightly overshooting the desired pH value and then back-titrating to pH 7. This provided some buffering capacity with minimum change in the ionic strength of the physiological saline solution.

Concentrated solutions of AO (10^{-2} to 10^{-3} M) were made up in distilled water and filtered through a Millipore type VM filter. The filtrate was used as a stock solution from which all succeeding solutions were made. It was stored at 4°C under a layer of paraffin oil in a glass-stoppered low-actinic glass flask. Tests of the stability of the stock solutions (reproducible fluorescence emission) were made for periods as long as 3 months, with no apparent change. Concentration of dye in the stock solution was determined by micro-Kjeldahl nitrogen analysis.

Starting with an aliquot of the stock dye solution, serial dilutions to concentrations as low as 6×10^{-10} M were freshly prepared for each experiment and used to calibrate the fluorometer. Solutions between 3×10^{-5} and 6×10^{-8} M were used for staining.

3. Cells

Leukocytes from the peritoneal fluid of female Webster white swiss mice (Rockland Farms) were used. One milliliter of paraffin oil was injected intraperitoneally to act as an irritant and cause the appearance of large numbers of leukocytes in the peritoneal fluid. At 15–18 hours after the paraffin oil injection, the mice were sacrificed by cervical dislocation. The leukocytes were harvested by repeatedly flushing the peritoneal cavity with buffered saline. The washings were transferred to a separatory funnel and allowed to stand at room temperature until the paraffin oil rose to the surface. The aqueous phase containing the cells was then removed. The cells were washed three times in buffered saline by centrifugation. After the final washing the pellet of cells was resuspended in 10 ml of buffered saline solution.

4. Staining of Cells with Acridine Orange

The final cell suspension was divided into three or four aliquots for supravital staining with acridine orange. These were placed in stoppered, low-actinic glass centrifuge tubes. To prevent drying of the pellet of cells, the following operations were completed on each tube before going on to the next. The suspension was centrifuged to form a pellet of cells and the supernatant decanted as completely as possible. The pellet was resuspended[2] in 6 ml of a solution of acridine orange chosen from the set of serial dilutions, 3×10^{-5} to 6×10^{-8} M. The centrifuge tube was stoppered and the contents thoroughly mixed by manually turning it end over end a number of times. A desicoted small stirring rod was used to loosen the pellet if necessary.

Staining was allowed to continue, with gentle mixing, until equilibrium had been reached. This was approximately 1 hour at room temperature. A 1-ml aliquot of the cell suspension was removed for cell counts and for making slides from which single cell spectra would be obtained. Air-dried spreads were also made. These were later treated with Wright's stain and

---

[2] Buffered saline remaining in the pellet did not appreciably change the concentration of the staining solution.

used to examine the leukocytes by conventional means. No direct comparison on an individual cell between AO-staining and Wright's staining was made.

The remaining 5 ml of dye-cell suspension was centrifuged, the supernatant was decanted and stored in a stoppered low-actinic glass centrifuge tube at room temperature until the recording of cell spectra was completed. Then the concentration of dye remaining in the supernatant was measured with the fluorometer.

The slides were prepared by placing a drop of the dye-cell suspension on a glass slide, covering it with a coverslip, and sealing with paraffin. Cell counts were made with a hemacytometer. Equilibration time is defined as the length of time after which no further dye uptake by the cells occurs and no further alteration in the fluorescence emission spectra can

FIG. 3. Photograph of line-selector oscilloscope display.

be detected. Note that the slides were made with cells suspended in their staining solution so as not to alter the equilibrium conditions.

IV. Fluorescence Microspectroscopy of Cell Preparations

The slides of AO-stained cells were allowed to warm to 30°C on the thermostated microscope stage before exposure to the exciting radiation. Under yellow or orange light to avoid exciting the dye, the slides were visually examined and a cell was selected and positioned to lie in the image of the spectroscope entrance slit. The image of the slit cannot be seen, but its position is defined by the cross hairs of a filar micrometer eyepiece. The slide was exposed to fluorescence-exciting radiation only during the actual recording of the spectrum. With manual operation, exposure to the fluorescence-exciting radiation is limited to approximately 1 sec. If a synchronizing shutter were utilized, exposure could be limited to approximately a sixtieth of a second. Exposure time could be made still shorter if one chose to use a flash lamp as the fluorescence-exciting source. However, a 1 sec exposure time does not produce appreciable fading of the fluorescence emission from the AO–cell complex.

With the oscilloscope camera set to multiple exposures, the following sets of information were all photographed upon the same frame:

1. The line-selector trace passing through the image of the emission spectrum produced by the fluorescing cell.

2. A line-selected trace displaying the emission spectrum from an area in the field close to the fluorescing cell. This is the baseline from which measurements are made.

3. Line-selected traces containing wavelength-calibrating information. By placing these at the top and bottom, the frame can later be aligned exactly with an overlay of the spectral dispersion of the spectroscope. The third line-selector trace carrying only one spectral line is inserted to avoid reversing the abscissa when analyzing the raw data.

An example of the recorded raw data is shown in Fig. 3.

TABLE I
HALF-VALUE SPECTRAL BANDWIDTH[a,b]

Wavelength (nm)	Slit = 0.06 mm (mm)	Slit = 0.20 mm (mm)
546	1.9	6.4
588	2.4	7.9
656	3.3	11.0
768	5.0	17.0

[a] For the prism spectroscope used in this equipment exclusive of the television equipment.

[b] Calculated from manufacturer's data.

A slit width of 0.06 mm was used when the average dye content per cell was greater than 1×10^{-15} mole of AO. For smaller values of dye uptake per cell, a slit width of 0.20 mm was used. Table I shows the half-value spectral bandwidths used at these slit widths for the region of the spectrum occupied by the fluorescence emission of AO-stained cells.

V. Instrumentation

A. The Fluorometer

The fluorometer used to measure the concentrations of acridine orange solutions is shown in the schematic diagram, Fig. 4. It was constructed by adding simple modifications to the instrument used for fluorescence microspectrophotometry. One attachment consisted of an adapter that mounted in front of the exit slit. It carried the cuvette holder and a high aperture collecting lens positioned between the cuvette and the entrance slit. Another adapter at the exit slit provided a light-tight coupling to the multiplier phototube housing. A lens, in the housing, formed an image of the slit on the photocathode. An end-on multiplier phototube (DuMont 6292, CBS 7817, EMI 9558, or equivalent) was used and no adjustment of the position of the photocathode with respect to the image of the slit was necessary.

A commercial fluorometer may, obviously, also be used. It should utilize spectroscopic dispersion (filter fluorometers may produce ambiguous results). Most important it must have adequate long-term stability. Measurements of dye solutions are made sequentially and the fluorometer must be stable at least over the length of time required for a series of measurements. The original set of serial dilutions of the dye is always

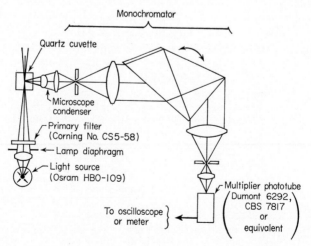

Fig. 4. Fluorometer, simplified block diagram. (From West, 1965.)

measured immediately before and after the measurements on the supernatants from the staining suspensions.

In the experimental set-up shown here, the multiplier phototube is supplied by a stable, variable high voltage power supply (Northeast No. RE 3004). The stability of this supply is of the order of one part in 10^4. The resistors that supply the dynode voltages are relatively low resistance. The current through these resistors is then very much larger than the signal (anode) current. Dynode voltage, hence, multiplier phototube amplification, is then insensitive to variations in light intensity over a considerable range. Care must be taken never to expose the phototube to strong light, as this may destroy its linearity. If the measurements of the serial dilutions are plotted logarithmically, the straight line portion of the curve will have a slope of 45° for linear operation. Departure from this slope indicates nonlinear operation (dye dilutions must be in the range where Beer's law is obeyed). Generally, this has been found to be due to a multiplier phototube which had been exposed to strong light, even if only for a short interval. Changing the phototube is the only remedy. Operation of such damaged phototubes is no longer sufficiently stable to warrant the time and effort of additional calibration curves.

The output of the phototube is usually fed to an oscilloscope, already part of the equipment, where the signal level is read from the trace position. A high input impedance voltmeter may be used in place of the oscilloscope. The oscilloscope has a very short response time compared to to the meter and permits a series of measurements to be made more rapidly.

A stable Hg-arc light source, described below, was used with a Corning CS 5-58 (5113) blue filter. The 436 nm Hg-line was the principal wavelength of fluorescence-exciting radiation. Solutions were contained in 1-cm fused silica cuvettes.

In operation the solutions of AO were allowed to come to room temperature (ca. 26°C) before measurements were made. The monochromator was set to a wavelength of 538 nm with a half-value bandwidth of approximately 12 nm. The phototube was operated with a supply voltage of 1300 V.

Irradiation of the solution to be measured was kept to a minimum. The exciting radiation was blocked until the cuvette was in position for measurement. Immediately upon irradiation, the fluorescence intensity was read from the vertical displacement of the oscilloscope trace. Less than a second of irradiation time was required to make a measurement. Measurements could be made of AO concentrations in the neighborhood of 10^{-10} M.

Overall stability of the fluorometer is such that readings are reproduced within approximately 5% on successive days (equipment turned off in the interim). While the use of a reference beam could, no doubt, improve the instrumental performance, it is doubtful that a useful gain in accuracy would result when pipetting and reading errors are taken into account.

B. The Light Source

A light source of sufficient intensity to excite a detectable amount of fluorescence must be used. The light source must be stable and essentially free from ripple. The high aperture of the lamp condenser lens, and the fact that the arc is imaged upon the entrance slit of a monochromator, require that the position of the arc be stable.

An Osram HBO 109[3] high pressure mercury vapor arc lamp was chosen for its high intrinsic brightness (approximately 140,000 Stilb, according to manufacturer's data). A power supply was designed to meet the above operating requirements (Fig. 5). Commercial power supplies such as Hewlett-Packard 6274 also give satisfactory results. The values of the resistors shown in Fig. 5 must be changed to accommodate the lower supply voltage (60 V). The important power supply characteristic in this application is freedom from ripple and noise.

The circuit diagram of the light source power supply is shown in Fig. 5. The design is conventional. Negative feedback is not used because of the difficulty of taking thermal time constants into account. As a matter of fact, feedback may even increase lamp instability. The no-load output voltage is approximately 90 V. At full load the input to the series resistors (R_4 and R_x) is approximately equal to the no-load output voltage. The transformer and choke have been designed with sufficient iron to prevent saturation. Their direct current resistance is small.

In operation, the voltage drop across the lamp is approximately 20 V. The relatively large difference in potential across the series resistors permits the value of series resistance to be considerably larger than the

---

[3] Equivalent lamps are manufactured by PEK and Sylvania.

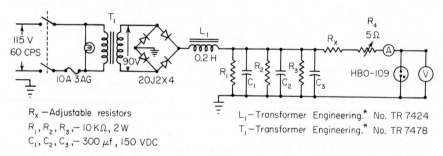

R_x — Adjustable resistors
$R_1, R_2, R_3,$ — 10 KΩ, 2 W
$C_1, C_2, C_3,$ — 300 μf, 150 VDC

L_1 — Transformer Engineering.* No. TR 7424
T_1 — Transformer Engineering.* No. TR 7478

Fig. 5. Power supply for Osram HBO-109 lamps, simplified schematic diagram. Transformer Engineering Corp., 2550 Brookpark Rd., Cleveland, Ohio, 44134.

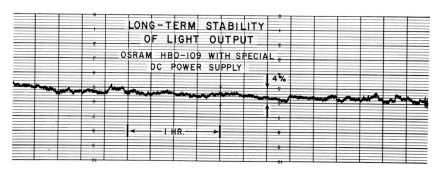

FIG. 6. Record of stability of Osram HBO-109 lamp light output. (From West, 1965.)

negative resistance of the lamp. The sum of the series resistance and the lamp resistance is positive, as is required for stable operation. Under these conditions, the lamp current is essentially a function of the magnitude of the external series resistance and the applied voltage.

The measured ripple in the output of the power supply and in the light output of the lamp is 0.5%. The light output is stable, within 4% over an interval of several hours. Figure 6 is a record showing the long-term stability of the lamp. For this test the image of the Hg-arc was brought to a focus on the entrance slit of a monochromator and the variation in intensity was measured at the exit slit. Thus, Fig. 6 is a composite of arc position stability and constancy of lamp brightness.

C. The Television Fluorescence Microspectrophotometer

The television fluorescence microspectrophotometer is assembled from commercially available components. The extremely high sensitivity of the image-intensifier orthicon (Morton and Ruedy, 1960), now commercially available (RCA 4470), makes possible the rapid recording of very weak fluorescence spectra. Where spectra of higher intensity are available (strong fluorescence or absorption) more conventional camera tubes such as image orthicons or vidicons may be employed. The latter camera tubes do not require modification of conventional television cameras; the image-intensifier orthicon does.[4] For any television system, the horizontal and vertical synchronizing pulses must be available for connection to the oscilloscope. Also provision must be made for adding the unblanking pulse from the oscilloscope to the video signal in the camera. This brightens that portion of the television raster which is selected for display on the line selector oscilloscope.

[4] Maryland Telecommunications, Incorporated, Cockeysville, Maryland.

"Line selection" has been described by Fisher (1952), Potts, West, and Shearer (1959) and West, Potts, and Shearer (1962). The additions to this technique that are required for television spectroscopy of the fluorescence emission from single cells have been described by West, Loeser, and Schoenberg (1960) and Loeser and West (1962). A block diagram of the experimental set-up is shown in Fig. 7. The light source and its power supply are the same as described above. The standard components of a television camera chain are not shown in the figure. A photograph of the experimental set-up is shown in Fig. 8.

In operation, the image of the arc was focused on the entrance slit of the monochromator used to provide fluorescence-exciting radiation. Lamp housing optics should be high aperture. Magnification should be sufficient to fill the entrance slit. The monochromator and microscope condensers were adjusted for Köhler illumination. The primary filter was used to reduce stray light from the monochromator to negligible levels. Both the wavelength setting of the monochromator and the primary filter can be varied to suit the requirements of the system under investigation. For acridine orange the monochromator was set to 436 nm with a Corning CS5-58 (5113) serving as primary filter.

The microscope was equipped with achromatic objectives. Achromatic objectives have higher transmission efficiency, a very important consideration, and the image is degraded to a lesser extent than is true for apochromats when the eyepiece is omitted. A Leitz 100×, N.A. 1.30 oil-immersion objective was used when the spectra from cells were recorded. The ocular was removed. The heating stage was maintained at 30°C.

The microscope was focused so that with the aid of the field lens of the

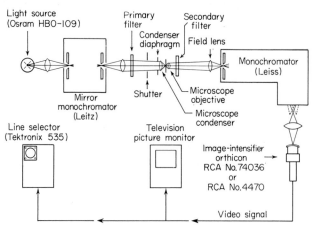

Fig. 7. Television fluorescence microspectrophotometry, simplified block diagram. (From West, 1965.)

FIG. 8. Photograph of experimental set-up.

fluorescence spectroscope, the entrance slit served as an aperture stop in the optical system. A high-efficiency, low-dispersion monochromator, with exit slit removed, such as the Leiss single-pass monochromator, serves as the fluorescence spectroscope. In this mode of operation the recorded emission spectrum was that produced by radiation from the entire cell. Visual examination could be used to determine whether there is nuclear or cytoplasmic fluorescence or both. It is possible to obtain an emission spectrum from any area within a cell by imaging the cell upon the entrance slit of the spectroscope. The concern in these studies, however, was the examination of the emission spectra from individual cells as a function of dye content per cell. It was, therefore, necessary to examine, spectroscopically, the emission from the entire cell. The secondary filter (Corning No. 3486 for acridine orange) which absorbs the exciting radiation is inserted between the nosepiece carrier and the body tube of the microscope. In this position the fluorescence of the filter itself is minimized.

A filar micrometer eyepiece, mounted on the viewing tube, was used to locate the image of the spectroscope entrance slit in the object plane of the microscope. By this means, an object could be visually positioned so that the radiation it emits passes through the entrance slit of the spectroscope without further adjustment. Of great help in accomplishing this rapidly is a centering microscope nosepiece (Leitz).

The radiation emitted by a fluorescing object on the stage of the microscope is dispersed into a spectrum by the spectroscope. The spectrum so produced is brought to a focus on the photocathode of the image-intensifier orthicon television camera tube. An electron image, the analog of the optical image, is produced. The photoelectrons are accelerated by a large potential difference (10–15 kV) to a phosphor target coated on a very thin transparent base. Electron optical lenses focus this stream of electrons to reproduce the optical image. The other side of the transparent base is coated with a second photocathode and is the beginning of the conventional image orthicon section of the image-intensifier orthicon tube.

The photoelectrons produced by the second photocathode are accelerated (approximately 300 V) and focused on a target, where a corresponding charge pattern is produced by secondary emission. This charge pattern is retained (stored) until scanned by the electron beam. The scanning beam traverses the target in a series of parallel, consecutive straight lines which, in sum, form a rectilinear array or raster. As the electron beam passes over the target it continually gives up electrons to the target to neutralize the stored local charge. The remaining electrons in the beam are returned to an electron multiplier section of the tube where, after amplification, they are collected by the anode. The anode current constitutes the video signal. The three-dimensional (position plus intensity) optical image has been converted into a two-dimensional signal (amplitude and time). Starting from any fiducial point in a raster one can locate any other point by simply stating the time interval.

The video signal is sent to a picture monitor and to the line-selector oscilloscope (Tektronix 535 or equivalent[5]). Using the vertical synchronizing pulse as the fiducial point, one can adjust the sweep delay circuit of the line-selector oscilloscope to select any given television line. A bright line, which corresponds to the oscilloscope sweep length, is superimposed on the image displayed on the picture monitor. The bright line indicates the portion of the image represented by the video signal displayed on the line-selector oscilloscope. The video information from any feature of interest may be selected by varying the delay introduced by the oscilloscope. In the present application the height of the cell spectrum covered approximately 10 television lines, and the line selector trace was adjusted to pass through the approximate center of the image of the spectrum.

---

[5] The oscilloscope cathode ray tube has a P11 phosphor or a P7 and a blue filter. Alternatively, one of the newer storage oscilloscopes may be used, set to single-sweep operation.

A 35-mm oscilloscope camera with a motorized film transport magazine (Beattie-Coleman) was used to record single-cell spectra. The camera was modified to provide either of two modes of operation: (a) multiple exposure or (b) single exposure with automatic film transport. The exposure time can be set and maintained at preset shutter speeds. In the single exposure-film transport mode, a data card, 24-hour clock, and frame counter are recorded.

Kodak Panatomic-X photographic film was used throughout because considerable enlargement is required before measurements are made on the recorded oscilloscope traces. Faster films may provide no exposure advantage while producing more grain.

D. CONSTRUCTION OF CORRECTED SPECTRA

The line selector oscilloscope display is a graph of intensity of fluorescence emission as a function of wavelength. Wavelength is plotted along the abscissa and intensity along the ordinate. Construction of corrected spectra from the photographic record of this display requires that the following factors be taken into account:

1. Background fluorescence
2. Nonlinearity of the television camera tube response as a function of light intensity
3. Spectral response of the camera tube
4. Spectral transmission of the secondary filter
5. Dispersion curve of the fluorescence spectroscope

The corrections were made as follows (Fig. 3):

1. Background fluorescence was accounted for by recording the video signal from an area immediately above or below the image of the spectrum displayed on the picture monitor along with the video signal from the spectrum itself. The video trace due to the background was used as a baseline for all measurements of amplitude. This amplitude measurement is representative of the intensity of fluorescence at a given wavelength.

2. The transfer function of the television camera tube (output current as a function of input light intensity) may not be linear. The transfer function of the television camera tube was experimentally determined in a separate set of measurements by interposing calibrated, neutral density filters between the microscope and the spectroscope. Uranium glass, cadmium sulfide, or uranyl nitrate particles served as a constant source of fluorescence radiation.

The resulting line-selected traces were recorded on the same photographic frame. A set of calibration curves was constructed from these data for each wavelength used in plotting the corrected spectrum (the transfer function may vary with position on the photocathode). Corrections to be applied to the recorded traces were read from these curves (Potts *et al.*, 1959; West *et al.*, 1962; Loeser and West, 1962). The image-intensifier orthicon used in these studies was supplied by the manufacturer with a close-spaced target and screen which provided an essentially linear transfer characteristic.

3. The intensifier-image orthicon (RCA Developmental Type No. C74036 was used for these data. The commercial version is RCA 4470), has a multialkali (S20) photocathode, the spectral response of which is shown in Fig. 9. For a given tube, the position of the peak of the spectral response curve may lie anywhere within the limits of the range of maximum value indicated in Fig. 9. The slope of the long wavelength skirt is essentially constant. The wavelength interval of interest for AO, 500–700 nm, always falls on the linear portion of the curve as indicated by the dashed lines in the figure. The camera tube spectral correction factors do not vary with shift in the position of the peak of the photocathode spectral response curve. Therefore, the spectral correction factors can be read directly from the manufacturer's data. However, spectra that exist in the range of the peak of the camera tube spectral response curve require individual spectral calibration.

4. The spectral transmission of the secondary filter, Corning CS3-69 (3486), was measured with a Cary recording spectrophotometer. Correction factors, as a function of wavelength, were obtained from the spectrophotometer recording. The spectral transmission of glass absorption filters varies with thickness and from melt to melt. This filter was chosen because it does not appreciably attenuate the 540 nm AO fluorescence peak. The Corning CS3-69 may be troublesome in simple photoelectric filter microscope fluorometers. In such instruments the Corning CS3-68 has been found most useful. It has the lowest intrinsic fluorescence of any of the sharp-cut filters and reduces the exciting radiation to undetectable levels. Filter fluorescence is unfortunately not controlled by the manufacturer and will vary with the individual filter of a given type. But the Corning CS3-68, in the author's experience, holds its own with respect to intrinsic fluorescence. Manufacturer's catalogs[6] should be consulted for specific filter information. Filter transmission curves plotted on a linear scale should be used with caution as the fluorescence emission is generally weaker than the exciting radiation by six orders of magnitude or more. Background, including filter fluorescence, should be determined

---

[6] Glass Color Filters, Optical Market Development Department, Corning, Corning, New York; Schott Color Filter Glass, Fish-Schurman Corporation, 70 Portman Road, New Rochelle, New York, 10802.

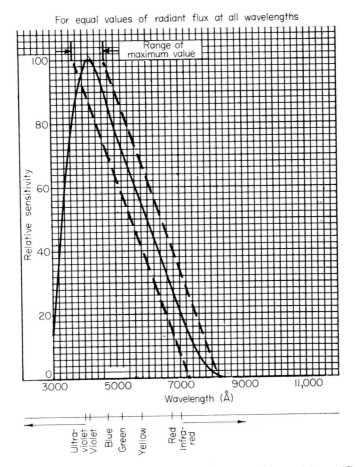

For equal values of radiant flux at all wavelengths

FIG. 9. Spectral-sensitivity characteristic of image-intensifier orthicon. (Courtesy RCA.)

experimentally. Dark field illumination will reduce the filter fluorescence, but also reduces the sensitivity to the desired fluorescence. Similarly, Wratten[7] gelatin filters may be used to shape the response of the glass secondary filter. They are heat sensitive and must be preceded by the glass filter. Interference filters, as primary or secondary filters, generally do not attenuate the undesired radiation sufficiently to be useful in filter instruments. Their narrow spectral bandwidth also limits their use for spectroscopic displays.

Most of the blue or UV primary filters have appreciable long wave-

[7] Kodak Wratten Filters, Kodak publication B-3, Eastman Kodak Company, Rochester, New York 14650.

length transmission which is transmitted by the secondary filters. The combination consisting of the Corning CS5-58 and CS3-68 has been found to serve a variety of applications and has relatively low background due either to filter fluorescence or long wavelength transmission by the primary filter.

Spectroscopic dispersion of the fluorescence-exciting radiation and the fluorescence emission, even when detection and measurement at only a single wavelength is desired, greatly reduces the dependence on the filters for low background. However, the primary and secondary filters ordinarily cannot be completely eliminated due to the stray light in the exciting and fluorescence spectroscopes.

5. The spectroscopic dispersion of the prism fluorescence spectroscope was determined by photographically recording the spectral lines from a mercury arc and a cadmium arc. A positive transparency was made of this spectrum on 35-mm film. An enlarged print was made of this spectrum. With a photographic enlarger, a positive transparency was enlarged so that the recorded mercury lines coincided with the calibrating spectral lines and an exposure made. Without moving the enlarging paper, a positive transparency of the spectral lines (usually just the Hg-lines) drawn on cross-section paper is then superimposed on the first exposure, and a second exposure is made after suitably adjusting the magnification. The doubly exposed enlargement, after development, shows the recorded spectra and the wavelength scale. Wavelength can be read directly and is absolutely accurate. The precision is adequate for fluorescence band spectra.

The corrected spectra are the result of applying the above-listed corrections to the raw data. Wavelength calibration of the recorded trace was obtained from an additional spectrum recorded on each frame which showed the positions of the 546 nm and 579 nm Hg lines. The corrected spectra are plotted as relative intensity versus wavenumber.[8]

VI. Results

A. Fluorometer Measurements

1. Fluorometer Calibration

The fluorometer was calibrated over a range of 3×10^{-3} to $6 \times 10^{-10} M$ acridine orange. Fluorescence emission was measured as a function of concentration at 538 nm with a half-value spectral bandwidth of approximately 12 nm. This wavelength corresponded to the maximum of the AO monomer emission band (Zanker, 1952). In very dilute solutions of the

---

[8] Wavenumber = $10^8/\lambda$(Angstroms).

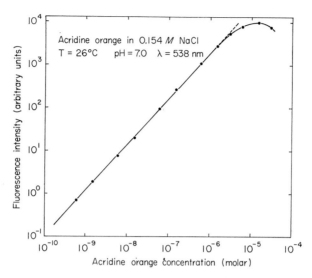

Fɪɢ. 10. Fluorometer calibration curve for acridine orange. (From West, 1965.)

dye, only the monomer is present. Making use of this peak gives maximum sensitivity.

A logarithmic plot of the data yielded a straight line from 6×10^{-10} M to approximately 1×10^{-6} M AO. Figure 10 shows a typical calibration curve. The slope is very nearly equal to unity. A calibration curve was determined for each experiment. The calibration curve shows that acridine orange obeys Beer's law up to a concentration of approximately 1×10^{-6} M. At concentrations higher than this, quenching of fluorescence emission at 538 nm occurs. The departure from linearity is due to the formation of dye polymers which reduce the concentration of monomer in the solution with a consequent reduction in the intensity of the fluorescence emission at 538 nm. With increasing concentration of dye, the fluorescence intensity at 538 nm reached a maximum and then progressively decreased. Because of this behavior the curve cannot be used for the measurement of concentration without prior knowledge of the concentration range being measured.

2. Concentration of Dye in the Supernatants

The fluorescence intensity of the dye in the supernatants, once equilibrium was reached, was measured, and the concentration was determined from the fluorometer calibration curve. The difference between the concentration of dye in the supernatant and the initial dye concentration, taking account of staining solution volume, was the amount of dye

removed from the solution and stored in the cells. This total divided by
the number of cells gave the average value of dye uptake per cell. The
initial concentration in solution divided by the number of cells gave the
amount of dye initially available per cell. Figures 11 and 12 are graphs of
the results of a number of such determinations. The data in these figures
do not, alone, provide information about the nature of the intracellular
components that formed complexes with the dye.

In Fig. 11, each point represents the average uptake of dye per cell for
a given amount of dye initially available per cell. The amount of dye taken
up by an individual cell is a linear function of the amount of dye presented
to the cell up to a concentration of approximately 6×10^{-15} mole of AO
per cell. This is not the limiting value of dye uptake per cell. At higher
concentrations of dye available per cell the relationship is no longer linear
and approaches saturation. It should be recognized that within the limits
of these experiments variations in the cell population do not alter the
shape of the curves.

Figure 12 shows the average dye uptake per cell as a function of
concentration of acridine orange (on a per cell basis) remaining in the
supernatant after equilibrium has been reached. The linear portion of the
curve extends over approximately two decades (from an average dye
uptake per cell of 3×10^{-17} to 3×10^{-15} mole of AO). The departure
from linearity, at the higher concentrations, is rapid. In both Figs. 11 and

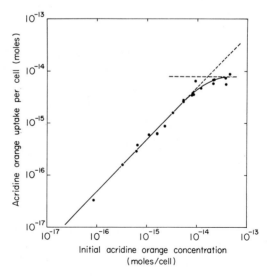

Fig. 11. Acridine orange uptake by mouse leukocytes as a function of initial dye
concentration. (From West, 1965.)

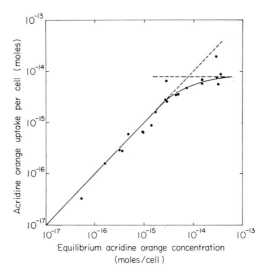

FIG. 12. Acridine orange uptake by mouse leukocytes as a function of equilibrium dye concentration. (From West, 1965.)

12 the curves may be described by two limiting asymptotes shown as dashed lines; one having a slope of unity, and the other a slope of zero. The intersection of the asymptotes shows that the average dye content per cell reaches saturation at approximately 8.0×10^{-15} mole of AO for the range included in these experiments.

B. VISUAL OBSERVATIONS OF THE FLUORESCENCE EMISSION OF CELLS

1. Wright's-Stained Preparations

The chromatin pattern of all of the cells stained with AO was similar to that obtained with Wright's stain.

2. Polymorphonuclear Leukocytes

At the smaller quantities of dye uptake per cell the fluorescence was associated with the chromatin network of the nucleus, which was clearly defined. The color of the fluorescence was green. The cytoplasm was essentially unstained except for an occasional cell showing brick-red granules. The nuclear fluorescence progressively changed to yellow and then to yellow-orange or orange as the amount of dye presented to the cell was increased. The cytoplasm, in these instances, was usually faintly green and occasionally a diffuse red-orange. Cells with a clump of red-orange fluorescing material in the cytoplasm have also been observed.

3. Lymphocytes

The nuclei of the lymphocytes showed the same fluorescence changes with dye concentration as did the polymorphonuclear leukocytes. With increasing dye concentration the cytoplasm became diffusely red-orange.

C. Fluorescence Emission Spectra from Individual Cells

The corrected fluorescence emission spectra from selected individual cells are shown in Figs. 13 through 19. It should be pointed out that there are variations in the fluorescence spectra from cells of a given type at a given intracellular dye concentration. The limits of the spectral variations for a given cell type at a given intracellular dye content are depicted in the figures. The shapes of the spectral curves are essentially the same for any given set of conditions, but the relative amplitudes of the maxima vary. There is strong reason to suspect the presence of additional fluorescing molecular species.

Once or twice a population of cells was obtained from the peritoneal exudate which was largely composed of lymphocytes. Observations of the spectra emitted by these cells showed that cell after cell provided a constant emission spectrum, the amplitude of the maxima and shape of the curves being essentially the same. (The observations were made on the line-selector oscilloscope.) The cell populations in the peritoneal exudates, however, usually contained both lymphocytes and polymorphonuclear leukocytes (PML). Under conditions of AO staining, most of the granules by which PML's are usually classified do not stain. Observation of supravitally stained fluorescing cells permitted only simple classification into lymphocytes and polymorphonuclear leukocytes. Thus, spectra from PML's may represent a variety of granulocytes. Consequently, minor variations in the fluorescence spectra are perhaps not surprising.

It should be noted that the number of samples was relatively small (approximately 100 corrected spectra). Thus, it is conceivable that there could be additional spectral variations. However, for each spectrum that was recorded, additional observations of the spectra from cells on the same slide were made visually on the line-selector oscilloscope. No marked differences were seen.

Figure 13 shows the changes in the emission spectra from individual PML's as the dye content per cell is varied. When the intracellular dye content is small, a single maximum is seen between 530 and 540 nm. As the concentration of dye within the cell is increased, a shoulder gradually appears and eventually emerges as a distinct maximum at approximately 660 nm. In some instances this maximum occurs at a longer wavelength,

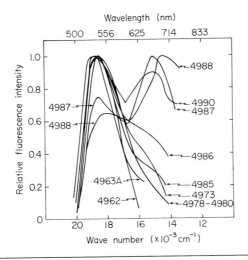

FIG. 13. Fluorescence spectra from individual polymorphonuclear leukocytes. (From West, 1965.)

Cell No.	Intracellular dye content (moles AO)	Remarks
4962	6.5×10^{-16}	—
4963A	8.9×10^{-16}	—
4978	3.7×10^{-15}	—
4980	4.9×10^{-15}	—
4985	5.8×10^{-15}	—
4986	5.8×10^{-15}	—
4973	7.1×10^{-15}	—
4990	7.6×10^{-15}	Orange cytoplasm
4987	9.2×10^{-15}	Red cytoplasm
4988	9.2×10^{-15}	Red cytoplasm

approximately 690 nm. The appearance of the long wavelength peak is associated with orange or red-fluorescing cytoplasm. A poorly defined isosbestic point is seen at approximately 580 nm.

The fluorescence emission spectra from individual lymphocytes at various intracellular dye concentrations are shown in Fig. 14. At low intracellular dye concentrations a single maximum between 530 and 540 nm is seen. As this concentration increases, a shoulder appears at approximately 580 nm which emerges as a definitive peak. At still higher concentrations a different situation exists. The peak at 580 nm is not seen, and a new shoulder appears at 660 nm. At the highest intracellular

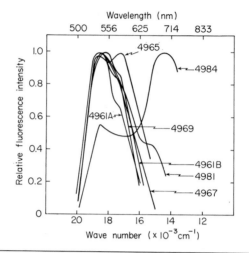

Fig. 14. Fluorescence spectra from individual lymphocytes.

Cell No.	Intracellular dye content (moles AO)	Remarks
4969	2.7×10^{-16}	—
4967	3.0×10^{-16}	—
4961A	6.5×10^{-16}	—
4961B	6.5×10^{-16}	—
4965	8.9×10^{-16}	—
4981	3.6×10^{-15}	—
4984	5.8×10^{-15}	Red granules in cytoplasm

concentrations measured a distinct maximum is present at 690 nm. An isosbestic point is found in essentially the same position as in the case of the polymorphonuclear leukocytes.

From a comparison between Figs. 13 and 14 differences can be seen in the fluorescence emission spectra of the two kinds of cells considered. These differences are more clearly shown in Figs. 15 through 19.

Figure 15 shows the fluorescence emission spectrum of a polymorphonuclear leukocyte (4962) with an average dye uptake of 6.5×10^{-16} mole of AO, and of two lymphocytes (4967 and 4965) with average dye contents of 3×10^{-16} and 8.9×10^{-16} moles of AO, respectively. The spectrum of the PML (4962) has a peak at approximately 540 nm. The location of this maximum and the 50% bandwidth are in close agreement with the data of Zanker (1952) for AO in dilute aqueous solution at pH 6.0

(see Fig. 2). The emission spectrum produced by the lymphocyte (4965) has two maxima of almost equal amplitude at approximately 540 and 580 nm. The spectrum resulting from lymphocyte 4967, which contains a smaller quantity of dye has a maximum at 540 nm and a suggestion of a shoulder in the neighborhood of 580 nm. The short wavelength skirts of the lymphocyte spectra are shifted slightly in the direction of longer wavelength, the larger shift occurring when the two peaks are apparent.

Figure 16 shows the spectral emission curves from three stained lymphocytes, one (4969) from a population that has taken up an average of 2.7×10^{-16} moles of AO per cell and the other two (4961A and B) from a population that has taken up an average of 6.5×10^{-16} moles of AO per cell. All three cells have essentially the same spectrum despite the fact that one of the cells (4969) has approximately 40% of the dye content of the other two. In each case there is a distinct fluorescence emission

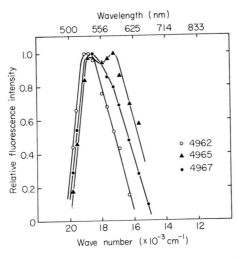

Cell No.	Cell type[a]	Intracellular dye content (moles AO)	Estimated percentage of available sites bound[b]
4962	PML	6.5×10^{-16}	2.6
4967	L	3.0×10^{-16}	1.2
4965	L	8.9×10^{-16}	3.6

[a] PML = Polymorphonuclear leukocyte; L = lymphocyte.
[b] See Table II.

FIG. 15. Fluorescence spectra from single cells. (From West, 1965.)

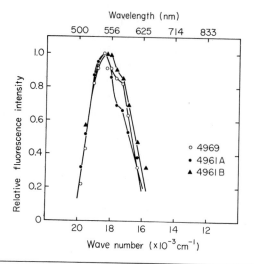

Cell No.	Cell type[a]	Intracellular dye content (moles AO)	Estimated percentage of available sites bound[b]
4969	L	2.7×10^{-16}	1.1
4961A	L	6.5×10^{-16}	2.6
4961B	L	6.5×10^{-16}	2.6

[a] L = Lymphocyte.
[b] See Table II.

FIG. 16. Fluorescence spectra from single cells. (From West, 1965.)

maximum at approximately 540 nm and a shoulder at approximately 580 nm.

Figure 17 shows the fluorescence spectra of three PML's (4963A, 4978, 4980) and one small lymphocyte (4981), having a higher intracellular dye concentration than shown in the previous figures. Despite the higher intracellular dye content, the PML's exhibit only a single maximum at approximately 540 nm. In contrast, the lymphocyte (4981) shows a shoulder at a longer wavelength. This appearance of a shoulder at longer wavelengths always occurred at smaller dye concentrations for the lymphocyte than for the polymorphonuclear leukocyte.

The two PML's (4978 and 4980) (Fig. 17) which contain 3.7×10^{-15} and 4.9×10^{-15} moles of AO, respectively, yield spectra with a peak emission of 540 nm and have a greater 50% bandwidth than found at a lower intracellular dye content, suggesting the presence of other fluorescing species. The spectrum from lymphocyte (4981) has a considerably greater 50% bandwidth than any of the polymorphonuclear leukocytes with approximately the same intracellular dye content. This is probably due to the contribution from the molecular species having maximum fluorescence emission at 580 nm.

Figure 18 shows the fluorescence emission spectra of three polymorphonuclear leukocytes (4984, 4985, and 4986) from a population of cells which have taken up 5.8×10^{-15} moles of AO per cell. The spectra from two of the PML's (4985 and 4986) have peaks at approximately 540 nm. However, at these higher concentrations definite shoulders are seen in the neighborhood of 660 nm. Visually, these cells had no red fluorescence. The PML (4984) has a different spectrum. The short wavelength peak is again at approximately 540 nm. There is a strong long wavelength peak at 690 nm which is almost twice the amplitude of the 540 nm peak. The

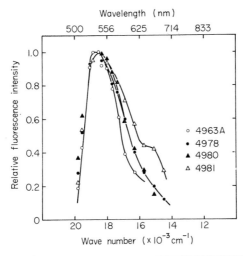

Cell No.	Cell type[a]	Intracellular dye content (moles AO)	Estimated percentage of available sites bound[b]
4963A	PML	8.9×10^{-16}	3.6
4978	PML	3.7×10^{-15}	14.8
4980	PML	4.9×10^{-15}	19.6
4981	L	3.6×10^{-15}	14.4

[a] PML = Polymorphonuclear leukocyte; L = lymphocyte.
[b] See Table II.

FIG. 17. Fluorescence spectra from single cells. (From West, 1965.)

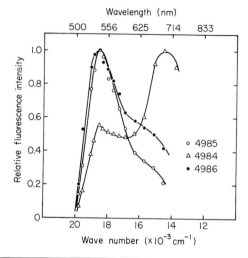

Cell No.	Cell type[a]	Intracellular dye content (moles AO)	Estimated percentage of available sites bound[b]
4984	PML[c]	5.8×10^{-15}	23.2
4985	PML	5.8×10^{-15}	23.2
4986	PML	5.8×10^{-15}	23.2

[a] PML = Polymorphonuclear leukocyte.
[b] See Tables II and III.
[c] This cell had red fluorescing granules in the cytoplasm.

Fig. 18. Fluorescence spectra from single cells. (From West, 1965.)

cell that produced this spectrum had deep red granules in the cytoplasm. The spectrum is probably the result of both nuclear and cytoplasmic fluorescence.

Figure 19 represents the spectra produced by PML's which contained still higher amounts of AO per cell. Visual examination showed that three of these cells (4990, 4987, and 4988) had orange or red cytoplasm. Cell 4973 had no visible orange or red fluorescing material in the cytoplasm. Nevertheless, the spectrum from this cell has a small shoulder at approximately 660 nm. Two cells (4987 and 4990) have a maximum at approximately 660 nm in addition to the one at 540 nm. The third (4988) has a red emission peak at approximately 690 nm. The relative amplitudes of the emission maxima at 540 nm compared to those of longer wavelengths are variable. In the spectrum of cell (4988) the short wavelength peak is shifted to approximately 560 nm. Comparison of the spectra from cells

4973 and 4990 (dye content approximately 7×10^{-15} moles AO per cell) with the spectra from cells 4987 and 4988 (9.2×10^{-15} moles AO per cell) shows the increased prominence of the long wavelength emission peak with increasing dye content per cell, a trend which was noted in discussing the previous figures. At the highest dye content per cell, the amplitude of the long wavelength peak exceeds that of the short wavelength peak. This was found for the lymphocyte at smaller intracellular dye concentrations (cell 4984, Fig. 14, which contains 5.8×10^{-15} moles of AO).

Figure 20 shows the fluorescence emission spectra of acridine orange in buffered physiological saline, pH 7.2. These are corrected spectra derived from data obtained with the television fluorescence spectrophotometer.

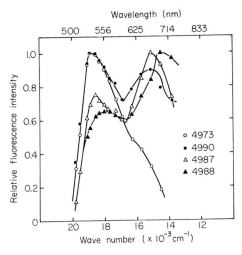

Cell No.	Cell type[a]	Intracellular dye content (moles AO)	Estimated percentage of available sites bound[b]
4973	PML	7.1×10^{-15}	28.4
4990	PML[c]	7.6×10^{-15}	30.4
4987	PML[d]	9.2×10^{-15}	36.8
4988	PML[d]	9.2×10^{-15}	36.8

[a] PML = Polymorphonuclear leukocyte.
[b] See Tables II and III.
[c] This cell had orange fluorescing cytoplasm.
[d] These cells had red fluorescing cytoplasm.

FIG. 19. Fluorescence spectra from single cells. (From West, 1965.)

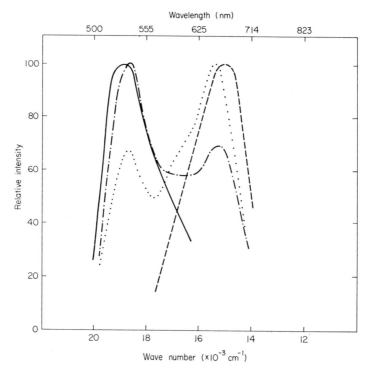

Wavelength (nm)

Fig. 20. Television fluorescence microspectrophotometer. Fluorescence spectra of acridine orange in aqueous solution: dependence on concentration. Citrate-phosphate buffered saline, 0.1 M, pH 7.2, 22°C, 1-cm light path. (Solid line) 1×10^{-7} M AO; (dashed line) 1×10^{-3} M AO; (dotted line) 1×10^{-4} M AO; (dashes and dots) 1×10^{-5} M AO.

Figure 21 shows a comparison among the fluorescence spectra of AO–polymer complexes and an AO–lymphocyte complex at large polymer to dye ratios. Again, these are corrected spectra derived from the data produced by the television fluorescence microspectropolarimeter.

VII. Discussion

In comparison with absorption measurements, fluorescence measurements are several orders of magnitude more sensitive. For example, for solutions of acridine orange in a 1-cm cuvette or of a complex of AO and substrate, the minimum concentration for absorption studies is approximately 10^{-6} to 10^{-7} M whereas concentrations approaching 10^{-10} M are useful for fluorescence studies. Similar differences in sensitivity are found when the dye is studied in single cells.

When the microscope is used to study stained biological structures, it is more useful to discuss sensitivity in terms of absolute quantity rather than of concentration. Inside the cell substances may exist in very high local concentration, but in exceedingly small absolute amounts. Calculation of concentration is difficult. Even more disturbing is the fact that considering only intracellular dye concentrations may lead to erroneous interpretations of the data since the dye may not exist in a free state inside the cell, or it may be restricted to some portion of the cell. When dye is bound to an intracellular substrate, the ratio of dye to substrate is the important parameter.

Localization and absolute quantity of a dye which binds to intracellular substrates are interrelated. The microscope does not affect this relationship while making it available for analysis. Thus, the use of the microscope for fluorescence spectroscopic studies effects, in engineering

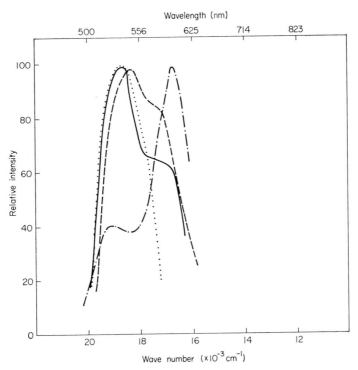

FIG. 21. Television fluorescence microspectrophotometer. Comparison of cell spectrum with fluorescence spectra of AO–polymer complexes. Citrate-phosphate buffered saline, 0.15 M, pH 7.2, 22°C (solid line). 10^{-7} M AO + yeast RNA P/D = 40; (dashed line) single lymphocyte P/D = 39; (dotted line) 10^{-7} M AO + salmon sperm DNA P/D = 50; (dashes and dots) 10^{-7} M AO + chondroitin sulfate P/D = 75. Solid curve and dotted curve slightly separated for clarity.

parlance, a tremendous gain in signal to noise ratio. Quantities as small as 10^{-16} moles cannot be handled in solution. Also, note should be taken of two additional factors: (1) 10^{-16} moles of AO per cell is not the lower limit of sensitivity. Perhaps another 10-fold decrease in detectable intracellular dye content is possible. (2) The recorded line-selected spectrum is that produced by only one of the television lines passing through the spectrum. The spectrum in these studies occupied four to ten television lines. These two factors together could account for approximately a 100-fold increase in sensitivity. It should be possible to obtain fluorescence spectra from as little as 10^{-18} moles (270×10^{-18} g) of AO or similar dye. It is interesting that Chance (1962) states a limiting sensitivity of approximately 10^{-19} moles of reduced pyridine nucleotide. For comparison, a mouse diploid nucleus contains 6×10^{-12} g of DNA (Swift, 1955) which corresponds to 0.019×10^{-12} moles DNA phosphorus/nucleus, assuming a phosphorus content of 10% for DNA.

Rapid fading upon excitation exhibited by some fluorescent molecular species does not result in distorted spectra when the image-intensifier orthicon is employed for recording the emission spectra. Thus, fluorescence microspectrophotometry is very well suited for studying living cells while interfering minimally with cell physiology.

Visual observations on cells stained with small amounts of acridine orange show that the dye is found almost exclusively in the nucleus and associated with the chromatin material. At higher intracellular concentrations of the dye, fluorescence can be seen in the cytoplasm. These results are in agreement with those of DeBruyn and his colleagues (1950, 1953), who observed, in vivo, a high affinity of proflavine (a diamino-acridine) for the intranuclear nucleoprotein and a low affinity for extra-nuclear nucleoprotein.

Despite the differences in sensitivity between fluorescence[9] and absorption measurements, there are definite relationships between the absorption measurements and the absorption and emission spectra for a given molecular species. For AO–NA complexes the long wavelength absorption peak (504 nm) (α-band, Stone and Bradley, 1961) and the short wavelength fluorescence peak (540 nm) both result from the same molecular species (complex II). Similarly, the short wavelength absorption peak (465 nm) (β-band, Stone and Bradley, 1961) and the long wavelength emission peak (660 nm) are both due to the same molecular species (complex I). One can generally predict some of the features of the fluorescence spectrum from the absorption spectrum and, conversely, the

---

[9] The experimental technique employed does not distinguish fluorescence from phosphorescence.

features of the absorption spectrum from the fluorescence spectrum. For AO–NA complexes, the presence of an absorption maximum at 504 nm is always accompanied by a fluorescence maximum at 540 nm and the 465 nm absorption maximum is always accompanied by an emission maximum at 660 nm.

The shape of the primary emission spectrum, that of the species that fluoresces uniquely at 540 nm, and the position of its peak may be altered by the presence of other (secondary) spectral bands. Usually, if the secondary spectral bands are far removed from the primary band, no noticeable effect on the primary peak will be observed. (This may not always be the case, depending on the shape of the curve for the different emitting species.) However, when the secondary spectral band is fairly close to the primary spectral band, then some mutual interaction between them will occur. The influence of one spectral band on the other also depends on their relative amplitudes (molar emission coefficients) and shapes. The influence is an additive one. There may be a shift in the position of one or both peaks, the skirt of one of the spectral bands may develop a shoulder, the half-value spectral bandwidth may be increased. Because of the influence of one on another, it is necessary to determine the entire spectrum in order to analyze the bands. This is equally true for fluorescence and absorption.

Except for very clearly defined situations, the complexity of the emission spectrum from single cells, makes the interpretation of measurements at one wavelength of doubtful value, a situation which is further aggravated when the number of fluorescing species increases. For example, the 580 nm peak, which appears in the fluorescence spectra obtained from AO-stained lymphocytes, shifts the location of the maximum of the fluorescence band ordinarily found at 540 nm to 560 nm. The magnitude of this effect varies across the width of the band, being large in the neighborhood of the long wavelength skirt and small in the neighborhood of the short wavelength skirt.

The molecular species which has an emission maximum at 580 nm would not appear to be due to an AO–NA complex since it is absent in the spectra from polymorphonuclear leukocytes. The spectrum of AO–yeast RNA (Fig. 21) might indicate that the 580 nm complex is due to RNA. However, the shoulder in the lymphocyte spectrum exists at a shorter wavelength than the shoulder in the RNA spectrum. One would expect the converse for the relative heights of the two shoulders. On the basis of these data, it appears that the shoulder in the RNA spectrum represents a molecular species with a peak emission at a wavelength longer than 580 nm. Thus, the molecular species with peak emission at 580 nm does not appear to be an AO–RNA complex. This is in keeping with the fact that this molecular species was not observed in PML's. These data are only preliminary and should be considered indicative rather than definitive. More work is required to elucidate the nature of the molecular species with peak emission at 580 nm.

Figures 20 and 21 do make the point that it is possible to obtain data from supravitally stained cells which is directly comparable with data from solution studies. The spectra of AO in aqueous solution shown in Fig. 20 agree very closely with those of Zanker (Fig. 2). This not only illustrates the accuracy of the corrected spectra, but demonstrates that the corrected spectra are independent of instrumental parameters and can be correlated with data from other laboratories.

Figure 21 and Figs. 13 through 19 demonstrate that the molecular species peculiar to AO–NA complexes are present in the complex spectra from individual cells. This is supported by the work of Loeser, West, and Schoenberg (1960) and Stone and Bradley (1961) and was discussed in Section 6,c.

Not apparent from the cell spectra, since they are normalized, is the variation in intensity of fluorescence as a function of intracellular dye content. The data, prior to being normalized shows the following: The intensity of the 540 nm peak continues to increase proportionately with increasing dye uptake per cell to a limiting value. Within the limits of these experiments, the 540 nm emission peak is not affected as the longer wavelength (660 nm) peak increases in amplitude at the higher intracellular dye concentrations. The formation of the complex that has an emission peak at 660 nm is dependent on the prior formation of the complex that emits at 540 nm. As the 540 nm complex approaches saturation, the formation of the 660 nm complex is initiated. In the intermediate concentration region, both kinds of AO–NA complexes are simultaneously being formed. This behavior is seen in the curves in Figs. 11 and 12.

Over the range of concentrations covered by these measurements quenching of the 540 nm peak has not been observed. In contrast, data from solution studies show the 660 nm fluorescing species (complex I) being formed at the expense of the 540 nm fluorescing species (complex II) (Stone and Bradley, 1961; Loeser et al., 1960). The reasons for this difference in behavior between AO–NA complexes in living cells and in solution can only be speculative on the basis of the available data. Aside from the designation of an area for future study, this observation emphasizes the need for comparison between solution studies and intracellular studies on living cells.

There are also other features of interest. The differences between the spectra from lymphocytes and polymorphonuclear leukocytes that have been recorded are indicative of underlying biochemical differences between these two types of cells. In a more general sense, this finding may be taken as representative of intercellular differences that may be detected and studied among a variety of cell types. Understanding the underlying reasons that give rise to the detected intercellular differences requires appropriate *in vitro* studies on model systems and additional experimental investigations on cells that are designed to satisfy the demands of the *in vitro* studies and the proposed theoretical analysis.

Another aspect of AO staining to which attention should be devoted is the matter of cytoplasmic staining. For supravitally stained cells, behavior may be divided into two classes: (1) Low intracellular dye content, chromatin of the nucleus fluoresces green to yellow-green. The cytoplasm is unstained to faint diffuse green. Some cells show deep-red fluorescing cytoplasmic granules. Cells are not affected by irradiation for long periods (cells have been observed for several hours with no alteration in morphology or fluorescence spectrum). The deep-red or brick-red granules when present fade very rapidly (within seconds) upon irradiation. Spectra have been obtained from some of these granules. Such spectra showed only a red fluorescence band with a peak at approximately 700 nm (West, 1963). The cells containing the red granules may be more sensitive to the fluorescence-exciting radiation than those without granules, but this matter has not been studied carefully. The red granules may be equivalent to the "acridine orange particles" of Robbins and Marcus (1963). Their experimental procedures, however, do not permit direct comparison. (2) High intracellular dye content: The nucleus fluoresces greenish yellow to yellow. The cytoplasm shows general orange or reddish orange fluorescence, the intensity depending on the intracellular dye content and the type of cell. This may correspond to what has been termed "cytoplasmic reddening" by Robbins and Marcus (1963). Again, no direct comparison is possible. Cells treated in this manner are very sensitive to the fluorescence-exciting radiation and begin to lose their morphological integrity in seconds. This is accompanied by further diffuse orange staining of the cytoplasm. The process, once started, is apparently irreversible. Once irradiated, the morphological changes continue even in the dark, but at a slower rate than with continuous irradiation. Spectra from such cells show a red fluorescence peak at approximately 660 nm which is characteristic of the AO–NA complex at high dye to NA ratios. Deep red granules may also be present. In this case the red fluorescence peak will be shifted toward longer wavelengths (see Figs. 17 and 18). One may also observe the progressive and fairly rapid increase in orange cytoplasmic fluorescence when a cell has apparently suffered some damage. Since complex I may be present even when not visually detectable, it is not clear at this time whether the damage is due to irradiation or other causes. But, one could presume that under conditions where most of the cells in a given population fluoresce green and are refractory to irradiation, the presence of orange fluorescence in the cytoplasm is indicative of cell injury or death. Similar observations have been reported by Wolf and Aronson (1961). Thus, differences in staining behavior between viable and dead or damaged cells are to be expected under properly controlled conditions. Bucherer (1943), May (1948), Strugger (1949) and Strugger et al. (1953) have proposed AO staining for detection of dead or injured cells.

The AO staining behavior of fixed biological material is not directly comparable with the AO staining behavior of living cells. This difference is due, in part, to the changes caused by the fixation procedures, and, in part, is due to the staining procedures. Generally, the goal in biological staining of fixed material is to produce an insoluble precipitate. Rigler (1966) has reviewed the AO staining of fixed biological material and added much new information. Rigler measured a number of the physical-optical properties of AO complexes in fixed cells and in solutions. These include fluorescence polarization, lifetime of emitted radiation, and absorption and fluorescence spectra. He relates the staining properties to the structural order of the substrate. Aggregation of dye on the nucleic acid which results in the long wavelength emission band (emission maximum approximately 660 nm) is associated with binding to a single-stranded random coil. According to this theory, when the dye is bound to a double stranded helix, only the short wavelength fluorescence band is present (emission maximum at approximately 540 nm). He relates the short wavelength emission band to the monomeric form of the dye with no nearest neighbor dye to dye interaction which could be accounted for by the intercalated model of Lerman (1961, 1963, 1964; Luzzati et al., 1961).

While similar spectroscopic behavior is observed with supravitally stained cells, it is doubtful if the red emission band (complex I) can be taken as a measure of the proportion of the nucleic acid in the single-stranded random coil form. Attaching such significance to complex I for supravitally stained cells requires a progressive denaturation of the intranuclear nucleic acids with increasing intracellular dye content. This does not seem reasonable in view of the tissue culture studies of cells grown in the presence of acridine orange (Wolf and Aronson, 1961) and the data reported here which shows that complex II (binding of the dye in monomeric form) attains a limiting value that is not altered on further additions of dye. While it is possible that irradiation causes denaturation of nucleic acid when bound to AO, it would be expected that such denaturation would be accompanied by spectroscopic changes. No such changes were observed during the short irradiation times (approximately 1 sec) used to record fluorescence spectra from supravitally stained cells. It is also interesting to note that optical rotatory dispersion studies of AO–DNA complexes (Neville and Bradley, 1961) display Cotton effects in the neighborhood of the absorption bands associated with the monomeric and aggregated forms of the dye complex. The Cotton effects disappear when the AO is bound to denatured DNA. The induced Cotton effect is a very complex phenomenon and in the absence of detailed analyses must be used with caution. Nevertheless, even at $DNA/AO = 1$, the presence of a Cotton region suggests that the DNA still exists as an asymmetric helical polymer, at least in part. The possibility of some configurational changes occurring in DNA when complexed with AO is not excluded.

As Rigler also stated, the findings from the AO staining of fixed biological material are not directly comparable with the results from solution studies and from supravitally stained cells. It is to be hoped that both approaches to cytochemistry will develop a common ground. Certainly Rigler's work is a long step in that direction.

The prominence of the 540 nm emission maximum in the fluorescence spectra from single cells, the appearance of an emission maximum at 660 nm with increased intranuclear dye content, and the association of the dye in both forms with the chromatin network may be taken as presumptive evidence that the major portion of the intranuclear dye content is complexed with the nucleic acids of the nucleus.

In view of the correlation between the results obtained with AO-stained cells and those obtained with AO–NA complexes in solution, and for the purpose of calculating the percentages of available sites bound on the NA molecule, one is tempted to make the assumption that the entire intracellular dye content is complexed with the nucleic acids of the nucleus. For this purpose the results are divided into two sets; one comprising those cells which had only nuclear fluorescence, and the other those cells which had cytoplasmic fluorescence.

Swift (1955) determined the DNA content of adult mouse diploid liver nuclei to be 6×10^{-12} g per nucleus which corresponds to 1.94×10^{-14} mole DNA-phosphorus per nucleus, assuming a phosphorus (P) content of 10% for DNA.

The hypothesis that the DNA content of resting cells is a constant is now well accepted. Mouse lymphocytes and polymorphonuclear leukocytes from the peritoneal exudate constitute a population of cells with constant DNA content.

The RNA content per cell may be variable and is certainly not as well known as the DNA content. Several independent measurements of the ratio of RNA to DNA in mouse lymphoid tissue and skin (Weymouth and Kaplan, 1952; Lombardo et al., 1952; Wiest and Heidelberger, 1953) have been made, which give a value of the RNA to DNA ratio of 0.3. This ratio was determined chemically and does not differentiate between nuclear RNA and cytoplasmic RNA. Nevertheless, it is useful to use the value of the RNA/DNA ratio as the upper limit of the RNA content of the nucleus in the calculations shown below. For metabolically active tissues, i.e., liver, the RNA/DNA ratio is much larger than the value shown above (Baxi et al., 1951). The total NA-P per nucleus calculated from these assumptions is 2.52×10^{-14} mole, which is equivalent to 0.78×10^{-12} g. The calculation is given below:

$$
\begin{aligned}
\text{Total (NA-P)/nucleus} &= \text{(RNA/DNA)(DNA-P/nucleus)} + \text{DNA-P/nucleus} \\
&= (0.3)(1.94 \times 10^{-14}) + 1.94 \times 10^{-14} \\
&= 2.52 \times 10^{-14} \text{ moles}
\end{aligned}
$$

The quantity of dye bound per cell is taken to represent an equivalent number of moles of Na-P. The percentage of sites bound is obtained by dividing the dye uptake per cell by the total NA-P per nucleus.

The estimated percentages of nucleotides bound as a function of intracellular AO concentration for cells with no cytoplasmic fluorescence are shown in Table II. These results resemble the situation found by Peacocke and Skerrett (1956) for the complexing of proflavine with DNA when the dye to DNA ratio was less than 0.22. These authors found the dye was strongly bound to the DNA under these conditions with a free energy of association of approximately -8 kcal/mole.

The spectra from lymphocytes at low dye uptake per cell and the general broadening of the half-value spectral bandwidth of the short wavelength band with increasing dye content per cell indicate that fluorescing molecular species other than dye-NA complexes are probably present. Such interfering molecular species will reduce the theoretically calculated percentage of NA sites bound. An increase in the calculated value will result when only the nuclear RNA is considered and not the total intracellular RNA, as was done above. Nevertheless, the values calculated above are useful for estimating the percentages of NA sites bound for cells whose emission spectra were recorded.

The emission spectra from lymphocytes show the appearance of the 660 nm band when approximately 14% of the sites are bound. In the case of polymorphonuclear leukocytes, the 660 nm band is not noticeable in

TABLE II

PERCENTAGE OF NUCLEOTIDES BOUND AS A FUNCTION OF
INTRACELLULAR AO CONCENTRATION FOR CELLS WITH
NO CYTOPLASMIC FLUORESCENCE[a]

Cell type[b]	Cell No.	Figure No.	Average intracellular dye content (moles AO)	Estimated number of nucleotides bound (% of available sites)
L	4969	16	2.7×10^{-16}	1.1
L	4967	15	3.0×10^{-16}	1.2
L	4961A	16	6.5×10^{-16}	2.6
L	4961B	16	6.5×10^{-16}	2.6
PML	4962	15	6.5×10^{-16}	2.6
PML	4963A	17	8.9×10^{-16}	3.6
L	4965	15	8.9×10^{-16}	3.6
L	4981	17	3.6×10^{-15}	14.4
PML	4978	17	3.7×10^{-15}	14.8
PML	4980	17	4.9×10^{-15}	19.6
PML	4985	18	5.8×10^{-15}	23.2
PML	4986	18	5.8×10^{-15}	23.2
PML	4973	19	7.1×10^{-15}	28.4

[a] Assuming that only AO–NA complexes are formed.
[b] L = Lymphocyte; PML = polymorphonuclear leukocyte.

the spectra until approximately 23% of the sites are bound. The appearance of the 660 nm band in the spectra of polymorphonuclear leukocytes at higher AO/NA ratios than was found for lymphocytes may be due to the presence of a larger amount of RNA in the polymorphonuclear leukocytes. The spectra from the latter cells are characteristic of AO–NA complexes. Interfering fluorescing molecular species are not apparent.

The calculations given above are based on average values for the entire cell population. Detailed information on the intranuclear RNA content from cell to cell was not available. Thus, the calculated values of percentage of sites bound represent an approximation for a particular cell. PML's were by far much more numerous than lymphocytes in the cell populations studied. This may explain why the data from PML's is in very close agreement with that of Peacocke and Skerrett. The data from lymphocytes do not fit as closely, the strongly bound species reaching saturation when approximately 14% of the available sites are bound. This figure is not necessarily in conflict with the other data. It probably indicates that the total number of available sites for binding dye is smaller in lymphocytes than in PML's.

It is of interest that differences between PML's and lymphocytes are displayed in these data and in the cell spectra. Once such differences are evident, they can lead to a number of additional cytochemical investigations. It is also worthy of note that spectroscopic differences between PML's and lymphocytes become evident at the lowest intracellular dye concentrations used in these studies.

Although the numerical results are approximate, they are, nevertheless, useful for comparing the intracellular behavior of the dye–NA complex with *in vitro* data from dye–NA complexes in solution. In addition, the ordinate in Figs. 11 and 12 may be rescaled in terms of "percent available" NA-sites bound. So labeled, a curve of this nature could be used for any cell type to quantitate the percentage of available NA-sites bound with the dye. Other fluorescing molecular species formed with the dye, when present, could interfere with the accuracy of the results. It may be possible to devise experimental procedures to account for interferences in a specific instance. Spectra from individual cells are a necessary part of this procedure.

The ordinate can also be labeled in terms of moles of DNA–P. In the latter instance, the y-intercept of the asymptote with zero slope can be given the value of the total NA content for the particular cell type from which the data were obtained. It should be possible to use such a cell, for example mouse PML's, as a standard with which the NA contents of other cell types can be measured.

Table III shows the estimated amount of dye bound per nucleotide at high intracellular dye concentrations, assuming all the dye is complexed with nuclear nucleic acid. However, all these cells either show cytoplasmic fluorescence or departures from the spectra anticipated for AO–NA complexes. Some of the cytoplasmic fluorescence may be due to molecular species formed by AO binding to polyanions other than NA. The data in Table III are not directly comparable with the data of Peacocke and Skerrett, which were concerned only with dye–NA complexes.

Estimates of an equilibrium ratio, K_e, which is similar to an equilibrium constant, K (the NA content per cell is assumed to be constant), can be made from the linear portion of the curve shown in Fig. 2. Assuming that all the dye that has entered the cell is concentrated in the nucleus, and assuming that the nuclear volume is 5 nm^3, it is possible to express the intracellular dye content in terms of molar concentrations. The equilibrium ratio, K_e, is obtained by dividing this value by the equilibrium value of the extracellular molar dye concentration derived from fluorometer

TABLE III
PERCENTAGE OF NUCLEOTIDES BOUND AS A FUNCTION OF
INTRACELLULAR AO CONCENTRATION FOR CELLS WITH
CYTOPLASMIC FLUORESCENCE[a]

Cell type[b]	Cell No.	Figure No.	Average intracellular dye content (moles AO)	Estimated number of nucleotides bound (% of available sites)
L	4984	18	5.8×10^{-15}	23.2
PML	4990	19	7.6×10^{-15}	30.4
PML	4987	19	9.2×10^{-15}	36.8
PML	4988	19	9.2×10^{-15}	36.8

[a] Assuming that only AO–NA complexes are formed.
[b] L = Lymphocyte; PML = polymorphonuclear leukocyte.

measurements of the supernatants after the staining reaction has reached equilibrium.

Table IV shows the calculated K_e in column (3). The average K_e is 1.8×10^5. The individual values are in fairly good agreement with the average. The assumption that K_e can be treated as an equilibrium constant permits calculating the free energy of association, $\Delta F°$, of acridine

TABLE IV
COMPARISON OF INTRA- AND EXTRACELLULAR ACRIDINE
ORANGE CONCENTRATIONS

(1) Intranuclear AO concentration (molar)	(2) Equilibrium extracellular AO concentration (molar)	(3) K_e = ratio $(1)/(2)^{a,b}$
5.6×10^{-2}	3.4×10^{-7}	1.7×10^5
5.8×10^{-2}	3.2×10^{-7}	1.8×10^5
1.3×10^{-1}	9.0×10^{-7}	1.4×10^5
1.8×10^{-1}	9.9×10^{-7}	1.8×10^5
7.0×10^{-1}	3.3×10^{-6}	2.1×10^5
7.2×10^{-1}	3.5×10^{-6}	2.1×10^5

[a] Average value of $K_e = 1.8 \times 10^5$.
[b] See text for assumptions made in determining K_e.

orange with the nucleus. From Eq. (3) $\Delta F^\circ = -7.3$ kcal/mole. This is, of course, an approximation.

It is of interest to compare the calculated value of the free energy of association with values obtained for *in vitro* dye–nucleic acid complexes. The free energy of association of proflavine with DNA is about -8 kcal/mole (Peacocke and Skerrett, 1956), and with acriflavine it is -9 kcal/mole (Oster, 1951). The free energies observed for the interaction of other dyes with nucleic acids can be calculated from the literature and bracket the calculated value for acridine orange on nuclei (Cavalieri *et al.*, 1951; Irvin and Irvin, 1954).

The free energy of association calculated here involves the process of dye entering the cell as well as the interaction of dye with the substrate and should not be taken to represent, exclusively, association of the dye in a particular complex. Also, the calculated value of ΔF° is probably somewhat low. The chromatin is not dispersed uniformly throughout the volume of the nucleus. If the actual volume occupied by the AO-chromatin complex were utilized in the calculations, K_e would be increased as well as ΔF°.

The shape of the curve in Fig. 12, i.e., the sharp knee, is characteristic of a complex with a fairly small dissociation constant. The curve is similar to the curves that result from the molar ratio method (Bauman, 1962) of studying complex formation.

The similarities between the data from solution studies of dye–NA complexes and the data from supravitally stained cells (including visual observation) offer strong support for considering that the observed behavior of supravitally stained cells is primarily due to AO–NA complexes. Over the range of concentrations used in the reported work, DNA is not distinguishable from RNA. The strong binding calculated above is associated with the short wavelength fluorescence band (approximately 540 nm) and is probably due to the monomeric form of the dye bound to the polyanion without nearest neighbor interaction. In keeping with the large free energy of association, this complex is stable and is unaffected by environmental variations within the physiological range. It is also stable in the presence of fluorescence-exciting radiation with no apparent phototoxic effects. The molecular species with emission at 660 nm is labile and phototoxic. The 660 nm emission band and the physical chemical behavior are characteristic of the binding of AO molecules to NA with nearest neighbor interaction. The formation of these two molecular species of AO bound to NA depends on the molar ratio of AO to NA-P in supravitally stained cells. Further, interaction between cells in a population of

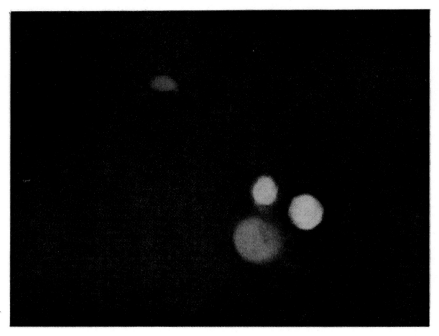

FIG. 22. Differential staining of mouse lymphocytes and ascites cell.

cells in the same staining solution does not occur. Therefore, one would expect a variety of staining behavior in a mixed population of cells placed in the same staining solution. Indeed, such is found to be the case experimentally.

An example that illustrates the latter point is shown in Fig. 22. The figure shows a mouse ascites tumor cell and two mouse lymphocytes which have been stained in a solution containing 3×10^{-14} mole of AO per cell. Figure 11 shows that for mouse leukocytes this amount of dye presented to the cell will result in saturation of the monomer AO–NA complex (peak emission at approximately 540 nm) and formation of the aggregated AO–NA complex (peak emission at approximately 660 nm). In contrast, tumor cells, which may have high degrees of polyploidy would not, under these conditions form the aggregated AO–NA complex (red emission). The ascites tumor cell fluoresces green, while the lymphocytes are yellow-orange (in an additive color system green and red appear yellow to the eye) in keeping with the prediction (see Fig. 11). Thus, supravital AO-staining may be useful for separating tumor cells from normal cells. Since the cytoplasm does not normally stain under these conditions, the increased amounts of cytoplasmic RNA found in tumor cells would play no role. However, increased amounts of intranuclear RNA, if present, would aid in separating tumor cells by increasing the value of the dye/cell ratio required for the red fluorescing form of the AO–NA complex to appear. Of course, if the normal cells being compared with the tumor cells contain other substrates which successfully bind the dye in competition with NA, then they would also require larger dye/cell ratios before exhibiting red or yellow fluorescence. However, this does not seem to be the case for peripheral blood cells.

VIII. Prospects and Future Applications

It is believed that the work presented here establishes the fact that it is possible to obtain biophysical cytochemical data from supravitally stained cells by taking advantage of the changes in the optical properties of dyes and dye–polymer complexes (Udenfriend et al., 1967). It should now be possible to conduct biophysical cytochemical studies as a function of cell type and as a function of physical, chemical, and biological parameters. In addition to AO, other dyes should be investigated (Porro et al., 1963; Turnbull, 1945). The possibilities for making direct comparisons between biophysical cytochemical data and data from in vitro model systems could stimulate increasing interaction between the physical chemist and the cytochemist in the hope that the theoretical foundations of cytochemistry will be extended.

Television fluorescence microspectroscopy, and similar microspectrophotometric techniques, are not limited to equilibrium studies. Studies on the kinetics of reactions are also possible as Chance has already demonstrated. Similarly, phosphorescence spectra may be investigated (the experimental apparatus described herein does not distinguish fluoresence from phosphorescence) with suitable modification of the experimental set-up.

Emphasis on the physical optical properties of dye–polymer complexes may bring forth new applications of the microscope. Every additional physical optical phenomenon that is made available to the cytochemist represents another facet of the dye–polymer complex of interest. Thus, it should eventually be possible for the biophysical cytochemist to employ a number of the tools and methods of the physical chemist and obtain sets of independent measurements which are nevertheless interrelated. One present possibility in this direction is concerned with optical rotatory dispersion. A microscope capable of being used as a microspectropolarimeter is being developed by West (1967, 1968). This instrument will be capable of measuring optical activity throughout the visible and ultraviolet regions of the optical spectrum. Since the Cotton regions of most biological macromolecules lie in the far UV, the measurement of induced optical rotation after dye binding is of great interest as it will permit studies on living cells. Such optical rotatory dispersion data are obviously closely related to fluorescence microspectrophotometry of supravitally stained cells and should also provide another avenue for the interchange of information between the cytochemist and physical chemist.

ACKNOWLEDGMENTS

The author gratefully acknowledges the advice and help of E. W. Abrahamson and M. D. Schoenberg. Special thanks are also due C. M. Loeser and A. M. Potts, without whose stimulation and support this work might not have been undertaken. Thanks are also due G. A. Hutchison for the color photograph.

GENERAL REFERENCES

Berlman, I. B. (1965). "Handbook of Fluorescence Spectra of Aromatic Molecules." Academic Press, New York.

Calvert, J. G., and Pitts, J. N., Jr. (1967). "Photochemistry." Wiley, New York.

Djerassi, C. (1960). "Optical Rotatory Dispersion Applications to Organic Chemistry." McGraw-Hill, New York.

Harrison, G. R., Lord, R. C., and Loofbourow, J. R. (1948). "Practical Spectroscopy" (D. H. Menzel, ed.). Prentice-Hall, Englewood Cliffs, New Jersey.

Hercules, D. M. (1966). "Fluorescence and Phosphorescence Analysis Principles and Applications" (D. M. Hercules, ed.). Wiley (Interscience), New York.

Jenkins, F. A., and White, H. E. (1957). "Fundamentals of Optics," 3rd Ed. McGraw-Hill, New York.

Konev, S. V. (1967). "Fluorescence and Phosphorescence of Proteins and Nucleic Acids" (S. Udenfriend, ed.). Plenum Press, New York.

Lowry, T. M. (1964). "Optical Rotatory Power." Dover Publications, New York.

Martin, L. C. (1966). "The Theory of the Microscope." Blackie, London.

Mayor, H. D. (1963). "The Nucleic Acids of Viruses as Revealed by Their Reactions with Fluorochrome Acridine Orange." "International Review of Experimental Pathology," G. W. Richter, and M. A. Epstein, eds., Vol. 2, pp. 1–45. Academic Press, New York.

Morgan, Joseph (1953). "Introduction to Geometrical and Physical Optics." McGraw-Hill, New York.

Nairn, R. C. (1964). "Fluorescent Protein Tracing," 2nd Ed. (R. C. Nairn, ed.). Williams and Wilkins, Baltimore, Maryland.

Passwater, Richard A. (1967). "Guide to Fluorescence Literature." Plenum Press Data Division, New York.

Pringsheim, Peter (1949). "Fluorescence and Phosphorescence." Interscience, New York.

Sani, G., Citti, U., and Caramazza, G. (1964). "Fluorescence Microscopy in The Cytodiagnosis of Cancer." Thomas, Springfield, Illinois.

Seliger, Howard H., and McElroy, William D. (1965). "Light: Physical and Biological Action." Academic Press, New York.

Snatzke, G. (1967). "Optical Rotatory Dispersion and Circular Dichroism in Organic Chemistry." Heyden and Son, Ltd., London (Distributed in the U.S. by Sadtler Research Laboratory, Inc., Philadelphia, Pennsylvania).

Strong, John (1958). "Concepts of Classical Optics." W. H. Freeman and Company, San Francisco.

Udenfriend, Sidney (1962). "Fluorescence Assay in Biology and Medicine." Academic Press, New York.

Wood, Robert W. (1934). "Physical Optics," 3rd Ed. MacMillan, New York.

Young, M. R. (1961). *Quart. J. Microscop. Sci.* **102**, 419–449.

REFERENCES

Albert, A. (1951). "The Acridines." Arnold, London.

Alexandrov, W. (1932–1933). *Protoplasma* **17**, 161–217.

Armstrong, J. A. (1956). *Exptl. Cell Res.* **11**, 640–643.

Armstrong, J. A., and Niven, J. S. F. (1957). *Nature* **180**, 1335–1336.
Aschoff, L. (1924). "The Reticulo-Endothelial System. Lectures on Pathology." Harper & Row (Hoeber), New York.
Bank, O., and Bungenberg de Jong, H. G. (1939). *Protoplasma* **33**, 512–530.
Bauman, R. P. (1962). "Absorption Spectroscopy," p. 421. Wiley, New York.
Baxi, A. J., Samarth, K. D., and Venkataraman, P. R. (1951). *Proc. Indian Acad. Sci.* **34**, 258–266.
Beers, R. F., Hendley, D. D., and Steiner, R. F. (1958). *Nature* **182**, 242–244.
Bergeron, J. A., and Singer, M. (1958). *J. Biophys. Biochem. Cytol.* **4**, 433–457.
Blout, E. R., and Stryer, L. (1959). *Proc. Natl. Acad. Sci., U.S.*, **45**, 1591–1593.
Borst, M., and Königsdörffer, H. (1929). "Untersuchungen über Porphyrie mit besonderer Berucksichtingung der Porphyria congenita." S. Hirzel, Leipzig.
Bradley, D. F. (1961). *Trans. N.Y. Acad. Sci.* **24**, 64–74.
Bradley, D. F., and Wolf, M. K. (1959). *Proc. Natl. Acad. Sci. U.S.* **45**, 944–952.
Bradley, D. F., and Wolf, M. K. (1960). *In* "The Neurochemistry of Nucleotides and Amino Acids" (R. O. Brady and D. B. Tower, eds.), pp. 89–108. Wiley, New York.
Briggs, R. (1952). *J. Gen. Physiol.* **35**, 761–780.
Bucherer, H. (1943). *Zentr. Bakteriol. Parasitenk. Abt. II* **106**, 81–88.
Cavalieri, L. F., Angelos, A., and Balis, M. E. (1951). *J. Am. Chem. Soc.* **73**, 4902–4906.
Chance, B. (1962). *Ann. N.Y. Acad. Sci.* **97**, 431–448.
Cornil, V. (1875a). *Compt. Rend.* **80**, 1288–1291.
Cornil, V. (1875b). *Compt. Rend. Soc. Biol.*, Ser. *6*, No. 2, pp. 200–206.
Dalcq, A. (1931). *Arch. Biol. (Liege)* **41**, 143–220.
Dart, L. H., Jr., and Turner, T. R. (1959). *Lab. Invest.* **8**, 1513–1522.
DeBruyn, P. P. H., Robertson, R. C., and Farr, R. S. (1950). *Anat. Record* **108**, 279–307.
DeBruyn, P. P. H., Farr, R. S., Banks, H., and Morthland, F. W. (1953). *Exptl. Cell Res.* **4**, 174–180.
DeLerma, B. (1940). *Boll. Soc. Nat. Napoli* **51**, 17–35.
DeLerma, B. (1942). *Boll. Soc. Nat. Napoli* **53**, 9–16.
DeLerma, B. (1949). *Ann. Ist. Museo Zool. Napoli* **1**, n. 4, 1–32.
DeLerma, B. (1958). *In* "Handbuch der Histochemie" (W. Graumann and K. Neumann, eds.), Band I, Teil 1, pp. 78–159. Fischer, Stuttgart.
Drebinger, K. (1951). *Arch. Entwicklungsmech. Organ.* **145**, 174–204.
Drummond, D. S., Pritchard, N. J., Simpson-Gildemeister, V. F. W., and Peacocke, A. R. (1966). *Biopolymers* **4**, 971–987.
Edsall, J. T., and Wyman, J. (1958). "Biophysical Chemistry," Vol. 1, p. 201. Academic Press, New York.
Ehrlich, P. (1879). *Arch. Anat. Physiol., Physiol. Abt.* pp. 166–169.
Ehrlich, P. (1909). *Ber. Deut. Chem. Ges.* **42**, 17–47.
Ellinger, P. (1940). *Biol. Rev. Cambridge Phil. Soc.* **15**, 323.
Ellinger, P., and Hirt, A. (1929). *Z. Anat. Entwicklungsgeschichte* **90**, 791–802.
Ellinger, P., and Hirt, A. (1930). *Arch. Exptl. Pathol. Pharmakol. Naunyn-Schmiedebergs* **150**, 285–297.
Ellinger, P., and Hirt, A. (1931). *Arch. Exptl. Pathol. Pharmakol. Naunyn-Schmiedebergs* **159**, 11–127.
Evans, H. M., and Schulemann, W. (1914). *Science* **39**, 443–454.
Eyring, E. J., Kraus, H., and Yang, J. T. (1968). *Biopolymers* **6**, 703–714.

Fikentscher, R. (1931). *Arch. Pathol. Anat. Physiol. Virchows* **279,** 731–739.

Fischl, V., and Schwenk, E. (1932). *Klin. Wochschr.* **11,** 1114.

Fisher, J. (1952). *Electronics* **25,** 140–143.

Förster, T. (1951). "Organisch Vererbindungen." Vandenhoeck & Ruprecht, Göttingen.

Goessner, W. (1949). *Verhandl. Deut. Ges. Pathol.* **33,** 102–109.

Goldman, M. (1968). "Fluorescent Antibody Methods." Academic Press, New York.

Guilbault, G. G. (1967). *In* "Fluorescence Theory, Instrumentation, and Practice" (G. G. Guilbault, ed.), pp. 297–358. Dekker, New York.

Hertwig, G. (1924). *Anat. Anz.* **58,** Suppl., 223–227.

Heschl, R. (1875). *Wein. Med. Wochschr.* No. 32, Columns 713, 715.

Hodgman, C. D. (1955–1956). "Handbook of Chemistry and Physics," 37th Ed., p. 1615. Chem. Rubber Publ. Co., Cleveland, Ohio.

Irvin, J. L., and Irvin, E. M. (1954). *J. Biol. Chem.* **206,** 39–49.

Jürgens, R. (1875). *Arch. Pathol. Anat. Physiol. Virchows* **65,** 189–196.

Kamnev, J. F. (1934). *Protoplasma* **21,** 169–180.

Keilin, D. (1925). *Proc. Roy. Soc. (London)* **B98,** 312–338.

Köhler, A. (1904). *Z. Wiss. Mikroskopie* **21,** 129–165, 273–304.

Krebs, A. T., and Gierlach, Z. S. (1951). *Am. J. Roentgenol. Radium Therapy Nucl. Med.* **65,** 93.

Krieg, A. (1954). *Experientia* **10,** 172.

Langridge, R., Seeds, W. E., Wilson, H. R., Hooper, C. W., Wilkins, M. H. F., and Hamilton, L. D. (1957). *J. Biophys. Biochem. Cytol.* **3,** 767–778.

Lehman, H. (1913). *Z. Wiss. Mikroskopie* **30,** 417–470.

Lerman, L. S. (1961). *J. Mol. Biol.* **3,** 18–30.

Lerman, L. S. (1963). *Proc. Natl. Acad. Sci. U.S.* **49,** 94–102.

Lerman, L. S. (1964). *J. Mol. Biol.* **10,** 367–380.

Levene, P. A., and Simms, H. S. (1925). *J. Biol. Chem.* **65,** 519–534.

Lison, L. (1935). *Arch. Biol. (Liege)* **46,** 599–668.

Loeser, C. N., and West, S. S. (1962). *Ann. N.Y. Acad. Sci.* **97,** 346–357.

Loeser, C. N., West, S. S., and Schoenberg, M. D. (1960). *Anat. Record* **138,** 163–178.

Lombardo, M. E., Travers, J. J., and Cerecedo, L. R. (1952). *J. Biol. Chem.* **195,** 43–48.

Luzzati, V., Mason, F., and Lerman, L. S. (1961). *J. Mol. Biol.* **3,** 634–639.

Mahler, H. R., and Cordes, E. H. (1966). "Biological Chemistry," p. 196. Harper & Row, New York.

Maron, S. H., and Prutton, C. F. (1965). "Principles of Physical Chemistry," 4th Ed., p. 305. Macmillan, New York.

May, J. (1948). *Zentr. Bakteriol. Parasitenk. Abt. I. Orig.* **152,** 586–590.

Mayer, H. D. (1963). *Intern. Rev. Exptl. Pathol.* **2,** 1–45.

Michaelis, L. (1947). *Cold Spring Harbor Symp. Quant. Biol.* **12,** 131–142.

Michaelis, L. (1950). *J. Phys. Colloid Chem.* **54,** 1–17.

Morthland, F. W., DeBruyn, P. P. H., and Smith, N. H. (1954). *Exptl. Cell Res.* **7,** 201–214.

Morton, G. A., and Ruedy, J. E. (1960). *Advan. Electron. Electron Phys.* **12,** 183–193.

Nassonov, D. (1930). *Z. Zellforsch. Mikroskop. Anat.* **11,** 179–217

Nassonov, D. (1932). *Protoplasma* **15,** 239–267.

Neville, D. M., Jr., and Bradley, D. F. (1961). *Biochim. Biophys. Acta* **50,** 397–399.

Norden, G. (1953). *Acta Pathol. Microbiol. Scand. Suppl.* **96.**

Olsen, R. A. (1960). *Rev. Sci. Instr.* **31,** 844–849.

Orgel, A. (1961). *J. Mol. Biol.* **3,** 762–768.

Oster, G. (1951). *Trans. Faraday Soc.* **47**, 660–666.

Peacocke, A. R., and Skerrett, J. N. H. (1956). *Trans. Faraday Soc.* **53**, 261–279.

Pfeffer, W. (1886). "Untersuchung en Aus dem Botanischen Institut zu Tübingen," Bd. II. Engelmann, Leipzig.

Policard, A. (1925a). *Bull. Histol. Appl. Physiol. Pathol. Tech. Microscop.* **2**, 317.

Policard, A. (1925b). *Bull. Histol. Appl. Physiol. Pathol. Tech. Microscop.* **2**, 167–180.

Porro, T. J., Dadik, S. P., Green, M., and Morse, H. T. (1963). *Stain Technol.* **38**, 37–48.

Potts, A. M., West, S. S., and Shearer, J. R. (1959). *A.M.A. Arch. Ophthalmol.* **62**, 485–499.

Price, G. R., and Schwartz, S. (1956). *Phys. Tech. Biol. Res.* **3**, 91–148.

Rabinowitch, E., and Epstein, L. F. (1941). *J. Am. Chem. Soc.* **63**, 69–78.

Ranadive, N. S., and Korgaonkar, K. S. (1960). *Biochim. Biophys. Acta* **39**, 547–550.

Reichert Optische Werke (1963). "Fluorescence Microscopy with Fluorochromes." W. J. Hacker Co., West Caldwell, New Jersey.

Richards, O. W. (1955). *In* "Fluorescence Microscopy in Analytical Cytology" (R. C. Mellors, ed.), pp. 5/12–5/13. McGraw-Hill (Blakiston), New York.

Rigler, R., Jr. (1966). *Acta Physiol. Scand.* **67**, Suppl. 267, 1–121.

Robbins, E., and Marcus, P. I. (1963). *J. Cell Biol.* **18**, 237–250.

Ruch, R. (1966). *In* "Introduction to Quantitative Cytochemistry" (G. L. Wied, ed.), pp. 281–294. Academic Press, New York.

Runge, W. J. (1966). *Science* **151**, 1499–1506.

Scheibe, O., and Eder, M. (1956). *Acta Histochem.* **3**, 6–18.

von Scheibe, G. (1938). *Kolloid-Z.* **82**, 1–14.

Schubert, M., and Hamerman, D. (1956). *J. Histochem. Cytochem.* **4**, 159–189.

Schümmelfeder, N. (1950). *Arch. Pathol. Anat. Physiol. Virchows* **318**, 119–154.

Sheppard, S. E. (1942). *Rev. Mod. Phys.* **14**, 303–340.

Sheppard, S. E., and Geddes, A. L. (1944a). *J. Am. Chem. Soc.* **66**, 1995–2002.

Sheppard, S. E., and Geddes, A. L. (1944b). *J. Am. Chem. Soc.* **66**, 2003–2009.

Singer, M. (1954). *J. Histochem. Cytochem.* **2**, 322–329.

Sjöstrand, F. (1944). *Acta Anat. Suppl.* **1**, 1–163.

Sjöstrand, F. (1946a). *Nature* **157**, 698.

Sjöstrand, F. (1946b). *Acta Physiol Scand.* **12**, 42–52.

Steiner, R. F., and Beers, R. F., Jr. (1961). "Polynucleotides," pp. 301–318. Elsevier, Amsterdam.

Stockinger, L. (1958). *Z. Naturforsch.* **13b**, 407.

Stone, A. L. (1964). *Biopolymers* **2**, 315–325.

Stone, A. L. (1967). *Biochim. Biophys. Acta* **148**, 193–206.

Stone, A. L., and Bradley, D. F. (1961). *J. Am. Chem. Soc.* **83**, 3627–3634.

Stone, A. L., and Bradley, D. F. (1967). *Biochim. Biophys. Acta* **148**, 172–192.

Stone, A. L., and Moss, H. (1967). *Biochim. Biophys. Acta* **136**, 56–66.

Strugger, S. (1940). *Deut. Tieraerztl. Wochschr.* **48**, 645.

Strugger, S. (1949). "Fluoreszenzmikroskopie und Mikrobiologie." Schaper, Hanover.

Strugger, S. P., Krebs, A. T., and Gierlach, Z. S. (1953). *Am. J. Roentgenol. Radium Therapy Nuclear Med.* **70**, 365–375.

Stübel, H. (1911). *Arch. Ges. Physiol. Pfluegers* **142**, 1–14.

Swift, H. (1955). *In* "The Nucleic Acids" (C. Chargaff and J. N. Davidson, eds.), Vol. 2, Chap. 17, p. 77, Fig. 6. Academic Press, New York.

Tonutti, E. (1946). *Schweiz. Med. Wochschr.* **76**, 778–779.

Turnbull, N. H. (1945). *J. Chem. Soc.* p. 441.

Udenfriend, S., Guroff, G., and Zaltzman-Nirenberg, P. (1967). *In* "Fluorescence Theory, Instrumentation, and Practice" (G. G. Guilbault, ed.), pp. 359–370. Dekker, New York.

Venkataraman, K. (1952). The Chemistry of Synthetic Dyes, Vol. II, p. 758. Academic Press, New York.

von Bertalanffy, L., and Bickis, I. (1956). *J. Histochem. Cytochem.* **4**, 481–493.

von Euler, H., Hellström, H., and Adler, E. (1935). *Z. Vergleich. Physiol.* **21**, 739–750.

Wasicky, R. (1913). *Pharm. Post* **46**, 877–878.

Weill, G., and Calvin, M. (1963). *Biopolymers* **1**, 401–417.

West, S. S. (1963). Unpublished observations.

West, S. S. (1965). *In* "Methoden und Ergebnisse der Zytophotometrie" (W. Sandritter and G. Kiefer, eds.). *Acta Histochem. Suppl.* **6**, 135–153.

West, S. S. (1967). *Biophys. Soc., 11th Ann. Meeting.* Abstr. p. 11.

West, S. S. (1969). *Ann. N.Y. Acad. Sci.* (in press).

West, S. S., Loeser, C. N., and Schoenberg, M. D. (1960). *IRE (Inst. Radio Engrs.) Trans. Med. Electron.* **ME–7**, 138–142.

West, S. S., Potts, A. M., and Shearer, J. R. (1962). *IRE (Inst. Radio Engrs.) Trans. Bio-Med. Electron.* **BME–9**, 159–164.

Weymouth, P. P., and Kaplan, H. S. (1952). *Cancer Res.* **12**, 680–683.

Wiame, J. M. (1947). *J. Am. Chem. Soc.* **69**, 3146–3147.

Wiest, W. G., and Heidelberger, C. (1953). *Cancer Res.* **13**, 246–249.

Williams, G. Z. (1955). *IRE (Inst. Radio Engrs.) Convention Record* **3**, Pt. 9, 131–137.

Wolf, M. K., and Aronson, S. B. (1961). *J. Histochem. Cytochem.* **9**, 22–29.

Zanker, V. (1952). *Z. Physik. Chem. (Leipzig)* **199**, 225–258.

Zanker, V., Held, M., and Rammensee, H. (1959). *Z. Naturforsch.* **14b**, 789–801.

Zeiger, K., and Harders, H. (1951). *Z. Zellforsch. Mikroskop. Anat.* **36**, 62–78.

Zeiger, K., and Wiede, M. (1954). *Z. Zellforsch. Mikroskop. Anat.* **40**, 401–424.

Author Index

Numbers in italics refer to pages on which the complete references are listed.

Bloom, D., 50, *89*
Blout, E. R., 102, 106, 107, 137, *164,* 233, *249,* 255, *318*
Blundell, M., 51, *90*
Bondareff, W., 72, 77, *89*
Bonner, W., 154, *166*
Bonner, W. A., 98, 154, 156, *166*
Borst, M., 269, *318*
Borysko, E., 189, *200*
Bostrom, R. C., 98, 159, *164, 166*
Bourne, G. H., 3, *86*
Bouwers, A., 102, *164*
Brachet, J., 97, *164*
Bradfield, J. R. G., 172, *199*
Bradley, D. F., 255, 259, 265, 304, 306, 309, *318, 319*
Brattgard, S. O., 161, *164*
Briggs, R., 263, *318*
Brown, K. A., 78, 81, *91*
Brown, R., 58, *86*
Bucherer, H., 308, *318*
Buddle, H. L., 41, *90*
Bullivant, S., 78, 80, 83, *86, 87*
Bulthuis, H. W., 102, *164*
Bungenberg de Jong, H. G., 264, *318*
Burch, C. R., 102, *164*
Burke, J. F., 78, *87, 90*
Burns, L., 205, *251*
Burstone, M. S., 34, 41, 42, 43, 54, 65, 67, 69, 71, 74, 75, 76, *87, 89*
Bush, V., 39, *87*
Butler, L. O., 51, *87*

C

Calvert, J. G., *317*
Calvin, M., 255, *321*
Caramazza, G., *317*
Carlson, L., 123, 159, *164*
Caspersson, T., 70, *87,* 96, 97, 100, 101, 115, 116, 124, 125, 128, 134, 135, 136, 137, 143, 149, 150, 159, *164,* 232, 237, *249*
Catchpole, H. R., 69, *87, 89, 90*
Caulfield, J. B., 67, *88,* 178, *199*
Cavalieri, L. F., 314, *318*
Cerecedo, L. R., 310, *319*
Chalkley, H. W., 219, 249, *250*

Chamberlain, P. J., 103, 108, 111, 126, 127, 128, 130, 138, 142, 144, 146, 147, 153, *164, 167*
Chance, B., 126, 132, 139, *164,* 202, 230, *250, 251,* 304, *318*
Chang, J. P., 32, 33, 35, 38, 78, 84, 85, *87, 89, 90*
Chase, W. H., 69, 71, 77, 78, *87, 91*
Chayen, J., 139, *164*
Chesterman, W., 40, *87*
Chilson, O. P., 10, *87*
Citti, U., *317*
Claude, A., 189, *199*
Clements, R. L., 51, *87*
Cobb, J. D., 71, *87*
Coltman, J. W., 214, 238, *250*
Commoner, B., 206, 225, 232, *250*
Conway, T. J., *166*
Coons, A. H., 29, *87*
Cooper, I. S., 17, *87*
Copeland, D. E., 24, 49, *87*
Copson, D. A., 47, *88*
Cordes, E. H., 272, *319*
Coriell, L. L., 2, 12, *88*
Corlette, S. L., 136, 137, 149, 150, *166*
Cornil, V., 264, *318*
Costello, L. A., 10, *87*
Cowley, C. W., 3, 4, 5, 6, 7, 8, 15, 22, *88, 92*
Craig, E. L., 73, *88*
Crawford, E. J., 70, *90*
Crowell, J., 26, *93*

D

Dadik, S. P., 315, *320*
Daems, W. T., 80, *91*
Dalcq, A., 263, *318*
Daneholt, B., 163, *165*
Danielli, J. F., 3, 21, 51, 70, *86, 88*
Dart, L. H., Jr., 267, *318*
Davies, H. G., 78, *88,* 97, 105, 114, 116, 117, 118, 121, 125, 134, 135, 137, 138, 148, 151, 153, 154, *164, 167*
Davis, B. J., 78, 79, *88*
DeBruyn, P. P. H., 262, 263, 265, 304, *318, 319*
Deeley, E. M., 78, *88,* 97, 114, 127, 142, *164, 167,* 202, *250*

SUBJECT INDEX